Macrobiotics a

Macrobiotics and Oriental Medicine

An Introduction to Holistic Health

by Michio Kushi
and Phillip Jannetta

Japan Publications, Inc.

Note to the reader: It is advisable to seek the guidance of a qualified health professional and macrobiotic counselor before implementing the dietary and other suggestions for specific conditions presented in this book. It is essential that any reader who has any reason to suspect serious illness in themselves or their family members seek appropriate advice promptly. Neither this or any other book should be used as a substitute for qualified care or treatment.

Published by JAPAN PUBLICATIONS, INC., Tokyo and New York

Distributors:
UNITED STATES: *Kodansha America, Inc., through Farrar, Straus & Giroux, 19 Union Square West, New York, 10003.* CANADA: *Fitzhenry & Whiteside Ltd., 195 Allstate Parkway, Markham, Ontario, L3R 4T8.* BRITISH ISLES AND EUROPEAN CONTINENT: *Premier Book Marketing Ltd., 1 Gower Street, London WC1E 6HA.* AUSTRALIA AND NEW ZEALAND: *Bookwise International, 54 Crittenden Road, Findon, South Australia 5023.* THE FAR EAST AND JAPAN: *Japan Publications Trading Co., Ltd., 1-2-1, Sarugaku-cho, Chiyoda-ku, Tokyo 101.*

First edition: June 1991

LCCC No. 85-081366
ISBN 0-87040-659-0

Printed in U.S.A.

Foreword

The traditional medicine of the Far East predates modern, scientific medicine by thousands of years. It has withstood the test of time and guided an untold number of people toward health and happiness. In recent years, Oriental medicine has gained the attention and respect of a growing number of modern health-care practitioners.

The philosophy that gave birth to acupuncture, shiatsu massage, moxibustion, palm healing and herbal medicine is profound and deep. Oriental medicine derives from an intuitive understanding of the law of change that governs all things, including an awareness of the nonmaterial energy that enlivens the human body and all of its functions.

As you will discover in this book, the practice of Oriental medicine cannot be standardized. Pulse diagnosis, for example, which is one of the methods of health evaluation used in the Orient, cannot be mastered fully without developing actual sensitivity to the currents of invisible energy, or *Ki*, that are constantly streaming through the human body and throughout the universe. The same is true in the practice of acupuncture, shiatsu massage, palm healing, and herbal medicine.

In this ancient system of health care, the ability to make an accurate diagnosis and implement the appropriate therapy depends upon the health, sensitivity and experience of the practitioner. Moreover, in the tradition of Eastern medicine, a physician needed to be a living example of health before being qualified to guide others.

The goal of Oriental medicine lies beyond the treatment of individual sickness. At this level, medicine becomes more educational than therapeutic, and doctors become educators who guide others toward a clear understanding of the principles of life and health. This is also the purpose of macrobiotics, which is based on an intuitive understanding of how factors such as daily diet, lifestyle, environment, and way of thinking contribute to health.

Macrobiotics is actually a way of life and not a treatment for specific illnesses. As hundreds of thousands of people around the world have discovered, this way of life offers a practical method, beginning with self-reflection and proper diet, to recover and maintain optimal health.

However, the ultimate purpose of macrobiotics and of Oriental medicine extends even beyond this. The aim of these traditional approaches is to create a healthy and peaceful society in which the understanding of health becomes part of everyone's daily life. If implemented widely enough, this approach would resolve war, hunger, crime, biological and psychological degeneration, destruction of the environment, decomposition of the family, and other planetary problems.

Interest in macrobiotics and Oriental medicine is growing throughout the world, most recently in Eastern Europe. This trend is an indication that we are now moving toward the development of a medicine of humanity, capable of synthesizing traditional and modern understanding and establishing planetary health and peace in the future. On a personal level, mastering the techniques and understanding the principles of these holistic approaches can lead to a deeper awareness of life, health, nature, and human origin and destiny.

This book is based on a seminar entitled "The Principles and Practice of Oriental Medicine" which I presented in London in June, 1975. This week-long seminar, cosponsored by the British Acupuncture Association, was to be the first of many visits to Western and Eastern Europe. It was attended by over 200 acupuncturists, medical doctors, shiatsu massage therapists, holistic practitioners, and macrobiotic teachers from throughout Europe.

William Tara and his associates at the Community Health Foundation and Kushi Institute in London, recorded over 40 hours of lectures. Edward Esko and Alex Jack, my associates in Boston, encouraged Japan Publications, Inc. to issue a book based on this material. Mr. Iwao Yoshizaki and Mr. Yoshiro Fujiwara, president and New York representative of Japan Publications, Inc., responded enthusiastically, and Phillip Jannetta, my associate in Tokyo, was asked to turn the material into a book. Phillip reviewed and edited the many hours of tapes, and supplemented the material with new information from my lectures at the Kushi Institute.

Phillip Jannetta has developed a practical understanding of both macrobiotics and Oriental medicine through his years of study, teaching and practice. He has been a student and associate of mine for the past fifteen years. In 1980, I and my wife, Aveline, certified Phillip as a macrobiotic teacher and counselor. Together with his wife, Yukiko, Phillip established a macrobiotic educational center in Tokyo in 1982, and now actively teaches throughout Japan.

I would like to express my appreciation to all of the friends mentioned above, for helping to create this book. I also thank the staff of Japan Publications, Inc. for designing and producing the finished volume. It is my hope that this book will lead to greater understanding between East and West, ancient and modern, and intuitive and scientific, in order to create a peaceful and healthy planetary culture.

Michio Kushi
Brookline, Massachusetts
April, 1990

Preface

This book is based on the teachings of Michio Kushi. Its basic outline comes from a seminar on Oriental medicine that Mr. Kushi presented in the early 1970s. At that time Oriental medicine was little known in the United States and its practice was classified as quackery. The situation was so muddled, in fact, that Mr. Kushi was threatened with legal prosecution for practicing medicine without a license when he passed around an acupuncture kit so that participants could see what acupuncture needles looked like.

Time has a way of rectifying misconceptions, however. Over the past decade and a half numerous colleges of Chinese medicine have opened in North America and Europe. They offer excellent curriculums and are staffed by teachers with extensive experience. A wide range of books have been published on the subject, both for professionals and the layman. Acupuncture is now recognized as a legitimate medical practice, although there are still restrictions.

My interest in traditional and Oriental medicine dates to Mr. Kushi's lectures, and I have continued to study with him and other teachers over the years. My macrobiotic counseling practice in Tokyo is based on the principles of Oriental medicine. In diagnosis, I use the traditional methods conceived in the Far East thousands of years ago, and refinements, based on the same principles, developed by George Ohsawa, Mr. Kushi, and others.

I have often used moxibustion, shiatsu massage, palm healing, and even the therapeutic effects of sound, for in-office, symptomatic relief. And, I always make dietary suggestions and lifestyle recommendations that are firmly based on these same principles. Quite often, individuals come to me as a last resort. For whatever reason, they are dissatisfied with the health care they have received from other sources.

It is a continual cause of amazement to me, that the root of seemingly inexplicable physical, psychological, and even spiritual problems, fall into focus with this simple orientation. There are times when it is disconcerting to have individuals and families come for what are to me obvious and commonsense suggestions. And yet the advice works, often to the surprise of the individual involved, and sometimes in dramatic fashion.

This is the first of three basic reasons that I readily agreed when approached with the idea to coauthor this book. It will take time, perhaps another generation, for the value of traditional and Oriental medicine to be fully recognized in the West. From the reactions of students in the classes that I teach throughout Japan, it is evident that people are ready to put this information to use now.

My second motivation reflects the theme of this book. Although the Oriental medical applications of acupuncture, moxibustion, herbal medicine and massage are gaining favor in the Western world, the full scope and implication of the orientation they represent are seldom discussed. The depth of the principles behind these practices is profound, and the breadth of their application is wider than we have begun to imagine. Now is the time for us to begin taking advantage of the insights and teachings of our ancestors.

Becoming a father was a further impetus for working with Mr. Kushi on this book. And this is where the significance of traditional and Oriental medicine draws the biggest surprise. Just as individuals develop problems and undergo treatment, families, communities, society, and modern civilization itself, are suffering. The signs, or symptoms, are all around us, including, but certainly not limited to, the staggering divorce rate, the threat of crime, the scourge of drug abuse, and the breakdown of our social institutions such as religion and education. Humanity, it seems, has lost its sense of meaning and direction in life.

In the year 2005, my eldest daughter will just be entering young adulthood. What will the world be like for our children? By any criteria, the prospects do not look bright. Unless there are drastic, worldwide changes, we can expect continual deterioration of all those factors that quality of life is commonly judged by. In 1985, for instance, the American Cancer Society estimated that one of every three children born that year will suffer from cancer sometime during their life. As if this were not serious enough, in its first issue of 1989, *Time* magazine devoted the cover story it usually reserves for the individual who has had the biggest impact on world events the preceding year, to "The Endangered Earth." Citing numerous environmental disasters, including drought, heat waves, forest fires, smog, pollution of the seas and sewage on the beaches, the article stated, "This year the earth spoke, like God warning Noah of the deluge. . . . Everyone suddenly sensed that this gyrating globe, this precious repository of all the life that we know, was in danger."

As we will see, these, and the various other problems facing humanity, are man-made. And they can be changed if we accept the concepts of personal responsibility and of the natural order of life. The very same principles that are now being successfully used for the relief of personal illnesses of the body and mind, can be applied to concerns of the family and of society as a whole.

I hope this book will change your life. It is meant to. If so, you will not stop there. Soon your attention will turn to your family, your friends, and your community. If enough individuals begin this process of personal development, my children, and your children, and children yet unborn, will inherit the basis of a planetary community founded on the tenets of harmony and peace. This indeed is the true goal of traditional and Oriental medicine and of macrobiotics. It is the dream that Michio and Aveline Kushi have dedicated their lives to realizing.

PHILLIP JANNETTA
Tokyo
Christmas Day, 1988

Acknowledgments

From its conception to final publication, the talents and energy of numerous individuals are necessary for the production of a book. To all those who contributed to this volume, I extend my deeply felt thanks.

In particular, I wish to extend my appreciation to George Ohsawa, who introduced in a practical and systematic way, the principles of life to the modern world. To Michio Kushi, and his wife Aveline, I owe a personal debt of gratitude. With their dedication to world peace, and their tireless teaching schedule, the Kushis have been a driving force over the last three decades in the holistic movement that is now extending across the planet.

The president of Japan Publications, Inc., Mr. Iwao Yoshizaki, has been extremely patient as this manuscript slowly came together, for which I am grateful. Mr. Yoshizaki deserves recognition for his efforts in making the wisdom of the East available to the Western world.

I owe a special thank you to all the students who have participated in the classes I have taught over the years. Their insights and questions have been a great help in my own development.

On a more specific level, I thank Edward Esko and Alex Jack, in Boston, for copyreading the final text, and to Craig Edwards and Kristin Newton, in Tokyo, for their kind feedback on the original manuscript.

To my wife, who manages to keep our household orderly despite raising a family, and who somehow finds time to dispense advise and teach cooking classes in both Japanese and English; and to our two daughters, whose energy and curiosity are an inspiration to me, I am grateful.

Finally, to my mother, whose passing away several years ago left a bigger gap in my life than I could ever have anticipated; to my father, whose sacrifices for his children I am only now coming to understand; and to my sister Deborah, and my brothers, David and Steven, who share and support the macrobiotic way of life, I extend a big thank you.

Contents

Foreword, 5
Preface, 7
Acknowledgments, 9

Part One: PRINCIPLES OF TRADITIONAL AND ORIENTAL MEDICINE, *15*

1. Oriental Medicine: An Overview, 17
Physics and Metaphysics, *18*
Modern and Traditional, *19*
Foundation of Oriental Medicine, *20*
When and Where, *23*
Five Principles of Oriental Medicine, *24*
East and West, *28*
Three Levels of Medical Practice, *30*
Classes of Treatment, *31*
Holistic and Symptomatic, *33*
Treatments, *34*

2. Ki: The Source of Life, 36
Ki: A Definition, *37*
Physical and Spiritual, *39*
Ki in Traditional Societies, *43*
Ki in Healing, *45*
Self in East and West, *46*
Ki in the Body, *47*
Planetary Body, *48*
The Forces of Heaven and Earth, *50*
In the Human Body, *52*
Male and Female, *54*
Two Types of Ki, *55*
Problems with Ki, *56*

3. Energy Cycles, 58
Yin and Yang, *58*
In the Western World, *60*
A Common Heritage, *64*
The Three Emperors of China, *64*
Ancient Techniques, *67*
Yin and Yang in the Body, *68*
Five Transformations, *69*
Examples of Application, *74*

Emotions, Mind, and Spirit, *75*
Energy Cycles, *77*
The Regulating Cycle, *79*

4. Meridians and Points, 81
Meridians, *81*
Meridians in the Embryo, *82*
Yin and Yang Meridians, *84*
Meridian Pairs, *86*
Course of Energy Flow, *89*
Origin of the Meridians, *102*
Points of Energy, *104*
Yu and Bo Points, *104*
Sei, Gen, and Go Points, *106*
Five Transformation Points, *109*
The Importance of Names, *112*

5. Diagnosis, 114
Purpose of Diagnosis, *116*
Methods of Diagnosis, *116*
Diagnosis by Seeing, *118*
Diagnosis by Listening, *121*
Diagnosis by Touching, *123*
The Pulses, *126*
Tongue Diagnosis, *129*
Meridian Diagnosis, *132*
Value of Traditional Diagnosis, *133*

Part Two: APPLYING THE PRINCIPLES, *135*

1. Food as Medicine, 137
The Infinite Range of Food, *137*
Seven Stages of Food, *139*
Complementary Views, *141*
Degrees of Control, *141*
Medicinal Applications, *142*
Energetics of Food, *147*
Atomospheric Energies, *148*
Using the Five Transformations of Energy, *149*
Body and Food Correspondences, *150*
Treating Symptoms with Food, *151*

2. Herbal Medicine, 153
Modern and Traditional Uses of Herbs, *153*
Value of Herbal Medicine, *154*
Standards of Application, *155*

Traditional and Modern Approaches Compared, *156*
Principles of Use, *158*
Five Transformations of Energy, *159*
Preparations, *160*
Conclusion, *161*

3. Prayer, 162
How We Use Sound, *162*
Sound as Energy, *163*
The Basic Sounds, *165*
Healing with Sound, *167*
Combinations of Sounds, *170*
Meditation, *171*

4. Palm Healing, 177
The Energy Circuit, *178*
Source of Healing Abilities, *179*
Generating Healing Abilities, *180*
Breathing Techniques, *182*
Detecting Ki, *183*
Treatments, *184*
Know Thy Self, *187*

5. Exercise and Massage, 189
Who Needs It, *189*
Physical Activity or Systematic Exercise, *190*
Five Guidelines to Follow, *192*
Two Poles of Exercise, *194*
Cultural Adaptation, *195*
East and West, *196*
Ki Exercises, *197*
Meridian Exercises, *198*
In Summary, *201*
Massage, *202*
A Generation Gap, *202*
The Origin of Massage, *203*
The Decline of Massage, *204*
Benefits of Massage, *205*
Complementary Approaches, *206*
In the West, *207*
Eastern Approach, *208*
Shiatsu, *209*
Applications, *211*
A Shiatsu Treatment, *212*
Self-Shiatsu, *213*

6. Acupuncture and Moxibustion, 216
Acupuncture, *216*
The Needles, *217*
Needing Techniques, *218*
The Treatment, *219*
Moxibustion, *221*
Production and Use, *222*
Treatments, *222*
Side Effects, *224*

Part Three: MACROBIOTIC HEALING: THE MEDICINE-TO-BE, *225*

1. Personal Well-being, 227
A Holistic Look at Illness, *229*
Difficulties Benefit Us, *230*
Mechanism of Illness, *231*
Impaired Discharge Ability, *233*
Ways to Accelerate Discharge, *235*
Macrobiotic Healing, *236*
Keys to Healing *236*
Curing an Illness, *240*
Spiritual Development, *241*

2. Family Health, 243
The Basis of Society, *243*
Beyond Personal Health, *245*
Love and Marriage, *246*
The Changing Family, *248*
Rebuilding Family Health, *249*
Spiritual Healing, *250*
The Time for Commitment, *252*

3. Society and the World, 254
An Epic End, *254*
Crisis and Opportunity, *256*
Good Intentions Are Not Enough, *257*
Solutions, *258*
A New Human Species, *259*
Conflicting Opinions, *260*
The Macrobiotic Solution, *261*
Change Moves from the Bottom up, *262*
The Crossroad, *262*

Bibliography, *263*
Index, *267*

Part One: Principles of Traditional and Oriental Medicine

INTRODUCTION TO PART 1

The concept of medical treatment—currently defined in terms of specialists, huge and impersonal hospitals, and space-age treatments—has been under siege for the past several decades. There is a growing unease, fostered both by reason and instinct, that contemporary health-care practices are somehow missing the mark: that treatments frequently do more harm than the illness, and that too few patients actually recover their original state of vitality following therapy. The desire for an alternative to interventive medicine is deeply felt, and, more and more often, openly discussed by laymen and professionals alike.

The very idea of illness itself is undergoing a similar alteration. The image of individuals being innocent victims of capricious or even malevolent external forces is rapidly becoming passé. Scientific research and common sense indicate that our state of health is directly linked to choices we make on a daily basis. Issues such as diet, exercise, smoking and drinking, personal relationships, home and natural environments, and a host of others, are being recognized as the keys not only to health and longevity, but to the actual quality of one's life.

Part 1 supports this reevaluation by introducing the theoretical groundwork of a very different approach to healing. Commencing with the basic precepts that characterize traditional and Oriental medicine, we move on to an in-depth exploration of Ki energy, a far-reaching concept destined to shatter society's one-dimensional view of life and human destiny. The human energetic system is the next topic, as our focus sharpens to considerations of individual well-being. The concluding chapter of this part reviews the distinctive diagnostic techniques that are the natural outcome of the metaphysical (as opposed to the analytical) worldview applied not only to healing, but to prevention and personal development as well.

Be warned, however, that this ancient ideology cannot be confined simply to concerns of physical health, or even to the broader issues of personal welfare. Rather, it is intimately joined to the entire social and natural environment within which human life unfolds. Join us now for an exploration of "holistic" medicine: a philosophy that our ancestors articulated many generations ago.

1. Oriental Medicine: An Overview

A civilization is a living, responsive, evolving entity. Its development is stimulated by the myriad influences each culture encounters over the long course of its individual life cycle. The manner in which a particular society chooses to deal with those questions basic to its existence is directly connected to its vision of life. From this collective cosmology comes responses to such challenges as how to secure a steady food supply, educate the young, care for the elderly, structure the family, articulate the individual's role in society, maintain internal and external stability, and deal with the fundamental issues of health: the prevention and treatment of illness.

The resulting social institutions that emerge to secure these needs, although appearing separate and distinct, are intimately related by a shared perception of how the world works. They are the natural extensions and physical expressions of the way a specific group of people interprets its place in the great scheme of life.

A dynamic, mutually dependent relationship develops within this social framework, as two opposite yet complementary forces interact to accommodate the contradictory necessities of fostering growth while maintaining stability. On the one hand, individuals with wisdom and foresight are needed to define the group's place in the world, and to establish goals and the methods for achieving them. This broad vision is matched by individuals with vigor and practicality, who have the skills and drive to accomplish the group's destiny.

The interdependence of these two orientations is clear. Without organization and the willingness to work, goals can never be realized. Without a clear judgment, aspirations large enough to accommodate the needs and expectations of both the individual and the group can never be established.

This polar relationship is a fundamental aspect of life. It exists within any and every process and phenomenon as the spark or energy that stimulates adaptation and evolution. Throughout this book, the interaction between opposite yet complementary forces is discussed, particularly as it applies to the two poles of medical practice: the modern, Western model, and the traditional, Oriental standard.

Often, comparisons will be made between the two partners in this union. It must be remembered, however, that it is indeed a partnership, that both members are essential, and that it is only when one begins to dominate that balance is upset, and extreme tendencies begin to appear. At some point in this scenario, a rebalancing must begin. On a social scale, this can happen because individuals and groups, leaders and organizations, recognizing that equilibrium has been lost, take steps to amend it. Or, if allowed to grow too large, this imbalance will naturally and automatically right itself, as the excesses of the dominate member leads to its own collapse.

Physics and Metaphysics

It is said that the science of physics is the mother of modern civilization. This basic science, involved in solving the apparent mysteries of the natural world, forms the underpinning not only for all other sciences, but for their practical applications in the form of technology, farming practices, legal, business, and educational systems, and, although difficult to see, morals and ethics as well. After all, the values we employ to determine good and bad, right and wrong, valuable and useless, are directly based on our worldview, as defined by the prevailing authority of science. In much the same way, physics is also the foundation of modern medical practice.

Metaphysics played a similar role in traditional times. Broadly defined as the attempt to understand the nature of life, metaphysics offers the mirror-image perspective to that provided by physics. It approaches reality by starting from a very large and general view, asking questions such as what is God, what is the purpose of life, and how does the individual human being relate to the natural world. Once these issues are resolved, the more mundane and specific considerations of day-to-day existence are addressed.

Physics begins its search for reality by exploring the basic properties of matter. The questions it seeks to answer are geared toward unlocking the secrets of the physical world. This approach has driven ever-inward as new discoveries and increasingly sophisticated technologies have extended our ability to unravel the laws of material existence. From this knowledge-base, first Western, and now modern civilization has fashioned its values and its strategies for life.

At one time, metaphysics was the dominate approach. In our day, physics holds sway. Like all other complementary relationships, neither partner can be considered true or false, right or wrong, or capable of offering the complete and final answers we seek. Rather, they represent opposite and mutually supporting ways of looking at life.

The difficulty arises when the acceptance and dependence on one approach overshadows, and then begins to exclude the other. Today, any attempt to introduce metaphysics into our view of life is labeled as superstition, and ignored. If the physical properties of a thing cannot be measured in a repeatable way, it is considered to be outside the boundaries of reality. Calling an idea non-scientific is tantamount to a death sentence to its prospects for any serious discussion.

This orientation seriously restricts our ability to adapt to the ever-shifting circumstances of life, particularly in recent times, when the rate of change is breathtakingly fast and still accelerating. It unnecessarily limits our options, drives us further along our path of excess, and guarantees the necessity of large-scale rebalancing sometime in the years ahead.

As a simple but serious example of this one-sided approach, modern science has produced many "wonder drugs" to fight infection and prevent infectious disease. However, indiscriminate use of such medications has weakened human immune ability, and by extension, the survival prospects of countless individuals. In addition, researchers have for years been reporting the development of "super" bacteria that have built up a resistance to the more common antibiotics. In the future, stronger and stronger drugs will be required to fight even routine infections, which in turn will have increasingly severe side effects. And, there is no reason to assume that microorganisms will not continue to adapt to these newer, more powerful medications.

Such unwanted (and unexpected) side effects are the by-products of an unnecessarily narrow and one-sided perspective. In dealing with infectious disease, science has failed to address certain factors, particularly the variables of individual susceptibility. Instead of the impossible task of eliminating "germs," a broader response involving individual participation in, and responsibility for, illness, including so-called contagious disease, needs to be fashioned.

Clearly, what is needed is a marriage of the modern and traditional views, of wisdom with knowledge, if humanity is to avoid foundering on the extremes of our conventional strategy to problem solving. We need to know not only the "how" of a sickness—how it develops and how to treat its symptoms—but also the "why"—why something like AIDS has appeared at this specific time, why it is rampant among certain groups, and in particular countries and social and natural environments, and why, after being exposed to the AIDS virus, certain individuals quickly come down with symptoms, while others remain symptom-free for months and years. The answer to these and similar questions demand a dynamic and comprehensive view of life.

Modern and Traditional

Two broad philosophies are compared in this book. They can be called the modern worldview and the traditional worldview. In addition, the adjectives Eastern and Western are applied. The modern, Western outlook and the traditional, Eastern view complement each other in many ways.

The former is generally concerned with linear, or one-dimensional time, seeks short-term gains, is logical and analytical, and is based on the science of physics. The latter deals with cyclical and multidimensional time, values long-term stability, is intuitive and comprehensive, and is rooted in metaphysics. Table 1 sums up the distinctions between these two value systems.

In the twentieth century, the modern, Western orientation has become not only the dominant but the pervasive view. Its influence is felt across the planet, from Bangkok to Quebec, from New York to Beijing, and has penetrated every aspect of daily life. Indeed, this particular belief system has spread so widely, that it is no longer accurate to speak of Western science or Western medicine, but rather of modern science and modern medicine. To the degree that their economies allow, the nations of the world have abandoned their distinct cosmologies in favor of our contemporary value system. They have recast their social institutions along Western patterns, despite the fact that modern nations are growing increasingly aware of the deficiencies of such systems.

A quick read of the headlines of a daily newspaper highlights these liabilities. Included are increasing rates of: drug abuse and crime, illiteracy and school dropouts; teenage pregnancies and unwed mothers; the homeless and destitute; single-parent families and the loss of the family as a social institution. Along with

Table 1 Complementary Orientation of Modern and Traditional Societies

Modern	Traditional
Analytical	Holistic
Divisive	Integrative
Compete/Struggle	Cooperate/Harmonize
Complex/Sophisticated	Practical/Primitive
Exploit and dominate nature and fellow humans	Cherish nature and fellow humans
Growth and consumption	Stability and renewal
Horizontal social order	Vertical social order
Individual profit	Family and community benefit
Logic/Reason	Intuition/Instinct
Materialistic/Scientific	Spiritual/Metaphysical
Mechanistic	Synergistic
Objective	Subjective
Sequential time	Cyclical time
Short-term gain	Long-term benefit
Specialists	Generalists
Theoretical/Conceptual	Practical/Common sense

destructive agricultural practices, planetary-wide environmental pollution, and the growing discrepancy between rich and poor nations, these are but a few of the most obvious side effects of our particular approach to life taken to its extreme.

Some countries have gone so far as to outlaw their ancient healing arts, others merely officially ignore them. This has happened despite the fact that health-care costs in industrial nations are consuming a large and growing percentage of their gross national products while the rate of degenerative disease, mental illness, and social disorder continues to climb.

It is interesting to note that traditional healing methods are still practiced, even in "modern" societies, in spite of public-relations campaigns waged by special-interest groups to discredit them, and often under the threat of legal penalties. These practices persist, not out of superstition or ignorance, but because they continue to prove themselves effective and cost efficient.

Foundation of Oriental Medicine

Oriental medicine cannot be separated from the philosophic base upon which the traditional and Eastern worldview rests. The relationship can be likened to the flower and roots of a plant. Although unseen and seldom appreciated, it is the roots that nourish and give form to the flower. Oriental medicine emerged and evolved directly from a particular approach to life, just as modern, Western medicine grow out of the unique worldview that was first articulated during the classical Grecian era and was then consolidated in Western Europe during the sixteenth and seventeenth centuries.

So close is the relationship between view of life and medical practice, that Oriental medicine can broadly be defined as the application of the Far-Eastern philosophy to the field of healing. Without such ideology, this unique system of medicine could not have developed, and where it is lost, the practice of Oriental medicine ceases to exists. In a similar way, each social institution in Far-Eastern countries reflects this parentage.

The term *Oriental medicine* actually refers to three factors:

1. The geographic location where this particular approach to healing developed and is still primarily employed.
2. The unique worldview that nourished this form of medical practice.
3. The traditional, holistic approach to personal, family, and societal well-being.

To our precise way of thinking, these categories may seem unnessarily broad. Without this wide context, however, it is impossible to understand, and thus appreciate and successfully use, traditional and Oriental medical applications in our modern, Western-oriented world.

In terms of geography, Oriental medicine was practiced primarily in the Asian countries of China, Korea, Japan, and India. (Other countries, including Tibet also share this approach.) Although the methods were slightly different, the under-

Fig. 1 Geographical Regions of Oriental Medicine Practice

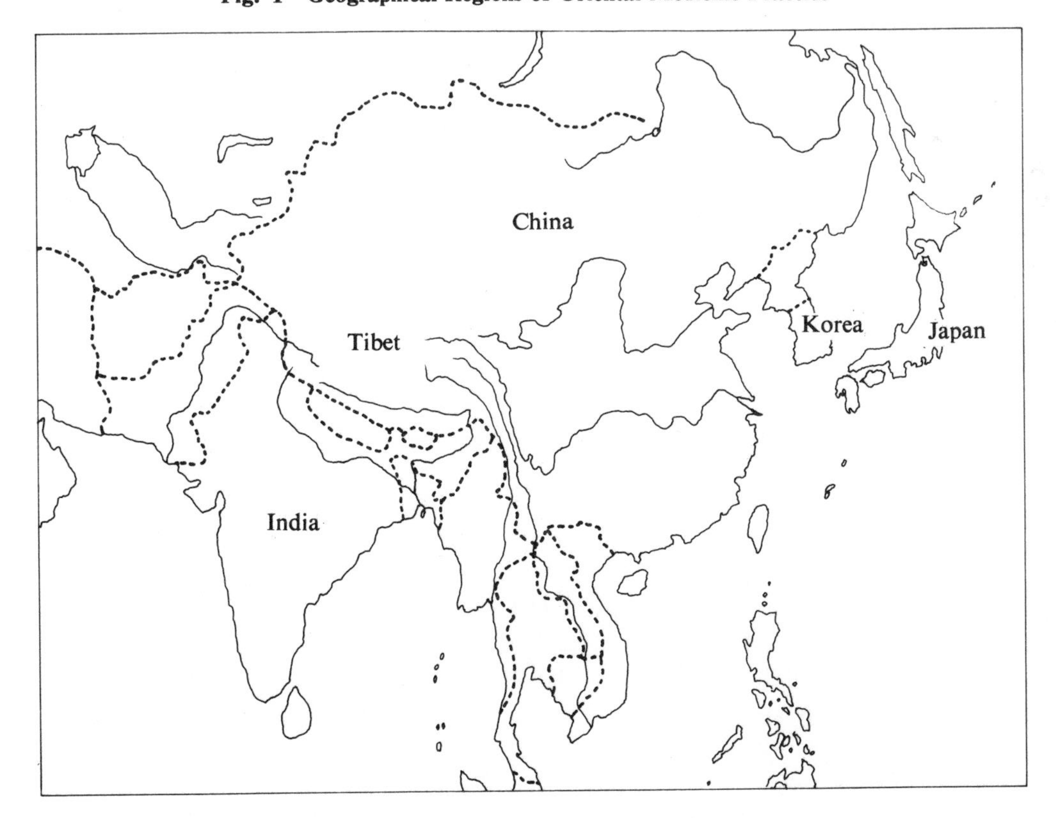

lying principles of India's healing arts were identical to those of its Far-Eastern neighbors. And, as we have seen, orientation, rather than specific application, is the criterion for defining Oriental medicine.

China's oldest book on medicine, the *Huang Ti Nei Ching*, or *The Yellow Emperor's Classic of Internal Medicine*, explains how distinct applications of the basic principles of Oriental medicine emerged in response to various geographical conditions. In the mountainous regions of western China, for example, medication, in the form of herbal and mineral preparations, was the most common method of treatment. People in this locale, adapting to the circumstances of their surroundings, took advantage of the myriad plants and mineral substances readily available to them. In other words, the people of western China applied the principles of Oriental medicine to their particular environment and circumstances.

In the coastal region of eastern China, along the Chinese sea, seafood was readily available. Surgical techniques were developed in response to the subsequent effects of the overconsumption of proteins and fats, especially of animal origin. These products tend to produce various types of tumors and cysts, and such diseases of the skin as boils and abscesses. Medical treatment was consequently geared toward the relief of such conditions.

In the cold, northern area, the application of heat, in the form of *moxibustion*, was developed as a method of therapeutic application. In the south, a hot and humid region, the more subtle technique of manipulating energy with the use of needles emerged, and is now commonly known as *acupuncture*.

Massage, exercise, and breathing practices began in the central region. As the *Nei Ching* explains: "The people of the regions of the center eat mixed food and do not (suffer or weary at their) toil. . . . These diseases are most fittingly treated with breathing exercises, massage of the skin and flesh, and exercises of the hands and feet. Hence the treatment with breathing exercises, massage and exercises of the limbs has its origins in the center regions [of China]."

In prehistoric Japan, medical application consisted mainly of *prayer*, or the use of sound to produce specific effects on the body and mind, and *palm healing*, or the use of the palms of the hands to direct energy for the treatment of physical and psychological problems. Even today in Japan, the term *Te Ate* (手当), or hand application, is used by the medical profession and the general public to refer to medical treatment. *Te* (手) means "hand," and *Ate* (当) means "application." Along with the specific treatments of prayer and palm healing, the Japanese of long ago used the adjustment of the individual's way of life, including diet, as the basis of healing.

The ancient Indian civilization developed such therapeutic and preventive measures as meditation, prayer, breathing techniques, herbal medicines, and physical exercise. Perhaps the most well-known branch of healing in India is *Ayurvedic* medicine. In practice, or application, Ayurvedic medicine differs from that found in the Far-Eastern countries. This is natural and understandable, as the environmental and social conditions of India differ greatly from those societies. The principles upon which Ayurvedics is based, however, correlate closely to those of Oriental medicine, just as the various approaches found in distinct regions of China shared the same foundation.

This brief overview illustrates the point that specific applications of the principles of Oriental medicine emerged to suit the unique conditions of various geographical areas. All such techniques, however, are based on a common worldview and a shared vision of the cause of illness. Moxibustion, massage, and acupuncture are applied along the body's meridians and points to harmonize energy flow. Palm healing, prayer, chanting, breathing practices, and meditation are also employed to make alterations in energy flow, although on a more subtle level. Dietary adjustment, and its offshoots, medicinal-food preparations and herbal medicine, are utilized in very precise ways to modify the flow of energy within the body.

When and Where

We cannot say for certain when or where Oriental medicine began. The *Nei Ching*, as mentioned above, is China's oldest medical text. Scholars generally estimate that the work was written sometime between the third and second centuries B.C., although the source of the book, the Yellow Emperor, is said to have lived about 2700 B.C. The *Nei Ching* contains references to times far earlier than the Yellow Emperor, when humanity lived to advanced ages. In the opening pages of the book, the Yellow Emperor asks his court physician:

> I have heard that people of ancient times had lived as long as one hundred and twenty years with no sign of weakening in movements, but people nowadays [in 2700 B.C.] become weakened in their movements at the age of less than sixty years old. Is this due to a change in natural environments or due to man's fault?

The answer to this question has important implications for all of us, and forms the basis of this book.

> The ancient people who knew the proper way to live followed the pattern of Yin and Yang, which is the regular pattern of heaven and earth, remained in harmony with numerical symbols which are the great principles of human life. They ate and drank with moderation, lived their daily lives in a regular pattern with neither excess nor abuse. For this reason, their spirits and bodies remained in perfect harmony with each other, and consequently, they could live out their natural life span and die at the age of over one hundred and twenty years.

It is generally thought that the *Nei Ching* is a summation of the medical knowledge gathered by generations of practitioners, extending back perhaps thousands of years before it was compiled in book form. This remarkable text may thus represent the accumulated healing experience from the very beginnings of the Chinese people.

Many aspects of Japanese culture have their origins in the Chinese civilization. The sixth and seventh centuries A.D. were a particularly active period of transmission. Japanese scholars, religious figures and government representatives were sent to China. They returned with the teachings of Buddha, a writing system based on ideograms, various arts and crafts, and the foundations of Chinese medicine. Transplanted to the island country situated off the coast of the Asian continent, this knowledge underwent a process of adaptation to suit the particular needs of Japanese society.

Historians tell us that many of China's cultural traditions may have their roots in the civilization of ancient India. The origins of Indian culture, dating back many thousands of years, are lost to us. Perhaps they were transported from the more ancient Sumerian civilization that developed along the Tigris and Euphrates river valley—the site of cultural developments that we take for granted in the twentieth century, including what is considered to be humanity's first system of writing, the plow and wagon wheel, a sophisticated system of measuring and surveying techniques, and the division of the day into hours and minutes.

Acupuncture is often considered to be a uniquely Chinese medical practice, and certainly a well-developed and widely used science of acupuncture has been used for thousands of years in China. In Korea, however, bone and stone needles have been discovered that date back to 3000 B.C. Although the material is different, the form of these needles is the same as modern Chinese needles.

In India, a figurine of a medicine man has been unearthed that is estimated to date from 2000 B.C. This ancient healer is holding an acupuncture needle in one hand and a medicine bag in the other. Evidence thus suggests that acupuncture was being practiced in India, Korea, and China, at least 4,000 to 5,000 years ago.

Records of Chinese medicine originate from the time of the Yellow Emperor, the third emperor of China. There is some dispute as to whether this figure is legendary or an actual historical personality. In the *Nei Ching* he is said to have lived around 2700 B.C. Long before this time, according to this work, various applications of Oriental medicine were already widely used.

We do not really know when or where Oriental medicinal practice began, and it may be impossible to determine precisely. We do know that, bounded by a common worldview, various forms of Far-Eastern medicine developed in response to the unique environmental conditions of specific locales. Later, these applications were compiled into a comprehensive medical framework, a small portion of which are now collectively known as Oriental medicine. Since it was the Chinese civilization that developed, gathered, and preserved many of these practices, Oriental medicine is now commonly called "Chinese medicine."

Five Principles of Oriental Medicine

Perhaps the major criticism of traditional and Oriental medicine heard today is that they lack coherence and a logical framework. Apparently based on superstition and a faulty concept of anatomy and physiology, they may represent humanity's best efforts under primitive circumstances, but contemporary science, medicine, and technology have rendered such practices obsolete. Once we realize, however, that the ancient healing arts are expressions of a value system that not only differs from, but is opposite to, our present orientation, the futility of trying to compare one with the standards of the other becomes obvious.

The ancient world, and the Far East in particular, can be characterized by five general principles that distinguish it from modern, Western civilization. These same attributes differentiate traditional medicine from modern medicine, or even from Chinese medicine as it is now practiced. These principles are the foundation of a very different way of perceiving reality, and as such, provide a unique opportunity for enlarging our view of life. They can be summarized as follows:

1. *Holistically Oriented—Non-Analytical.* In Oriental countries there was a long-held doctrine prohibiting autopsy. (For centuries, this was true in Western countries as well.) This precept developed out of respect for the human body, and also from the idea that the analytical approach to life, the taking apart of a thing in the attempt to understand it, was a mistake that threatened the loss of the overall or comprehensive view necessary for every member of society.

The premise was that in any situation, each factor was related to others, and all were organically connected in a synergistic relationship. In the human body, for instance, one organ or one system cannot be understood or treated apart from the whole. An individual, in turn, must be grasped as a unity or totality, rather than as series of isolated and independent parts. This is as true for the totality of the Self—the physical, emotional, intellectual, and spiritual aspects of our being—as it is for the physical body.

Not limited to medical practice, this principle had a social application as well. Individuals were not perceived as independent beings pursuing their lives in isolation, but rather as part of an organic whole—a family, a community, and a society—from which they received and contributed benefits. This is the source of the concept of harmony that is a cornerstone of Oriental civilization.

The Chinese and Japanese ideogram for harmony is 和, pronounced as *Wa* in Japanese. It consists of two parts. The left side (禾) refers to "cereal grain plant," such as rice or wheat. The right side (口) is the character for "mouth." The complete ideogram signifies "peace" or "harmony," reflecting the understanding that one who eats whole grains will be balanced or harmonious.

On the social level, the idea of *Wa* implies that a culture whose diet is based on grains will coexist peacefully with the forces of nature, and that the interaction of its citizens will likewise be amiable. This concept of harmony is a fundamental element of Far-Eastern civilization, and is essential in our study of Oriental medicine.

In contrast to this peaceful state, an individual who regularly ate meat was described by the adjective *niku niku suki* (meat, meat like) in Japanese. This term describes a person who is greedy, egocentric, aggressive, or self-centered. A culture based on animal-food consumption was thought to exhibit similar tendencies. It was seen to be destructive within, to the surrounding environment, and to the other cultures it came into contact with. These characteristics are opposite to the state of *Wa*.

2. *Spiritual Orientation—Non-materialistic.* In ancient civilizations, and particularly in the Orient, the physical or material world was perceived in terms of *Ki*-energy, invisible vibration, or spirit. This outlook reflected the

understanding that behind all physical existence lies a nonphysical reality. Every plant and animal was seen as a manifestation of spirit. The same was true of inanimate objects like stones, valleys, mountains, and streams. Even man-made items were recognized as having a spiritual existence. Their value and beauty were based on the degree of harmony of the energy pattern they manifested.

The medical interpretation of this view held that all sickness had its origins in the disruption of the body's energy flow. Various applications that adjusted or rebalanced this subtle energy were thus developed and successfully used to treat physical, psychological and spiritual problems.

On the social level, this principle implied that the basis for human relations was the natural order of harmony and compromise within the group, rather than competition and individual profit made at the family's or community's expense. While personal initiative was valued and individuality respected, personal gain or advancement were less important than the cooperation and good relations with others that produced benefits for all.

Material goods were perceived as reflections of the spiritual world. They were used with care and were meant to provide years and even generations of service. The natural world, seen as a reflection of the spiritual, was respected. No monetary value could be placed on natural resources, which were considered to be the collective possession of the group. Individuals were seen as caretakers, using and renewing, and passing on to the next generation. Social institutions were patterned after the natural order of life, so that benefits passed smoothly from individual to group and from group to individual. Unnecessary accumulation and waste were both recognized as violating the principles of nature.

3. *Cause-oriented—Non-symptomatic.* In traditional medical practice, the emphasis was on finding and changing the cause of a problem, rather than on the temporary relief of symptoms. If, for example, a herbal preparation was applied to some form of skin disease, the outbreak may disappear. And yet the case was not considered cured. Most instances of skin disease represent the discharge of internal excess. The cause is poor-quality blood and body fluids, which in turn are created by improper dietary practices. By making dietary adjustments, the blood quality changes, the cause will be eliminated, and the skin problem will disappear.

But our search for the cause must continue. Why did the individual eat and behave in such a manner as to create skin disease. One's view of life, which is the source of this behavior, must also be changed if true healing is to be achieved. Cause to cause to cause is the way we go, following this third principle of traditional medicine.

Applied socially, this precept was expressed as the concept of *On* (恩). This ideogram consists of two parts, 因, referring to "cause," and 心, denoting "mind." The implication is that we never forget the cause and origin of life. On a daily level, we acknowledge all those who have helped or benefited us. We cherish the kindness we have received, and we strive to return it, not just in the amount received, or with interest, as in a business transaction, but following the example of nature, continuously. On a wider scale, we recognize our dependence on the natural world that sustains us, and to the larger forces that make our life possible.

To our parents and ancestors, spouse and children, teachers and advisors, seniors, friends, society as a whole, and finally to life itself, we acknowledge our source or "roots," and ceaselessly extend our appreciation. This is the spirit of *On*.

4. *Intuitive—Non-conceptual.* Traditional and Oriental medicine are based on intuition and common sense, and in this regard can be called "primitive" in comparison with the sophistication and complexity of modern medicine. The operative premise is simplicity. Instead of huge clinics, complex equipment, numerous specialists and medical technicians, and extensive and expensive treatment, less equipment and simple applications are desired.

Ideally, there is no medication and no direct treatment as we normally think of it. This final stage of medical practice involves guiding by one's words and example, and influencing by one's presence so that people instinctively understand the way to bring their lives into harmony with the forces of nature. In the meantime, of course, treatments are employed, following the principle of intuition and simplicity.

On a social level, the intuitive and commonsense orientation appears in a culture's approach to the practical aspects of daily life. The family structure, for instance, consisted of several generations living in the same household. Economically and ecologically, this is a very efficient arrangement. Each generation contributed to the family's well-being, and, in turn, was supported and cared for by the others. Society was thus strengthened, and its resources freed for productive uses, rather than stressed with the need to provide not only economic support but the various other social services usually existing in a family setting. The community served as an extended family, providing additional support, guidance, and sense of belonging to its members.

Social order was maintained more from personal ethics, family supervision, and community standards, than on laws and police enforcement, thus negating the need for a complex legal and penal system. These were considered impractical, costly, and ultimately unworkable.

5. *Practical—Non-theoretical.* Although it has a comprehensive and profound theoretical basis, the philosophy and practice of traditional medicine are not divorced from everyday life. The theory is accessible enough to be understood by all people, and broad enough to be applied to all areas of life.

Medically, this means that individuals and families are capable of understanding the cause and mechanism of illness, and are able to treat most problems by themselves, at home. The simplest treatments are used, and the ingredients and equipment required are those commonly found in the family kitchen.

Socially, this principle means that solutions to the basic considerations of society are based on a functional, uncomplicated, long-term approach, rather than on theoretical, complex, stopgap solutions. The emphasis is on stability and renewal in contrast to short-term gain and the cycle of consumption and discarding, which is the driving force of our consumer society.

In the area of agriculture, for instance, this principle of practicality has allowed farmers to harvest food from the same fields for hundreds and even thousands of years. This differs greatly from the documented hazards of modern agricultural practices which include the demineralization of the soil, the destruction of the soil's microorganisms—which are essential for plant growth—the poisoning of the ground water with pesticides and chemical fertilizers, and the annual loss of tens-of-thousands of tons of topsoil to wind and rain erosion.

To summarize, the principles upon which ancient civilizations were based acknowledged the oneness and interdependence of life. Recognizing that humanity is but one member of the planetary family, our ancestors strove to live in harmony with the forces of nature, rather than to dominate them. Traditional medical practice reflected this outlook. Its primary concern was with the therapeutic aspects of daily life. A properly ordered lifestyle was viewed as the most efficient means of prevention, and reestablishing balance by the simplest methods avaliable was the ideal healing technique.

East and West

The five principles of traditional and Oriental civilization are the basis of ancient societies in general, and specifically of the Far East. They contrast sharply with the values of modern society, and with the Western worldview. Indeed, they are actually their complementary opposite.

It is well-known that in many ways, East and West are opposite. In *Acupuncture and the Philosophy of the Far East*, George Ohsawa summed up the differences this way: "The worlds of the Orient and the Occident are opposite ends of the same pole. In the Orient, the direction of East corresponds to what is West in the Occident. Thus it follows that in many ways the Oriental mentality is the mirror image of the Occidental way of thought."

This fact can be the source of misunderstanding and frustration, as many contemporary business executives and governmental officials can no doubt vouch for. As a simple example of the differing points of view, when an Oriental (Chinese, Korean, or Japanese) addresses an envelope, he will write in the sequence of country (if it is an international letter), state, city, and then the street address. Finally, when adding the individual's name, the family name comes first, followed by the given name. (Supporting the idea that the traditional orientation was at one time worldwide, some Eastern European countries still use this progression as well.)

Writing moves from right to left, and in vertical columns, as compared to the Western method of writing left to right in horizontal lines. And, instead of using alphabetical letters to create words, which are then grouped together to produce

Fig. 2 Complementary Writing Styles: East and West

1. George Rice
2. 123 Boylston Street
3. Brookline, MA.
4. U.S.A.

←

4. 3. 2. 1. ↓

1. アメリカ合衆国
2. マサチューセッツ州 ブルックライン
3. ボイルストン街一二三
4. ライス・ジョージ

Lines read from top to bottom and from right to left.

Line 1. U.S.A.
Line 2. Massachusetts, Brookline
Line 3. Boylston Street, 123
Line 4. Rice, George

concepts, ideograms, or symbols that more directly convey an idea or represent a thing, are used.

This single example accurately depicts two very different approaches to life. One, the traditional and Eastern view, starts with the general and moves to the particular, and is ordered along a perpendicular axis which is reflected in the distinct social structure in Oriental societies. The hallmark of this vertical social orientation is the respect extended to one's seniors and the guidance and support offered to one's juniors.

The other, the modern and Western view, starts with the particular and moves to the general. It is ordered along a horizontal axis, which is reflected in a social pattern in which individuals are treated similarly, regardless of age or experience.

As opposites, the Eastern and Western worldviews offer contemporary society the tools to fashion a broad-based, flexible approach to the seemingly insolvable problems confronting us as we approach the twenty-first century. Having taken the mechanistic and analytical approach to its extreme, humanity is now facing the inevitable necessity to rebalance. This change can come about in a deliberate and peaceful manner, if we exercise our judgment and make decisions based on a comprehensive perspective. If we assume that everything is fine, or that solutions to the critical health, ecological, economic, and social problems now confronting our planet can be found within our one-sided framework, we will insure that profound changes will force themselves upon modern civilization sometime in the near future.

The consequences of our narrowly focused attitude reverberate throughout society. Attempts to solve social problems as if they existed independently both of each other and from society's overall orientation will be futile, just as they have proved to be in the field of medicine. The exploding drug-abuse problem in modern societies offers a clear example. The issue runs far deeper than availability and low prices. People of all ages and socioeconomic positions are desperately trying to redress biological and psychological imbalances within themselves; imbalances directly related to a lifestyle and value system that have little relation to the natural order of life.

The choice is ours: we can either adopt a flexible approach and learn to live in harmony with the forces of life, or we can continue to resist them. Resistance is a form of violence that inevitably generates an opposite force to offset it.

Three Levels of Medical Practice

Traditional and Oriental cultures recognized three general levels of medical practice and three levels of practitioners. These categories represent a succession of ever-wider spheres of understanding and influence. They are reached as the physician gains insight through experience and reflection.

- On the first level of application, a doctor treated the symptoms of illness. It was said that such an individual could cure physical sickness.
- At the second level, the doctor's treatment was geared toward the patient as a whole, his way of eating, way of thinking, and in general, his way of life. It was said that at this level, a practitioner could care for the person.
- A physician on the third or highest level dealt with the larger issues of community life, and ultimately with the major problems of his time. Such a healer was regarded as being qualified to care for society.

In this progression, as a practitioner's understanding grew, he moved from the field of symptomatic treatment to one of guidance, and finally, to a role of educator and philosopher. The training of such a physician obviously differed greatly from current medical-school programs. A would-be traditional doctor apprenticed himself to a practicing physician who had mastered the highest level of application. The pupil would live with the practitioner, and work closely with him. He would study not only his teacher's technique, but also his ideology and way of life. After five or even ten years, the apprentice would begin to practice on his own.

As time went by, the maturing physician would need books on philosophy, science, astronomy, political and social studies, in addition to his medical texts. He was developing his understanding of civilization, of nature, and of the universe, to make himself a healer capable of dealing with issues from all areas of life.

No school can teach such a comprehensive understanding. Development is a matter of personal initiative. Formal education is, of course, needed to learn specific skills and general principles. But this is merely the start. Even learning how to apply techniques on a symptomatic level takes experience and insight.

The ability to administer to the needs of society requires not just an understanding of illness, but of food, lifestyle, emotions and intellect, family concerns, economic forces, social and governmental questions, technology, the cycles of nature, and spiritual affairs. To reach this level of practice, a very deep wisdom is required. This is one reason why educators and philosophers were and are still held in such high regard in Far-Eastern countries, and why Oriental families place great emphasis on their children's education.

The qualifications of a traditional physician contrast sharply with those commonly expected of a doctor today. Three factors in particular summarize the ideal.

The individual should: (1) be in good health, (2) have a clear and comprehensive judgment, and (3) desire to work for the good of all people. Obviously, such a definition may not fit the requirements of a doctor in the modern sense. After all, we do not necessarily expect our practitioners to be examples of physical and mental health or to have a sweeping knowledge of human affairs. Yet these were the kinds of attributes that traditional healers were expected to possess. Beyond dealing with physical complaints, such individuals guided people on all levels of human existence. In this sense, their practice was not limited to personal health considerations, but extended to the complete spectrum of community concerns.

As modern research continues to point out the host of interrelated factors affecting an individual's health, and as we come to acknowledge our intimate connection with the natural world, the concept of holistic medicine will become generally accepted. As this happens, our perception of a physician's role in society will grow increasingly broad. The work of our healers will then expand to include the myrial influences that contribute to personal and societal well-being.

Classes of Treatment

Just as traditional societies recognized assorted levels of healers and medical practice, they also made distinctions between classes of treatment. These start with consideration for the immediate symptoms, and extend, from cause to cause, to nurture the person as a whole, or the Self in the largest meaning of the word.

1. The first level of treatment dealt with symptoms through the use of acupuncture, massage, herbal medications and surgical techniques.
2. Symptoms were treated on the second level through the more subtle adjustment of Ki-energy by means of meditation, palm healing, prayer, and the like.
3. On the third level, dietary adjustments were employed to eliminate symptoms and to bring the patient's condition back into balance. Food was used not from a nutritional point of view, but as a very precise means of regulating the body's energy flow.
4. Guidance was the form that health care took on the fourth level. Problems were eliminated by recommending alterations in the patient's lifestyle.
5. In the final or highest level of traditional medical practice, treatment took the form of education. The physician dealt with the patient's view of life—his self-image, his goals and aspirations, and his concept of his origin and destiny.

When a patient visited a physician, immediate problems were addressed by treatments on levels one through three. But the healer was not satisfied with the mere elimination of symptoms. His goal was to enable the patient to understand the cause of the problem, so it would not be produced again. In this sense, the physician worked to change the patient's future. By doing so, he also altered the individual's past, in that, the patient's memory of his illness changed from one of sorrow and regret to one of gratitude, marking the start of a new, freer way of life.

Thus, if the person did create some problem for himself later on, he would be

Table 2 Modern and Traditional Approaches to Medicine

	Modern/Western Medicine	Present-day Oriental Medicine	Traditional Medicine (the medicine-to-be)
Aim:	Remove symptoms	Reestablish balance within body	Harmonize with larger forces of nature
Approach:	Analyze/divide	See body as a unit	See entire Self
Attitude:	Fear/violence	Harmony	Faith based on understanding
Physician's task:	Suppress symptoms	Stimulate body's healing ability	Allow the forces of nature to heal
Cause:	External factors (germs, heredity, stress, pollution, etc.)	Energy imbalances caused by lifestyle (improper diet, lack of exercise, etc.)	Ignorance of the principles of life
Treatments:	Drugs/surgery chemicals	Natural substances and simple treatments	Education
Personal participation or responsibility	Little or no participation or responsibility	Patient receives treatment and lifestyle advice	Total responsibility and participation
Time frame:	Results should appear as quickly as possible	Gradual as balance is restored over days, weeks and months	Healing takes place in a natural manner with no concern about time
Cost:	Capital intensive	Some extra cost	Little or no extra cost
Equipment:	Specialized and sophisticated equipment	Simple equipment	No special equipment

Note: Rather than excluding the other two categories, traditional medicine encompasses and goes beyond them to establish true health and the base for lasting personal development.

able, in most cases, to personally make the adjustments necessary for relief. He would accomplish this by self-reflection, in order to discover how he was producing the condition. Perceiving the cause, the individual would be in a position to eliminate whatever symptoms he was experiencing. In addition, he would recognize his personal responsibility for the difficulty, and the specific ways he had been out of harmony with the forces of nature. Recovery thus becomes an educational process leading to a greater degree of independence and insight.

This orientation is vastly different from the current situation in which an individual takes medication or undergoes some other form of treatment to relieve the symptoms of a problem. Once the immediate discomfort disappears, the illness is considered cured. There is no personal participation in the healing process, no self-reflection, and no search for the cause. Clearly, this is a frustrating and dangerous approach to personal well-being. The distinctions between the modern and traditional approaches to healing, along with a third orientation, which will be discussed in the following section, are summarized in Table 2.

Holistic and Symptomatic

Three types of medical practice are compared in this book: (1) modern, Western medicine, (2) present-day Oriental medicine, commonly referred to as Chinese medicine, and (3) traditional, Oriental medicine, which is the basis of macrobiotic healing, and which can also be called the medicine-to-be. Each of these medical systems is based on a distinct philosophy and has its own unique characteristics.

Modern medicine is symptomatic. When a patient consults a doctor, various tests are given to determine the nature of the problem. Depending on the diagnosis, specific treatments will be prescribed. If the symptoms disappear, the patient is considered cured. If not, another line of treatment is begun, perhaps after additional tests, or consultations with a specialists.

This approach represents a divisive and mechanistic view of the body. It presumes that body parts and functions are isolated and unrelated to the whole. It supposes that treatment for one problem will not affect other parts and areas of the body, and, most serious of all, it ignores the cause. This orientation is a reflection of our modern view of life, which is based on analysis, rather than synthesis, and of producing results in the short-term, regardless of the cost incurred.

If the same patient sees a practitioner of Chinese medicine, diagnosis and treatment will concern itself with identifying and eliminating the underlying cause of the problem. For example, if there is an ear problem, in the modern approach, the patient may see an ear specialists. In Chinese medicine, there are no specialists. The very idea of a specialist goes against the character of this approach to healing.

In this case, the Chinese-medicine practitioner will not limit himself to examining the ear. He realizes that at the very least, some other part of the body will be affected, and perhaps the ear problem is merely a symptom of a disorder with some other organ, gland, or system. This orientation is based on an organic worldview, one that regards life as an undivided, dynamically interrelated unity. From this perspective, each aspect of life is connected with, and dependent on the whole.

In the medicine-to-be, the traditional practice of many thousands of years ago, even this approach is unsatisfactory because it fails to address certain questions. Why, for instance, did the individual create such a problem in the first place. The answer lies in the patient's way of life, and finally on his view of life. What is his self-image, what does he envision as his purpose in life, what are his aspirations and his expectations. These issues must be addressed to solve the basic cause of sickness. Once broad-based answers to these and similar questions are answered, lifestyle changes come easily and often spontaneously, and most often, the reason why the individual visited the physician in the first place—the symptoms of his imbalanced way of life—will quickly disappear.

Of course, symptoms are treated on this level as well. However, symptomatic relief is not considered an end in itself, and in fact is deemed only a minor point in the overall treatment. This is because symptoms are recognized as being merely the effects, or reflections, of a disorder.

In the Bible, there are many examples of healing performed by Jesus and his disciples. One interesting recommendation that Christ frequently gave, after curing, was to go and sin no more. This injunction can be interpreted as an admonition that the individual get his life in order, so as to avoid producing sickness again by violating the laws of God. In macrobiotic terms, we would say, self-reflect, discover how and why you created this problem for yourself. Learn how to deal with the cause by living in harmony with the forces of nature.

Treatments

The attitude toward symptoms, and the treatments used in these three distinct medical approaches, differ greatly. Modern medicine, because it is based on analysis and separation, has adopted an outlook of fear and violence. Starting from the perspective of self and others, and the resulting assumption that the individual must fight to survive in a hostile environment and compete for a limited number of diminishing resources, it is logical to see sickness as an enemy that must be destroyed with whatever means available. Symptoms are regarded as alien, an enemy, and a threat that must be eliminated. And, patients are considered to be helpless victims, casualties of some malevolent and mysterious force.

Consequently, the methods employed, and even the terminology used by the medical profession, is war-oriented. The cover story of a recent issue of *Time* magazine reported the latest findings on the human immune system. The opening paragraphs of this article illustrate our point.

> It is a jungle out there, teeming with hordes of unseen enemies. Bacteria, viruses, fungi and parasites fill the air. . . . This menagerie of microscopic organisms, most of them potentially harmful or even lethal, has a favorite target: the human body. In fact, the tantalizing human prey is a walking repository of just the kind of stuff the tiny predators need to survive, thrive and reproduce.

These remarks accurately sum up the approach to health care taken by science and medicine. Humanity is portrayed as being a vulnerable, fragile island, alone in a sea of hostile forces. The goal is to construct ever-more efficient ways to defend ourselves from attack.

Our hospitals resemble battle fields where lethal chemicals, razor-sharp instruments, and high-energy bombardments are, in an ironic twist, used in the name of healing. The education and talents of some of our most creative researchers, and a large portion of our national wealth, are devoted to the development of ever-more efficient weapons in the misguided war against sickness.

In Oriental medicine, symptoms reflect disharmony within the body, and between the body and the external world. This is to say, in some way, the individual has grown imbalanced with the forces of nature. Problems are thus removed by reestablishing overall balance. To accomplish this, various techniques are of course used, but with a difference. Treatments are given from the perspective of a broad-based understanding of the forces of life, rather than from a narrow, materialistic view. Their purpose is not to destroy but to harmonize.

On a wider scale, traditional medicine, the medicine-to-be, attempts to bring an individual's total way of life, not just bodily functions, into harmony. Realizing that the weather, the seasons, relationships, social conditions all change, the goal is to bring understanding and flexibility into one's life. Ideally, we proceed along a path that will harmonize our total Self, and not just bodily functions, with the larger forces of existence. By learning to maintain balance as we pass through the ever-changing circumstances of life, we claim our heritage as free human beings.

The above comparison may sound unnecessarily harsh when discussing modern and Western medicine, and excessively optimistic when discussing traditional and Oriental approaches. Contemporary medicine has its value, and the creativity, dedication, and hard work of our scientists and health-care practitioners need to be recognized. Indeed, much of the problem comes about because individuals refuse to take responsibility for their own well-being. They live self-destructive lives, fail to practice any form of preventive health care, and visit a doctor long after symptoms have appeared. Being in such drastic condition, it is little wonder that equally extreme measures are required to help them.

The criticism is that modern, interventive medicine is too often seen as the only alternative, and is frequently used in cases where it is not only unnecessary, but counterproductive. This situation seriously restricts our ability to understand and treat the causes of illness, and offers no hope for a coherent system of prevention. It also generates serious side effects which weaken overall vitality and immune ability, thus setting the stage for other, perhaps more serious problems later on.

The way an expectant woman was routinely dealt with until very recently is a good example. Her pregnancy was treated as an illness, and her delivery as a medical emergency. The latest products of the high-tech and pharmaceutical industries were brought to bear on the completely natural process of childbirth. This attitude is now changing, but still, tens-of-thousands of births in modern countries are unnecessarily complicated by questionable medical practices. And this is but one simple example.

Earlier in this chapter, we discussed the five principles of Oriental medicine. Inherent in each of these is the assumption that there is an order and a pattern in life, and that this order is both understandable and applicable to every aspect of human affairs. In the remaining chapters of this part we will discuss this order and explain how our ancestors applied it to the area of healing.

2. Ki: The Source of Life

The accomplishments of Far-Eastern civilization—its sciences and arts, its technology and philosophy, its social patterns and statecraft—are branches growing from a living tree. In the following pages we pursue the philosophical roots of this tree. Chapter 3 covers the underlying principles which form its trunk, and chapter 4 examines the particular branch known as Oriental medicine. Finally, in chapter 5, we explore diagnostic methods, which, in this analogy, can be considered the stem from which hangs the fruit of traditional medical practice.

With this overall perspective, we will be in a position to appreciate the role of medicine in pre-modern cultures and in Oriental countries. And, where appropriate, we will be able to flexibly adapt this approach to our own particular time and unique set of circumstances.

To understand the worldview upon which Oriental and traditional medicine are inseparably based, we must first come to terms with the concept of Ki-energy. Whatever the subject, a student of ancient and Far-Eastern cultures will soon discover that the reality of a nonphysical energy permeating physical existence abides at the heart of the old-world order.

The idea of Ki lies outside our modern vision of life. This is not to deny the fact that certain individuals and schools of thought in Western civilization have recognized and articulated a theory of a nonphysical basis for the physical world. Rather, the general or overall orientation in contemporary science and philosophy is based on the material in contrast to a nonmaterial explanation of existence.

One of the most well-known examples in modern times of the recognition of the nonmaterial nature of reality is Einstein's assertion that mass or matter is a form of energy. Simply stated, this implies that the physical world is fashioned by currents of energy rather than from discrete and static physical building blocks. Another physicist, living about the same time as Einstein, came close to a scientific understanding of Ki. Ernest Rutherford (1871–1937) discovered that if the frequency of its electrons is altered, the structure of an object will immediately change in response. In other words, physical form is generated by energy patterns.

Needles to say, these revolutionary concepts (along with related theories that have been put forth more recently) have profound implications for all branches of science and thought. Eventually, their influence will be reflected in the way we as individuals approach our daily life. In the meantime, the energetic nature of reality remains far removed from our collective consciousness.

Ki is thus a difficult concept to interpret in Western terms. Further complicating the situation is the unique nature of this energy:

1. Ki is the foundation or source of the relative world, much like atoms were once considered the basic substance of matter. As such, all manifestations of nature, including the more subtle qualities of emotion, mind,

and spirit, are products of Ki. As we shall see, Ki is more like a process or an activity than an object, whereas our modern outlook focuses on the ability to isolate and replicate measurable phenomenon. This fact effectively eliminates the possibility of our recognizing the existence and function of Ki—and of the more subtle aspects of the Self as well—as long as we insist on the completeness of our modern perspective.

2. Ki exists in various states, much like matter-energy exists in the solid, liquid, gas, plasmic, and vibrational states. This characteristic will be discussed in detail in chapter 3. It is enough, for now, to acknowledge the implication that our view must be both flexible and wide if we are to embrace the dynamics of this primary energy.

Ki: A Definition

Ki can be broadly defined as the movement of nontangible energy or vibrations between the two primary poles in the universe. Ki encompasses all material and nonmaterial phenomenon in creation (the relative world). Its meaning embraces emotional expression and intellectual preferences; atmospheric conditions such as temperature and pressure; physical traits including hard and soft, large and small, and heavy and light; sensory stimulations such as colors, sounds, tastes, odors, and the various qualities of tactile stimulation. It takes in all motion and movement, and the full spectrum of vibrations and waves flowing in the universe. Each of these attributes is actually a different state of Ki.

By way of clarification, we can define life as movement, growth, and development. Life is distinguished by motion and change, and it includes states before and after the relatively narrow range of awareness encompassed within the plant and animal kingdoms. Although different in scope from human existence, life is a universal condition, found everywhere in creation and manifested in all objects and processes. The planet has life. The solar system and galaxies are alive, as are mountains and rivers, molecules, atoms, and preatomic particles.

While the breadth of consciousness and the speed of change varies, the difference between things is one of degree rather than of quality. From this larger view, we can say that Ki is a universal state, existing everywhere. Wherever there is life or motion there is Ki, and as we shall see, life exists at every stage of manifestation in the relative world.

One common explanation of Ki is that it is energy, or the flow of energy. Thus, the term "ki-flow" is commonly used in English-language texts on Chinese medicine. As far as it goes, this explanation is fine. Yet the concept of energy is somewhat different in the East and West, and in modern and traditional societies. Sometimes *energy* refers to simple mechanical motion; sometimes to calories or heat; sometimes to electricity, magnetism, gravity, or atomic decomposition; sometimes to waves or vibrations; and sometimes to spiritual and metaphysical existence beyond the range of sensory perception. All of this, the detectable and nondetectable, our ancestors called Ki.

Earlier we cited Einstein's theory of energy and matter as an example of a Western and modern understanding of Ki. But this is only partially correct. The energy

Einstein had in mind seems to be the more perceptible qualities of light, heat, motion, and so on. These are the products or reflections of the more refined force, but are not Ki itself.

If we limit our definition of Ki to perceivable energy, our vision of reality is incomplete. The realm of Ki extends from the infinitesimally shortest wave to the infinitely longest wave, from the fastest motion or speed to the slowest, from the most condensed state of matter to the most refined stage of energy.

Objects that we see as solid matter are those that are vibrating at a slower rate than ourselves. Because the pace of their movement and development is less active, they appear to be fixed and unchanging. Objects or processes that have a faster motion than ourselves, we classify as either liquid, gas, plasma, or vibration.

Water, for example, exists in liquid form in the temperature range of four to one-hundred degrees centigrade. When the temperature drops below this threshold, water begins to solidify. This is to say, its molecular motion and vibrations slow down, causing water to change its form. As the temperature rises above one-hundred degrees centigrade, molecular activity and vibration increases. Liquid thus begins to turn to gas as its molecules start to separate. If the temperature is further increased, the atoms themselves begin to disintegrate, as the electrons resolve into waves of energy, and the gas-state of water becomes plasma.

Fig. 3 Various States of Water

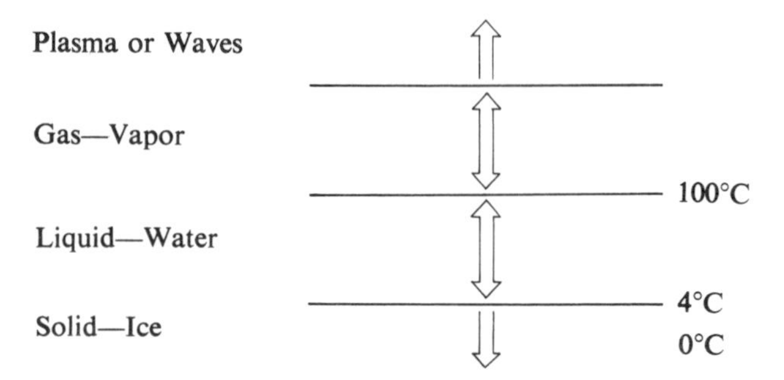

As its rate of vibration increases, the physical nature of water becomes correspondingly less dense. A decreasing rate of vibration causes water's structure to become progressively more solid.

Phenomena whose vibratory rate is extremely fast or slow exist outside the range of our senses, and thus beyond the scope of what we consider reality. Obviously, this does not negate the existence of the object in question. Rather, it illustrates the limits of the physical senses, and the various devices we use to amplify them, to perceive the totality of life. Beyond the domain of sensory perception, forces exist which we are constantly interacting with. We can become aware of, and consciously make use of these energies, just as peoples in the ancient world did. We begin this process by acknowledging and properly nourishing the totality of the Self in all its dimensions.

In teaching how to observe the energy body, for instance, students are directed to regard the area around an individual rather than focusing in on the head and face. This is similar to the way that infants look at objects and people. Babies do not see the physical features as much as the energy surrounding whatever they are gazing at.

This simple practice reflects a pattern of visual perception that is opposite to our modern habit of concentrating on the physical center of a thing. This, in turn, is another example of how one's worldview influences all aspects of life. Contemporary society is oriented toward a materialistic and analytical understanding, and the manner in which we view things (both literally, when we use the eyes to focus in on something, and figuratively, when we use the mind to judge or evaluate), supports this value system. As science has discovered, we tend to see what we expect to see, and to find what we are looking for, even in the supposedly controlled conditions of a laboratory experiment.

It is thus important to realize that it is from our own perspective that we judge the nature of objects and processes. Reality is relative to our personal perceptions, and, perception differs from one historical period to another, from society to society, from individual to individual, and within individuals, from moment to moment, according to one's condition.

This is not to suggest that there is no ultimate reality against which personal judgment can be weighed. Rather, insight varies according to one's breadth of consciousness. As long as awareness is limited to the relative, ephemeral world, our grasp of reality will be conditional.

This is the point of the often-repeated story of a group of blind men attempting to describe an elephant. One feels the powerful trunk, another, a massive foot, the third, a strong leg, and the last, the swishing, flexible tail. These individuals proceed to depict the animal according to their personal and limited perception, and needless to say, end up with very different accounts. Each man is correct according to his own set of experiences, and yet, lacking a comprehensive view, all fail to accurately portray the elephant.

Physical and Spiritual

Based on a nonmaterial understanding, or a more spiritual perspective, traditional societies interpreted life in terms of Ki. In contrast, the outlook of the modern world is more materialistic, and physically oriented. By themselves, neither view is complete. And, at their extreme, both offer a distorted vision of life.

It is certainly a mistake to limit our perception of reality to what the physical senses can observe. This sort of attitude ultimately creates feelings of isolation, in individuals and groups, and is the basis for the exploitation of the natural world and of other cultures and people. If we are separate beings, in competition with one another, such manipulation may seem justifiable.

On the other hand, to turn one's back on physical existence, in favor of the spiritual, is to reject our living heritage as human beings on this wonderful planet. We have both a physical and spiritual awareness, which simply means that we are capable of fully interacting with life on the macrocosmic as well as the microcosmic levels. In a very real sense, the process of personal maturation is the mechanism by which we come to fulfill this birthright by living as self-realized human beings, fully participating in the multiple dimensions of reality.

Have you ever wondered at the apparent uniqueness of the human species? As part of the animal kingdom, we exercise free will and self-awareness to an unprecedented degree. We strive for physical comfort and material wealth while concerning ourselves with questions of a spiritual nature and of survival of consciousness after death. The Bible explains the position of humanity in the scheme of life in this way: "And God said, Let us make man in our image, after our likeness: and let them have dominion over the fish of the sea, and over the fowl of the air, and over the cattle, and over all the earth, and over every creeping thing that creepeth upon the earth."

Philosophers and scientists have long sought to identify the source of this animal/angel duality. From a "macro" or metaphysical point of view, the riddle of this paradox becomes clear.

Humanity stands at the intersection of the two basic motions of life. We are the terminal point of a huge process of *physicalization*, in which consciousness moves from the oneness of infinity to individual awareness. At the same time, we stand on the threshold of the equally vast journey of *spiritualization*, moving from individual to infinite realization. To ignore one is to deny our origin. To disregard the other is to reject our future.

Fig. 4 Complementary Spirals of Life

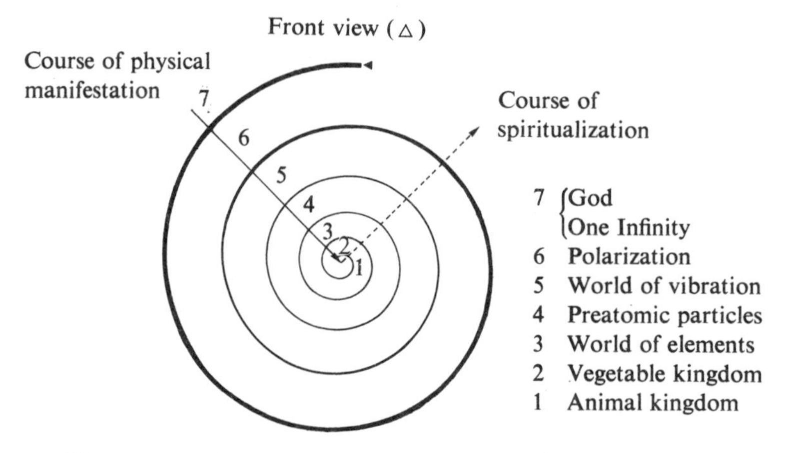

The space outside of the spiral is the unmanifested, undifferentiated ocean of Infinity, and the worlds within the spiral are the relative and ephemeral worlds.

In the alternating cycle of life, consciousness proceeds in a centripetal spiral from the macrocosmic state of infinite oneness to the microcosmic level of human awareness. At its most condensed point, consciousness begins the opposite course toward oneness via a centrifugal spiral.

Figure 4 illustrates this successive development from universal to individual awareness, and from individual to universal consciousness. The process unfolds in a seven-staged progression and moves in a *logarithmic* spiral. This means that each stage on the inward journey is the condensed replica of the one preceding it, and each step on the outward journey is the expanded reproduction of the one before it. The seven stages of physicalization progress as follows:

1. Unity, One Infinity, or infinite motion at infinite speed.
2. Duality, bifurcation, or division of infinite oneness into the two universal poles of centrifugality, or expansion, and centripetality, or contraction.
3. The polarity between these two forces generates energy or vibrations which signify the beginning of the relative world.
4. Energy or Ki condenses to preatomic energetic spirals. The two universal poles are mirrored in the negatively charged electron and the positively charged proton.
5. The more condensed world of atoms and elements emerges from the preatomic realm as even more tightly bound energy spirals.
6. The vegetable kingdom arises as the spiralic syntheses of the elements. The growth and decomposition of plants reflects the wave-like process of expansion and contraction.
7. The animal kingdom develops from the vegetable world, and represents a still more concentrated form of energy and consciousness.

   Human beings are the most recent product of the animal kingdom. We are consciousness in its most individualized state. From this point, personal awareness begins to move in the opposite direction, ultimately merging with Infinity.

The fertilization of the human egg initiates the course of spiritualization, which is the complemental journey to the process of physicalization. As we mature, perception expands to embrace ever-larger dimensions. Ultimately, we transcend the duality of the relative world to grasp the oneness of existence. It is at this point that we see beyond the contradictions and duality of day-to-day existence to experience the oneness of life. We thus begin to exercise the universal judgment referred to earlier.

The seven stages of spiritualization can be described in terms of the unfolding of consciousness, a process also depicted in terms of the evolution of judgment or awareness. It loosely (and potentially) coincides with the various stages of an individual's life and should be viewed as a natural growth process, just as is the course of physical maturation. Since our origin is Infinity—as already explained—each of us carries universal judgment within us. Self-realization is a matter of nurturing health on all levels of being to insure the proper development of consciousness. (This matter will be covered in Part 3.) The spiral of spiritualization unfolds through the following dimensions:

1. *Primary or Mechanical Consciousness:* Beginning with the fertilization of the ovum, and continuing throughout life, the growth and functioning of our body proceeds automatically, via various complementary activities such as contraction and expansion, inhalation and exhalation, taking in and giving out. This is reflected in the involuntary metabolic actions occurring at every level of organization, including reflexive actions.

2. *Sensory Consciousness:* Soon after birth, the awareness of physical stimuli begins to emerge, enabling us to participate in the various sensory experiences of our world. This includes feedback from the five senses, and also awareness of complementary sensations such as hot and cold, pain and pleasure, and so on.

3. *Emotional Consciousness:* During childhood our awareness expands to include the dimensions of sentiment and emotion. We begin to experience the polarities of life in such forms as joy and sadness, love and hate, fear and confidence. As this consciousness matures, our sense of the aesthetic becomes more refined.

4. *Intellectual Consciousness:* As we build on our experiences and insights gained on previous levels, our interaction with life expands to include the intellect. With the emergence of intellectual curiosity, we begin to form concepts and theories about our world, and to recognize such complementary qualities as cause and effect, reasonable and unreasonable, logical and illogical. It is at this stage that we articulate our worldview.

5. *Social Consciousness:* The use of our intellect gradually leads us to a major milestone: awareness enlarges beyond personal concerns to encompass our participation in group relationships. We start to see the dynamics of family and community interaction. As our social consciousness unfolds, we begin to consider questions of an ethical and moral nature such as right and wrong, and good and bad. Our awareness gradually expands to accommodate social and then global concerns.

6. *Philosophical or Ideological Consciousness:* Experiences within the previous realms impel us to a wider dimension of awareness in which we start to wonder about issues of a metaphysical nature: What am I? What will happen to me after death? Why does disaster overtake individuals and groups of innocent people? How is it that people succeed by immoral behavior. We are searching for universal truths, and entertain the complementary qualities of justice and injustice, truth and falsehood, and material and spiritual reality.

7. *Universal or Absolute Consciousness:* Active participation in the ideological dimension eventually brings insight that transcends the duality of the relative world. We see that all antagonisms are complementary and emerge from the same source. For instance, we realize that love and hate are actually mirror expressions of a single emotion, and can readily turn into one another. By extension, we recognize that these (and other) sentiments originate on each level of consciousness, so that a single concept such as love can be expressed in a mechanical, sensory, emotional, intellectual, social, ideological and absolute manner.

Universal consciousness is built upon and includes each of the previous realms, and its attainment results in freedom in the widest sense of the world.

At this point we become free human beings, able to flexibly participate in all stages of awareness and to reconcile all contradictions.

The stages within each of these two distinct motions are in no way separated or isolated from one another. As their spiralic motion indicates, each is based on and exists within, the preceding level, and each is a necessary preliminary to the state that follows. Individual phases merely represent landmarks along the constantly moving wave of life. This intimate relationship between the infinite and the individual is the basis of the affirmation by societies throughout the world that "As above, so below," and that "Mankind is created in the image of God." It is also the source of the concept of the macrocosm and the microcosm found throughout traditional and Far-Eastern societies.

Ki in Traditional Societies

Traditional peoples, recognizing the wave-like, spiralic motion of life depicted in Figure 4, lived with an energetic vision of reality. In China this energy is called *Ch'i*, in Korea, *Ghee*, in Japan, Ki, and in India, *Prana.* As mentioned earlier, this concept has also been recognized in the West as well. Various names have been used in this context, including life-force, ether, bio-force, and electromagnetism.

Oriental people still use hundreds of words in reference to Ki in their daily language. Unfortunately, although the expressions are still part of the vocabulary, the understanding of the underlying concept is vanishing as the modern, materialistic value system is embraced. Examples of the usage of Ki-related words from the Japanese language include:

In the natural world:

- *Ku-Ki* (air), the Ki of the sky
- *Ten-Ki* (weather), the Ki of heaven
- *Den-Ki* (electricity), the Ki of thunder
- *Ji-Ki* (magnet), the Ki of magnetism
- *Ka-Ki* (fire), the Ki of fire

Individual character:

- *Ki-Sho* (personality), the character of Ki
- *Ki-Sho ga Tsuyoi* (strong personality), the character of Ki is strong.
- *Ki-Sho ga Yowai* (weak personality), the character of Ki is weak.
- *Yu-Ki* (courage), the Ki is active.
- *Ki ga Chiisai* (coward), the Ki is small.

The concept of Ki has a social application as well. The word *Fu-Kei-Ki* (不景氣) means the "Ki is dull or inactive." It is used to describe an individual who looks cheerless. On a wider scale, it refers to hard times in general, or a slump in business activity. The opposite word, *Ko-Kei-Ki* (好景氣), means the "Ki is lively, brisk, or active." As an adjective, it is used to describe a time of economic prosperity, or a brisk period of business.

Japanese people refer to sickness as *Byo-Ki* (病氣), meaning "the Ki is disturbed." Even today in Japan, all doctors use this term, even if they are practicing Western medicine. They do not speak of the body as being ill, but of a sickness or disruption of the individual's Ki. On the other hand, *Gen-Ki* (元氣) is the word for health. Literally meaning "the source of Ki," the implication is that Ki is the origin of vigor and well-being and of life itself. These two images clearly reflect the view of the body as a pattern of energy. They are holdovers from the time when metaphysics was the dominate frame of reference.

Traditional peoples saw the physical body as a very dense, very compacted form of vibration. Other aspects of the Self were recognized as more refined states, differing according to their specific natures. In the same way, all things, objects or processes, can be classified along a continuum from the most refined to the most dense state of Ki. *Hito* (人), the Japanese word for "human being" or "person," is divided phonetically into two syllables. One of the meanings of *Hi* is "fire," and one of the readings of *To* is "spirit" or "ghost." The ancient perception of a human being was thus one of a "fire ghost," or "mass of vibrating energy": a very different notion than that articulated by contemporary science and medicine.

In comparison to the physical body, emotions are reflections of a less-dense state of energy, with a range of variation according to the quality of the emotion expressed. Depression, for instance, is a heavy and stagnated energy state, while happiness indicates a light and clear vibration. Instinctively, we all perceive this energetic quality of emotions, as witnessed in the fatigue we feel when in the company of an unhappy individual, and the pleasure we take in someone who is cheerful and lively.

Thoughts are still-more refined forms of vibration, again with variation. A dark, pessimistic outlook generates more dense, inactive energy, while bright, optimistic thoughts embody vibrations in a more active and subtle state. The spiritual Self represents our existence in an even more expanded energy body. Differences in the spiritual awareness among individuals suggest distinctions in the quality of this more extended Ki.

Physical body, emotional consciousness, mental orientation, and spirituality—these seemingly different aspects of the Self simply reflect various qualities of energy, or phases along the continuum from individual to infinity. There are no boundary lines separating them. The journey from the physical to the spiritual is a gradually expanding spiral of energy, and that from the spiritual to the physical is a contracting energy spiral. Spiritual Ki constantly transforms into mental and physical Ki, and physical Ki changes into mental and spiritual Ki. The individual Self encompasses all levels of energetic consciousness. As religion and philosophy teach, we are indeed made in the image and likeness of God.

For our study of traditional healing, the implication of this relationship is that the physical body is constantly altered by the mind, and that both aspects are influenced by the spirit. In the same way, the spirit and the mind can be, and are continually modified by the quality of our physical health. This is the root of our freedom as human beings.

Fig. 5 Two-way Influence on the Self

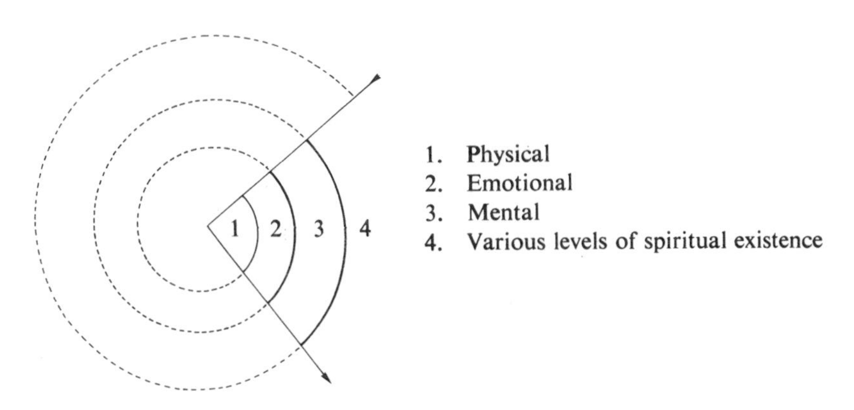

The more subtle aspects of the Self interpenetrate the denser qualities.

Through daily lifestyle practices, we are able to intentionally create the quality of our physical body, our mentality, and our spirituality. Or, we are free to leave the character of our consciousness on these various levels to the chance influences we come into contact with. Whichever way we choose, the deliberate or haphazard path to life, we ourselves are the final arbiter of our present circumstances and our future destiny.

Ki in Healing

In modern medicine, illnesses are classified according to the nature of their symptoms. We thus speak of headaches, toothaches, and backaches, referring to pain in specific areas. The degenerative diseases, too, follow this pattern. Arthritis indicates inflammation and/or deformation of the joints; diabetes to problems with insulin; and cancer with the uncontrolled growth of cells.

From the perspective of Ki, physical illness is a reflection of imbalance in the energy flow within the body. Physical problems, such as those mentioned above, are merely the symptoms of this disruption, and not its cause. When treating a specific condition, traditional healers consequently sought to identify the source of the energy imbalance, and then employed various means to correct it.

In order to normalize the Ki flow, and thus eliminate the symptoms, we can of course work directly with the body, making temporary adjustments with such treatments as acupuncture, massage, herbal medications, exercise, and so on; and long-term changes with alterations in lifestyle and diet. At the same time, the mind, as well as the spirit, will be affected by a physical problem, and both can also be employed in a coordinated response to healing. Ideally, we will use each aspect of our Self to create well-being and continued personal growth. And, until we do, permanent recovery will be impossible.

The behavioral symptoms of mental illness also reflect a disharmony of Ki, although on a more subtle level. Wild, chaotic actions, anger and aggression, sadness and fear—these and other examples are reflections of distorted energy states.

In turn, such imbalances affect the physical organs and systems in very specific ways, as researchers investigating human immune ability are now discovering. Reflecting the two-way flow of energy described above, physical disorders also have a direct influence on our emotional, mental and spiritual states. (The dynamics of this relationship will be detailed in the next chapter.)

In order to treat psychological problems, we can again proceed directly from the energy level most affected, through counseling, self-help practices, and so on. Knowing, however, that the body and the spirit are being influenced by our mental state, we can and should address these areas as well. Physical exercise, for example, can be a way of releasing pent-up energy that may be manifesting as frustration or anger. Prayer and meditation can calm the Self, provide perspective, and help give us insight into the nature of our problem. Each of these factors also directly influences Ki-flow. In the same way, to deal with spiritual problems, we can work with various spiritual practices. Yet, realizing the profound impact our spiritual consciousness has on our total being, and recognizing the two-way flow of Ki, we would be well advised to begin making adjustments in each aspect of our life.

Because the body, mind, and spirit are different manifestations of the same energy, or Ki existing at varying degrees of condensation, and because all aspects of the Self are intimately connected, each must be in balance before real health is achieved. This represents the total or holistic approach to healing and personal development. It is the reason why one-dimensional strategies do not work in the long run. Failing to recognize the entirety of our Self, they accentuate one aspect while ignoring and possibly arresting the growth of others. In the short term, such practices may help redress specific imbalances and they can be profitably used for such purposes. However, to secure overall and long-term well-being, a comprehensive approach, which includes all areas of life, is necessary.

Self in East and West

Traditional and Oriental cultures recognized the interrelated influence of the spirit, mind and body. Their healing arts were predicated on this dynamic interaction. This holistic view echoes the modern, scientific notion that energy is a form of matter, and matter is a state of energy. In ancient times, this concept was made possible by the recognition that: (1) the definition of life can be extended to all things, (2) that life itself is movement in various degrees of complexity, and (3) that Ki is produced wherever there is movement.

The teachings of Jesus acknowledge this two-way relationship. In *The Gospel According to Thomas*, Jesus is quoted as saying: "If the flesh came into being because of spirit, it is a wonder. But if the spirit came into being because of the body, it is a wonder of wonders. Indeed, I am amazed at how this great wealth [spirit] has made its home in this poverty [physical body]."

The distinctions of body, mind, and spirit are of course recognized in the modern and Western world, yet they are viewed in a way that is opposite to the traditional orientation. Rather than being related and interconnected, these aspects of the Self are considered unrelated and independent. This idea was distinctly expressed by

Rene Descartes, the French philosopher and scientist who, in the seventeenth century, established the methodology still used by modern science. Reacting against the narrowness and rigidity of the scholarship of his time, Descartes declared that only ideas that were clear and distinct were to be used in scientific pursuit.

Trying to improve the situation, however, Descartes went to the opposite extreme. He articulated a theory of life that was mechanistic and dualistic. There is no relation between the mind and body, Descartes stated, and animals, including humans, are nothing but complex machines.

From this perception came the rigid separation of scientific fields, including medicine and psychology. Well-defined boundaries for each discipline exist, and the education of practitioners within each category seldom overlaps. There is little crossover or attempt to unify accumulated discoveries, partly due to the progressive complexity and flood of details that the analytical approach generates. With the emergence of specialists and then subspecialists within each department, the boundaries have become ever-more sharply defined, and the range within each discipline increasingly limited.

Currently, we live in the age of specialization. And when its limits are understood, the value of this approach is undeniable. However, once a thing or a concept has been taken apart, it must be reintegrated for a comprehensive understanding, and for a congruent system of problem-solving. Otherwise it is too easy to lose sight of the web of relationships we all live within.

In writing this book, for example, we start with a general picture of the ideas we would like to present. Then a detailed outline is made to help focus and clarify them, and work proceeds chapter by chapter. Once the writing is finished, however, the entire manuscript must be read to ensure the logical connection within and between chapters, and a smooth progression of concepts. The first chapter represents an overview, the last chapter a synthesis, and the chapters, in-between provide the supporting details. In this sequence, we move from the general to the particular, and then from the specific back to the large view.

Perhaps in the isolated world of scholarship or research science, the body can be reduced to its smallest components, which are then studied as discrete phenomena. In reality, the body is far more than the sum of its physical parts, just as a human being is far more than the physical body. As we continue our investigation of the traditional healing arts, the practical value of this concept will become apparent.

Ki in the Body

Among some practitioners of Chinese medicine, the idea persists that the body exists and Ki runs through it. This image is somewhat backward however. The physical body did not come first. The flow of Ki initially created the form of the body, and during fetal development, various nutritional factors gathered along this pattern to produce the components of physical structure. Ki forms a multi-dimensional configuration around which the physical body materializes.

For example, when we make pottery, the first step is to fashion the clay into the desired shape. Often forgotten, however, is the fact that before starting to work, we already have created a mental image or energy pattern of what we want to make. Then, in order to firm the shape we have made, motion or vibration must be applied. Through the centrifugal force generated on the potter's wheel, the figure is set, and by the centripetal force produced by the intense heat of baking, it is solidified.

Pottery, of course, is not alive in the sense that plants and animals, or even mountains or streams are. In the body of naturally generated life, Ki-flow comes before physical form. To see this process clearly, our relationship to the larger patterns of life should be understood.

Planetary Body

The correlation between the macrocosm and the microcosm is a recurring theme in this book. The concept implies that individual objects and processes are replicas of a series of increasingly larger phenomenon, culminating in the oneness of Infinity. This relationship is clearly seen in the correspondence between the human body and the various celestial influences we absorb.

From outside the solar system, *centripetal*, or inward-moving force, continuously rains inward toward the sun. *Cosmic rays*, or energy from the cosmos, is the general name science gives to the measurable part of this energy. In the opposite direction, the sun constantly generates *centrifugal*, or outward-moving force, in the form of light, heat, and various other types of radiation, collectively known as *solar wind*. The sun emits energy at practically all wavelengths of the electromagnetic spectrum, ranging from long radio waves to the shorter microwaves and infrared, light, ultraviolet, and X-rays. We sense the ultraviolet rays as heat, and see the light waves as color. The other forms of radiation are not perceived with the physical senses.

In order for the sun to burn, it must be continually supplied with energy from the outside. And, as long as the sun burns, it will generate energy outward. In the midst of these outward- and inward-moving forces, the planets in our solar system run in an interrelated and dynamically balanced way.

Fig. 6 Energetic Forces in the Solar System

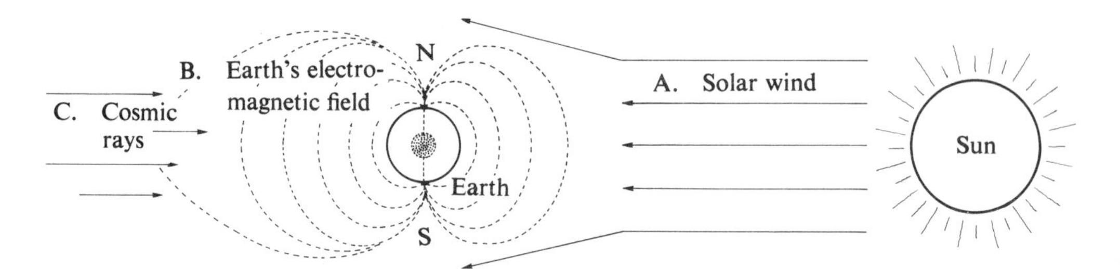

A—The sun generates outgoing energy, called solar wind. From the earth's perspective, solar wind is incoming.

B—The earth's rotation generates outgoing forces, some of which are identified as the planet's electromagnetic field.

C—Cosmic rays stream in toward the center of the solar system.

Between these two forces, a third source of energy exists. Our planet is in constant motion. It rotates on its axis once approximately every twenty-four hours and revolves around the sun roughly once every 365 days, traveling at about 30 kilometers every second. And, as part of the solar system, the earth moves around the center of the Milky Way Galaxy in a huge, two-hundred-million-year cycle. The speed of this journey is estimated to be from 190 to 270 kilometers per second.

These motions of the planet produce immense centrifugal forces, or energy actively moving from the center of the earth outward into space. This energy appears in such forms as the *Van Allen belts*, which are bands of high-energy, charged particles, that surround the globe. Because of the influence of the solar wind, these forces do not extend far on the side of the planet facing the sun, and they are lengthened on the side facing away from it. The solar wind pushes and elongates this energy toward the periphery of the solar system much as the smoke of a fire will be blown downwind on a breezy day.

Fig. 7 Planetary Energy Body

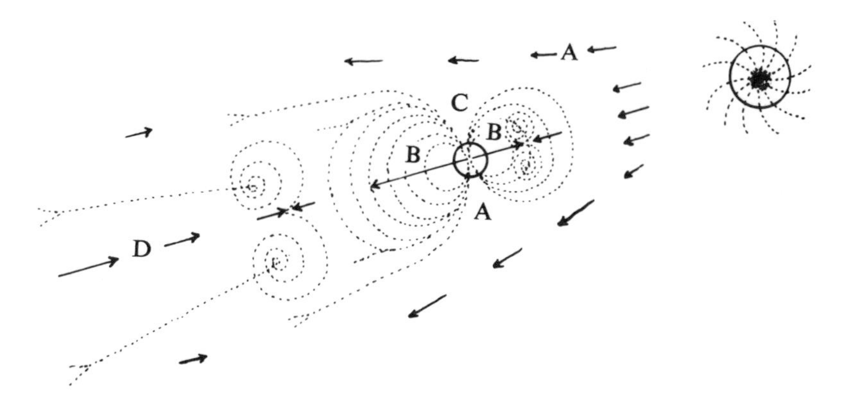

As the earth (C) rotates, electromagnetic orbits are generated and formed around the earth. Incoming solar wind (A) from the sun and the centripetal force from peripheral space (D) collide with the centrifugal force generated by the earth's rotation (B), and form a human-like aura of electromagnetic or plasmic energy around the earth.

The interaction of the centripetal force coming into the solar system from deep space, and the centrifugal force, generated outward by the sun, together with the belts of energy produced by the earth's movement, create a huge, human-like form around our planet. At various points within this energy body, the inward-moving and outward-moving forces collide. This impact generates vortices of energy that spiral out to produce the limbs and other features of this electromagnetic figure. The human body manifests, under similar influences, as a miniature reproduction of the planet's energy form. The earth is not unique in this regard. Each of the other planets has its own distinct energy figure as well.

On first reading, this analogy may seem difficult to accept. Although described in different imagery, the earth's energy body is recognized by scientists. Illustrations of it can be found in many astronomy books. The same is true of the complementary energies that create this form. The forces of solar wind, cosmic rays, and the earth's own magnetic field are established scientific facts. What is not recognized is the interaction of these forces, and the influence they exert on the surface of the planet.

The Forces of Heaven and Earth

On the earth, we, as well as our fellow inhabitants—both animate and inanimate—are created and nourished by the interaction of the forces of centripetality and centrifugality. These two energetic motions are not received in equal amounts, however. On this planet, the ratio is approximately 7: 1, centripetal force to centrifugal force, with a range of about 5: 1 to 10: 1.

This 7: 1 ratio is not an arbitrary figure. It is echoed throughout nature, as well as in the arts, technologies, and religions of traditional cultures around the world. It is also supported by numerous scientific findings. The earth's *escape velocity*, for instance, refers to the amount of energy that is required to lift a given object free of the planetary gravitational forces. The ratio, given in science textbooks as being 7.4: 1, is a particularly accurate reflection of the proportion of these two forces interacting on the earth. On other planets this ratio is different, depending on the size and mass of the planet, its distance from the sun, speed of rotation, and other factors.

Ancient peoples recognized the existence and influence of these complementary forces. *Earth's force* was the name given to the energy generated outward by the planet's rotation. The opposite energy, coming in from distant space toward the center of the planet, was called *Heaven's force.*

When viewed from above the north pole, the earth rotates in a counterclockwise direction. This motion generates expanding forces that move in an opposite or

Fig. 8 Earth's Electromagnetic Field

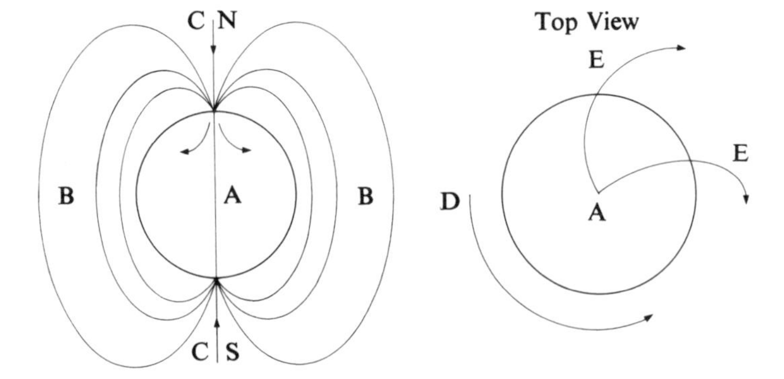

A—Planet earth
B—Electromagnetic fields generated by the planet's rotation (earth's expanding force)
C—Relatively open areas in the planet's energy field
Primary entrance points for Heaven's incoming force
D—Direction of the earth's rotation (counterclockwise) when viewed from the top
E—Direction of Earth's expanding force (clockwise)

clockwise direction. Although both forces are felt throughout the planet, the primary entrance points of Heaven's force are the north and south magnetic poles. (This is the source of the *aurora borealis* and the *aurora australis*, or northern and southern lights.) The direction of its inward motion is the same as the planet's, counterclockwise.

At the equator, Earth's force is generated with exceptional force. As mentioned above, its direction is clockwise. Reflections of this expansive force are the tropical forests with their large, varied, and lush growth of vegetation, and the profusion of animal life along the equatorial belt. This contrasts to the contractive influence of Heaven's force which results in the lack of vegetation in the polar regions, and to the smaller and less-varied plant and animal growth in northern areas.

Individual processes and phenomenon on the earth reflect the influence of these two forces, although in different degrees. Some reveal proportionally more Heaven's force—a more compact shape and/or active function—and others more of the Earth's force—a more extended shape and/or less active function. Despite this difference, however, all things are constantly charged by both energies.

From the north and south magnetic poles, Ki whirls in to the center of the earth, forming a highly charged channel of energy that runs through the deepest part of the planet. The collision of these incoming energies produces the opposite, or outward-moving energetic helixes. The earth's molten and magnetic core, the mantle, and the crust are created by spirals of this centrifugal force, as are the oceans, atmosphere, and belts of energy surrounding the planet.

Fig. 9 Energetic Nature of Fruit

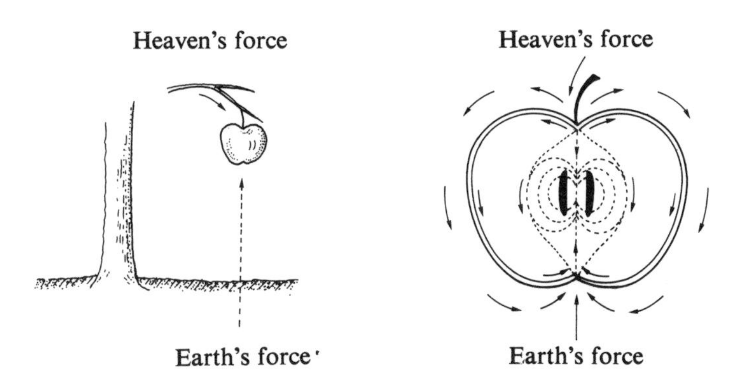

The interaction of Heaven's and Earth's forces at a fruit's center generates outward-moving energy spirals that then produce the seeds, core, pulp and skin, as well as an energy field around the physical structure.

The same process is repeated in all living things. Fruits are a simple example. The core is the central area where seeds are generally produced. The fruit's pulp is similar to the earth's mantle, and its skin corresponds to the earth's crust. The indentations found on the top and bottom of a piece of fruit show the influence of Heaven's and Earth's forces. A more elongated bottom, as is seen in strawberries, indicates that the downward motion of Heaven's force is stronger.

In the Human Body

In human beings, Heaven's force enters most actively at the hair spiral on the top of the head, situated toward the back, and moves in a contracting spiral down through the center of the body. Earth's force enters from the feet and the region of the sexual organs, and proceeds in an expanding spiral up through the body. The flow of these forces creates a *primary channel* of energy (also called the *spiritual channel* to highlight its energetic nature), situated deep within the body.

This channel runs vertically, parallel to the spine. It represents our basic connection with the forces of the universe much as the central nervous system represents the principal pathway of less refined sensory vibration to and from the brain. The importance of the primary channel to our well-being and the development of our consciousness will become apparent as we continue our study.

At various locations along the primary channel, Heaven's and Earth's forces collide, just as these same centripetal and centrifugal forces interact in the energy body surrounding the earth. In humans, the resulting energy spirals form seven areas of highly charged Ki. These are called *chakras*, or wheels of energy, in Indian philosophy, and the term is now commonly used in English.

In the upper region of the body, the major energy center is created in the mid-

Fig. 10 Body's Major Energy Centers

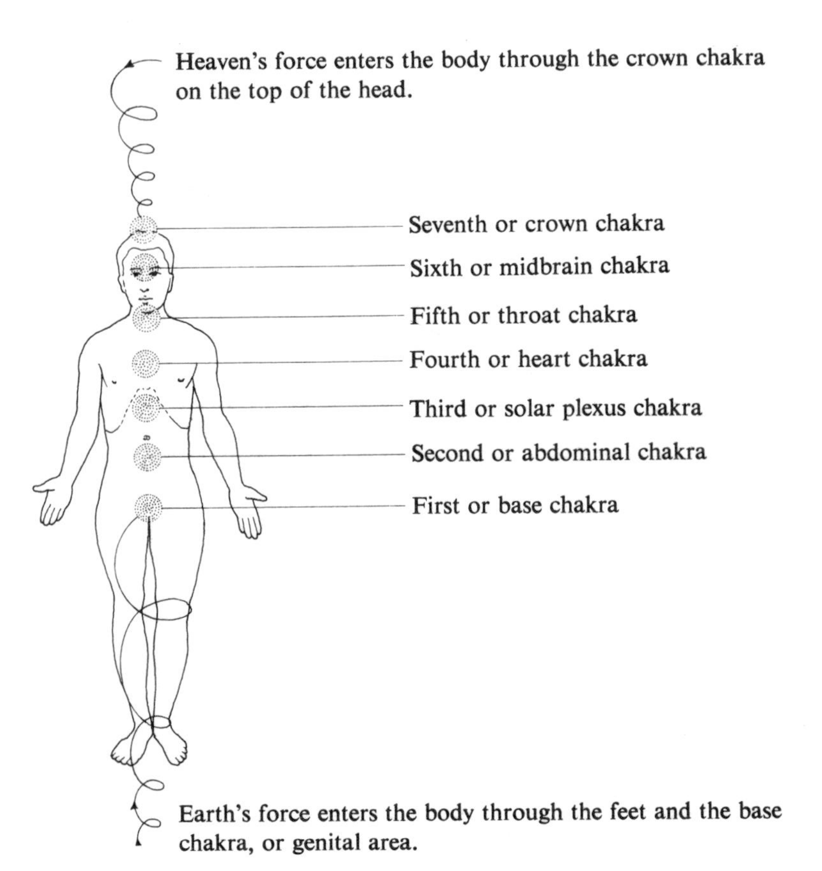

brain area, the most central, condensed region of the brain. Being very compact, this center attracts stimulus, or Ki, and then distributes this charge to the billions of brain cells. The *midbrain chakra* is the center of our consciousness, and influences numerous mental and physical processes.

In the lower body, the major center is in the area of the small intestine. In Japan, a country receiving strong centripetal forces, the importance of this chakra has long been recognized. This is reflected in the variety of terms used to refer to it, including *Ki Kai* (氣海), or "ocean of Ki," *Tan Den* (丹田), or "central field," and *Hara* (腹), or "abdominal center." In other, geographically and climatically distinct countries, the proportion of Heaven's and Earth's forces differs. As a result, other chakras are generally more active, and both their own importance, and the distinct qualities they influence, are stressed by the cultures in these locales.

The abdominal center can be considered the base of our physical vitality. It processes physical food, while the midbrain center handles nonmaterial nourishment. It is related to the functions of the small and large intestines, the bladder, and the genital area.

Between these two centers is the *heart chakra*, which becomes the center of the circulatory system. Being the fourth or central of the seven chakras, this chakra plays a major balancing role between physical and mental processes. Emotional consciousness is the result of this interaction, and is manifested as an acceptance of all people, conditions and changes. The heart chakra governs compassion and openness. Physically, it oversees the body's energy distribution system. It provides a strong charge of Ki to the blood and body fluids, and is the driving force for their distribution throughout the body.

During embryonic development, the respiratory system develops from the digestive system and the excretory system is created as a division of the circulatory system. The importance of these three chakras—the midbrain, heart and abdominal centers—is reflected in the fact that, collectively, they control the body's major systems.

The other chakras created by the interaction of Heaven's and Earth's forces are: the *throat chakra*, located at the base of the tongue, which influences speech and breathing patterns; and the *solar plexus* or *stomach chakra*, which governs the organs in the middle of the body—the spleen, pancreas, stomach, liver, and gallbladder. The exit and entrance points of these energies, the head spiral and the genital region, also form energy spirals. They regulate comprehensive influences: (1) the head spiral unifies the physical, mental and spiritual aspects of the Self into a universal consciousness, and (2) genital region chakra combines physical and mental processes to produce adaptability to our surroundings.

Individual chakras are activated by different qualities of Ki, and vibrate at different rates. In addition, each is active at certain times of the day, of the year, and at particular stages in an individual's life. Each generates unique physical, psychological, and spiritual influences.

Traditional cultures recognized these distinct properties and used them in diagnosis, healing, and personal development. They employed various breathing practices, meditations, chants, physical exercises, dietary adjustments, colors, sounds, and numerous other techniques to foster the effects they desired. (We will discuss these applications in greater detail in subsequent chapters.) The mental and spiritual functions of the chakras include:

- *The crown or seventh chakra:* Governs the higher or unified aspects of consciousness. It is the source of inspiration and universal understanding.
- *The midbrain or sixth chakra:* Is associated with reason and wisdom, and a breadth of understanding that we often call spirituality.
- *The throat or fifth chakra:* Speech and other forms of expression are controlled by this center.
- *The heart or fourth chakra:* The qualities of love and emotional development, as well as the sense of personal and social harmony, are associated with the heart chakra.
- *The solar plexus or third chakra:* Influences the qualities of will and perseverance.
- *The abdominal or second chakra:* Vitality and equilibrium are regulated by the abdominal center.
- *The genital region or first chakra:* Governs the qualities of reproduction and regeneration.

Male and Female

Throughout history, a variety of terms and images have been used to depict the complementary poles of distinct qualities, processes, and objects. In the emotional sphere, love and hate form one such polarity; in the field of psychology, the conscious and subconscious, and left- and right-brain thinking perform a similar function; in economics we talk about bears and bulls, and boom and bust; and we often describe an object as being either valuable or useless.

Male and female represent the two poles of humanity. As such, there is a difference in the degree of influence that the individual forces of Heaven and Earth exert on men and women. The male is charged more by Heaven's force, the female more by Earth's force. In each case, both energies are always active, and yet one force is somewhat stronger. Within the same sex, the ratio of these forces also differs, so that three males or females could be arranged in a line, with one reflecting more the influence of Heaven's force, one more the influence of Earth's force, and the third falling somewhere in-between.

In the female, the rising, expanding Earth's force predominates. In the male, the descending, contracting Heaven's force dominates. This varying influence is reflected in the differences in the male and female body, and in the distinct psychological and spiritual orientation of men and women. Each of these aspects exists in a complementary and opposite relation, revealing that male and female are the two poles of humanity. (This is why these terms "male" and "female" are often used generically to connote positive and negative, receptive and active, and other pairs of complementary qualities.) Each sex has qualities that the other lacks. This is the basis of the strong, magnetic-like attraction between the sexes. In nature, opposites attract each other to create balance or harmony.

Two Types of Ki

The complementary nature of what is commonly considered separate objects and processes has been pointed out already. The mechanism of Ki-flow is no exception. From our perspective, there are two general aspects of this energy:

1. Ki that we absorb from the outside, originating from sources near at hand, such as the type of clothing we wear, the people we interact with, the types of music, books, and movies we enjoy, and from the particular environmental setting we live in. We also receive Ki from influences originating farther away, including the moon, planets and sun, the constellations, and from infinite space. This more expanded, external Ki, takes a centripetal or inward path into our body. It moves from an expanded to a contracted state.

   The principal sources of external Ki are the forces of Heaven and Earth, which travel along our primary channel to the various chakras, from which they are distributed, via the meridians, to every cell in the body.

   We also receive Ki directly through the skin. The finer type charges the cells directly, while the less-refined typed is processed by the nervous system.

2. The opposite type of Ki is generated from within the body. It takes a centrifugal course, moving outward from the body's core, eventually to the furthest reaches of the universe. Internal Ki is generated by the blood, which in turn is created primarily by the food and drink we consume.

   In this process, plants, which are the basis of all food, even if they are eventually eaten in the form of animal products, convert and concentrate the Ki from the sun, soil, water, and atmosphere. We alter this Ki by the way we prepare and eat the plants. Digestion prepares food for assimilation, and makes its Ki available to the body. Blood is the transformed essence of what we eat. It carries a highly charged Ki which is distributed outward from the centrally located heart to all parts of the body.

   An additional influence on this internally generated Ki is respiration. However, since the quality of our breathing—the speed and depth of our breaths, and the efficiency of oxygen absorption in the lungs—is directly regulated by the quality of our daily diet, breathing can be considered a secondary factor.

   The exception is the consciously controlled breathing techniques used to generate specific physical and psychological qualities. In such cases, the breath is being used to direct Ki to one or more of the body's chakras or energy lines.

The more yang, internally generated Ki forms our cells, tissues and organs. The more yin, externally originating Ki activates and charges them. By balancing these two types of Ki in accordance to our personal circumstances, we create the quality of our physical health, emotions, mentality, and spirituality. In addition, by making specific adjustments in Ki, we can effect changes in the quality of each of these realms.

It may seem that we have little control over the external Ki we receive, but this is far from being the case. There are several distinct means to influence this flow of energy:

1. We have the freedom of choice over the Ki we receive from sources near to us. After all, we choose the type of clothing, furnishings, friends, entertainment, occupation, and environment we interact with on a daily basis.

2. By modifying the quality of our internal Ki, we directly influence both the type and the amount of energy we attract from external sources. The primary way to accomplish this is by making dietary adjustments, which will immediately begin to alter the quality of our blood, and thus the character of Ki we generate. (The role of diet, not only in the prevention or relief of sickness, but also in fostering personal growth, will be discussed in detail in Part 2.)

3. Physical activity is an additional tool at our disposal. It produces the benefits of breaking up stagnation and hardness in the body, so that internal Ki flows smoothly and the intensity of its charge is increased. Furthermore, movement enhances the essence of internal Ki, making it strong and clear. This, in turn, creates the polarity needed to attract a vibrant stream of external Ki.

The energy we receive from physical food and from nonmaterial food exists in a complementary relationship. Beyond a certain point, the more we take of the former, the less of the latter we are capable of using. If we overeat, we reduce our reception of external Ki, and weaken the quality of our internal Ki. This fact is readily experienced after a large meal. Mentally, we are apt to be sluggish, and it is not likely that we will have the initiative for physical exertion.

Problems with Ki

Sickness, whatever its symptoms, represents an imbalance in the flow of Ki. In general, this imbalance is reflected in one of two ways: (1) sickness caused by an overactive, excessive, or hyper flow of energy, and (2) sickness resulting from an underactive, deficient, or hypo energy charge. In Oriental medicine, the overactive state is called *Jitsu-Sho* (実症), or "full symptom," and the underactive state is called *Kyo-Sho* (虚症), or "empty symptom." These states are now commonly referred to simply as *Kyo* (虚) and *Jitsu* (実).

A fever is a good example of a Jitsu or full symptom. Excessive energy is vigorously being discharged via heat, and is often accompanied by similar mechanisms such as sweating, frequent coughing, and perhaps swelling and inflammation. In the opposite case, low blood pressure, stones—often located in the nasal sinuses, kidneys, or gallbladder—and mucus deposits in various locations in the body are examples of Kyo or empty symptoms. Such conditions reflect a stagnated or blocked state of energy.

The various types of therapies used in Oriental medicine represent the attempt to bring an imbalanced Ki flow back into harmony. All treatments can be broadly classified into either one of two categories, which correlate to the two types of illnesses listed above: (1) stimulating and supplying additional energy when the symptoms indicate a deficiency or Kyo state, or (2) producing a calming and draining effect when the condition reflects an excessive or Jitsu energy flow.

The criteria used for selecting the appropriate treatment will be explained in chapter 3. In Part 2 we will discuss the specific ways in which these adjustments can be made. Before addressing the application of traditional and Oriental medical techniques, however, we need to know more about the nature of Ki as it flows within the human body.

3. Energy Cycles

In chapter 2 we used the image of a living tree to symbolize the structure of Far-Eastern civilization. The roots of this metaphorical tree are represented by the concept of a nonmaterial energy, or Ki, underlying the relative world. In this chapter, we will discuss the trunk of the tree—the various cycles of energy as it moves between the primary poles in the universe.

Yin and Yang

Most people would agree that motion or change is a constant fact of life. Common sense, experience, and scientific research support the observation that all things—objects as well as processes—are in a perpetual state of movement. With a moment's consideration, a refinement can be added to this insight. Change does not take place in either a random or an haphazard fashion. Rather, there is an order to the way events unfold.

In some cases, this pattern is obvious, as in the progression of the phases of the moon and the seasons of the year, and in the life cycles of plants, animals, and even civilizations. Due to their rate of change—extremely fast or slow—this design is less apparent in other processes. The life span of an atom or of a star are illustrations of this point. Whatever the scale in the dimensions of space and time, however, nothing is exempt from the universal principle of change.

Polarity, or the motion between opposite poles, is life's fundamental mechanism of movement. It governs the cycle of birth, growth, and decay of all things, material, mental, and spiritual. As discussed earlier, the two partners in this relationship are centrifugality and centripetality. In the Far East, the outward-moving force is called *yin*, and the inward-moving force is called *yang*. These are the basic tendencies or motions in creation; the two extremes encompassing the continuum of existence. The elemental polarity that yin and yang represent is reflected on all levels of existence. And, the pattern of their interaction regulates every dimension of life, from the subtle realms of thought and spirit to the workings of the natural world.

It is important to realize that the terms yin and yang can be used only in comparison. They do not represent isolated phenomena, but rather show relative tendencies, compared in a dynamic way. We cannot say that a thing is yin or yang, but only that in comparison to A, B is more yin or more yang. Throughout this book we thus use the seemingly vague terms, "more yin" and "more yang" for descriptive purposes. Rather than being a source of frustration, this ambiguity, or relativity, puts us in touch with the paradoxical nature of reality.

Much as we might wish otherwise, nothing in life is completely and continuously good or bad, right or wrong, friend or enemy. As international events illustrate, yesterday's adversary is today's strategic and trading partner, and today's surpluses too often become tomorrow's shortages. In the same way, the luxuries of one generation become necessities for the next, and new technologies—designed to improve the quality of life—have frequently caused more problems than they were meant to solve.

By helping us unify the opposite tendencies within any pair, the principles of yin and yang can be used to unlock the mysteries of life. They enable us to perceive the dynamic relationship at work within and between any category we wish to study. For instance, under the general heading of vitamins, the fat-soluble vitamins, including A, D, E, and K, are more yang, and the water-soluble vitamins, including C, B_2, B_6, and niacin, are more yin. (Vitamin B_{12}, another water-soluble vitamin, is more yang.) The effects of particular vitamins on the human body will differ according to their yin or yang nature. This is why there is such a controversy over the medicinal effects of vitamin C.

In the field of cancer research, investigators report conflicting results. The outcome of one test indicates that the vitamin seems to help relieve the symptoms of cancer. Another test is inconclusive, while a third produces the opposite effect. Restricted within the limits of analytical reasoning, scientists are unable to recognize that within the general category of cancer, there are two poles: cancers caused by excessive yin, and those caused by excessive yang. In addition, there are varieties produced by a combination of both extremes.

Being more yin, vitamin C may help relieve the symptoms of a yang-caused illness, such as colon cancer, but for a yin-caused problem, like leukemia, vitamin C may actually accelerate the disease process. The same set of dynamics are at work in any illness, physical or mental. Let us use the more benign condition of baldness as one further illustration. Hair loss at the peripheral (more yin) regions of the head, commonly known as a receding hairline, is in most cases caused by excessive yin: moist, expanded hair follicles are unable to anchor the root. When balding occurs in the central (more yang) areas, the cause is most often excessive yang: follicles become dry and brittle, leading to loss of hair. Here we see a clear example of how the same symptom (hair loss) can result from opposite conditions—an insolvable problem from the either-or approach. Total baldness is produced by the combination of both excesses.

Displaying the primary mechanism of cause and effect, all situations develop as a result of the interaction of yin and yang. For this reason, no matter how complex a problem may appear at first glance, it can be resolved within the framework of the principles of these forces. With this dynamic understanding, even the riddle of apparently irreversible disease can be unlocked.

Medicine, for instance, distinguishes numerous varieties of tumors. They are categorized by the material they are composed of, their location in the body, and their rate of growth. Methods of treatment are many, and vary according to the type of tumor. Despite this superficial variation in appearance and behavior, the basic process of tumor formation is similar and straightforward. The cause, as should now be clear, is either an excess of yin or an excess of yang, or an excess of both factors. (The process of tumor formation will be discussed in Part 2.)

In the Western World

Contemporary society, of course, recognizes the polar nature of life as well. Daily language is full of complementary terms such as conservative and liberal, god-fearing and atheist, sophisticated and naive, and more basic pairs, such as love and hate, happy and sad, good and bad, friend and foe, male and female, and positive and negative. But modern and traditional societies view the complementary and antagonistic nature of these pairs differently.

Instead of recognizing the inherent partnership and interaction between contradictory qualities, our outlook tends to be dualistic: with an either-or attitude, we want one attribute without its opposite, seeking wealth for ourselves without realizing that someone else may be impoverished, labeling one thing as valuable and another valueless, desiring health while pampering ourselves with comforts.

In *The Gospel According to Thomas*, Jesus warned against this dualistic attitude when he said, "You do not realize who I am from what I say to you, but you have become like the Jews [a general term used to describe unbelievers], for they either love the tree and hate its fruit or love the fruit and hate the tree."

Another problem for us is that the adjectives used to describe the opposites in pairs of polarities convey nuances of meaning that prevents their application to the general classification of complementary opposites. It would make no sense to call a plant's roots (yang) friend and its leaves (yin) foe, and then include summer and winter in the same respective categories. Thus, the Oriental terms, yin and yang, carrying only the broadest of meanings, are used in macrobiotic teaching.

This lack of comprehensive terms was specifically addressed by British historian Arnold Toynbee (1889–1975). In his multi-volume classic, *A Study of History*, Toynbee divided world history in 26 civilizations and analyzed their life cycle according to the dynamics of challenge and response. Early in the work he wrote:

> Of the various symbols in which different observers in different societies have expressed the alternation between a static condition and a dynamic activity in the rhythm of the Universe, Yin and Yang are the most apt, because they convey the measure or the rhythm directly and not through some metaphor derived from psychology or mechanics.

Table 3 provides an overview of the characteristics created by the motions of yin and yang. At first glance the factors within each classification may seem unrelated. With a little study and experience the logical connection will become clear, and the value of such a comprehensive tool will be appreciated.

The relationship between elements listed in each column in Table 3 can be briefly explained as follows.

- The yang or centripetal force creates contraction, which in turn leads to downward and inward movement toward the center, thus producing a smaller size, a heavier weight, and a harder texture. This pressure generates a faster molecular speed and a hotter temperature. At the point beyond which con-

Table 3 Characteristics of Yin and Yang

	Yin ▽*	Yang △*
Attribute	Centrifugal force	Centripetal force
Tendency	Expansion	Contraction
Function	Diffusion	Fusion
	Dispersion	Assimilation
	Separation	Gathering
	Decomposition	Organization
Movement	More inactive, slower	More active, faster
Vibration	Shorter wave and higher frequency	Longer wave and lower frequency
Direction	Ascent and vertical	Descent and horizontal
Position	More outward and peripheral	More inward and central
Weight	Lighter	Heavier
Temperature	Colder	Hotter
Light	Darker	Brighter
Humidity	Wetter	Drier
Density	Thinner	Thicker
Size	Larger	Smaller
Shape	More expansive and fragile	More contractive and harder
Form	Longer	Shorter
Texture	Softer	Harder
Atomic particle	Electron	Proton
Elements	N, O, P, Ca, etc.	H, C, Na, As, Mg, etc.
Environment	Vibration . . . Air . . . Water . . .	Earth
Climatic effects	Tropical climate	Colder climate
Biological	More vegetable quality	More animal quality
Sex	Female	Male
Organ structure	More hollow and expansive	More compacted and condensed
Nerves	More peripheral, orthosympathetic	More central, parasympathetic
Attitude, emotion	More gentle, negative, defensive	More active, positive, aggressive
Work	More psychological and mental	More physical and social
Consciousness	More universal	More specific
Mental function	Dealing more with the future	Dealing more with the past
Culture	More spiritually oriented	More materially oriented
Dimension	Space	Time

* For convenience, the symbols ▽ for Yin, and △ for Yang are used.

traction cannot continue, the opposite process begins. In the above example, the generation of heat is the catalyst for the reverse motion.

• The yin or centrifugal force creates expansion, which leads to upward and outward motion toward the periphery, producing a larger size, a lighter weight, and a softer texture. This leads to a slower molecular speed and a cooler temperature. Then, at the point of extreme expansion, when the yin force is depleted, contraction begins again. In the above example, cold is the stimulus for contraction and the cycle begins once more.

Fig. 11 Example of the Yin and Yang Cycle

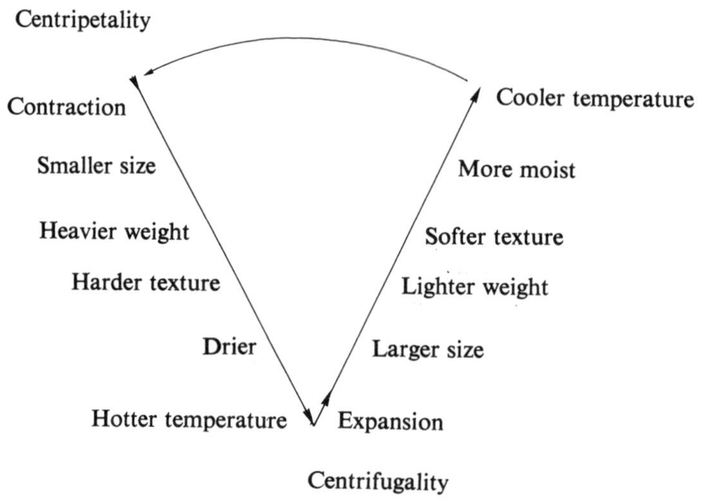

Centripetality

Contraction

Smaller size

Heavier weight

Harder texture

Drier

Hotter temperature

Cooler temperature

More moist

Softer texture

Lighter weight

Larger size

Expansion

Centrifugality

The principles of the interaction of these two primary forces are called the *Unifying Principles*, or the *Order of the Universe*. George Ohsawa, the man who introduced the application of yin and yang to the modern world, summed up this relationship in the Seven Theorems of the Absolute World and the Twelve Principles of the Relative World. These have subsequently been simplified into the Seven Universal Principles and the Twelve Laws of Change.

The Seven Universal Principles

1. All things come from, are sustained by, and return to one Infinity.
2. Everything is in continuous motion. Change is the only constant in the universe.
3. All opposites are complementary.
4. Nothing is identical.
5. Whatever has a front (apparent side) also has a back (hidden side).
6. The bigger the front, the bigger the back.
7. Whatever has a beginning has an end.

The Twelve Laws of Change

1. Infinity, or Oneness, differentiates into complementary and antagonistic tendencies, called yin and yang.

2. Yin and yang are created continuously by the movement of the infinite universe.
3. Yin represents centrifugality. Yang represents centripetality. The interaction of yin and yang produce all phenomena in the relative world.
4. Yin attracts yang, and yang attracts yin (opposites attract one another to make balance).
5. Yin repels yin and yang repels yang (likes repel one another to maintain balance).
6. Yin and yang, combining in various proportions, are the source of everything in creation. The degree of attraction or repulsion between phenomenon is in proportion to the difference of their respective yin and yang forces.
7. Within any one thing, yin and yang are constantly changing into one another.
8. Nothing is exclusively yin or completely yang. (Both forces exist in all things.)
9. Nothing is neutral. Either yin or yang is dominant in everything.
10. Large yin attracts small yin. Large yang attracts small yang.
11. At its extreme, yin produces yang, and yang produces yin.
12. Physical existence is yang at its center and yin on the surface.

The importance of the concept of yin and yang, and the dynamics of their interaction as expressed in the above principles and laws, cannot be overstated. While they are essential to our understanding of Oriental medicine, they are equally practical in all aspects of life. For the individual, they govern the realms of mental and emotional well-being and of spiritual growth, just as certainly as they shape and regulate the physical body. Society exists as a macrocosm of the individual. Its various interactions, growth patterns, and life cycle are similarly ordered by the forces of yin and yang.

These principles and laws represent the Unifying Principles of life itself. Following the criteria for medicine listed in chapter 1, they are:

1. Comprehensive, or holistically oriented.
2. Based on an energetic vision of reality.
3. Concerned with underlying causes rather than effects.
4. Based on common sense and intuition rather than abstract theory.
5. Universally applicable.

One day these principles will form the basis of our formal education. In the meantime, parents are encouraged to introduce children to them at home, before schooling begins, and in a manner appropriate to their age and abilities. Young minds are flexible and intuitive. The facility with which youngsters master these concepts is a confirmation of their inherent authenticity. As the English poet Keats wrote, "beauty is truth, truth, beauty . . ." and both, we might add, are found in simplicity.

A Common Heritage

The recognition and application of the principles of complementary opposites cannot be attributed to any particular civilization, region, or historical period. Being universal, they are the heritage of all humanity. They have been understood and applied throughout human history, and around the world. Our ancient forebears recorded their insights in their mythologies and sacred books, in their holidays and festivals, in their calendars and celestial observations. Each aspect of traditional culture reflected the interplay of polar forces in creation. Different images and symbols were of course used by various societies to depict the basic motion of life, yet everywhere the meaning was the same.

In the Orient, the study of the complemental nature of life continued uninterrupted for many thousands of years. At some point in the past, however, this understanding began to decline, and a dynamic application was gradually replaced by custom and ritual. These eventually solidified into a rigid and irregular application, lacking relevance to contemporary conditions. The spectacle of primitive or traditional societies renouncing their cultural heritage in favor of present-day values is thus an understandable if regrettable occurrence.

In the Western world, this traditional understanding was gradually supplanted by an opposite approach that lead eventually to our modern worldview and way of life. More recently, this orientation has become the accepted standard around the globe.

This alternating historical pattern once again reflects the cycle of movement from one pole, in this case the nonmaterialistic view, to its opposite, the materialistic view. It also mirrors the principle that, at its extreme point, a thing will begin to change into its opposite.

The German philosopher, Georg Wilhelm Friedrich Hegel (1770–1831), described the evolution of civilization in a comparable manner. He envisioned development as a cyclical pattern in which progress unfolds through the interaction of complementary forces. A process begins with an initial unified state, or *thesis*, which generates its opposite, or *antithesis*. These opposites combine into a higher state of unity, or *synthesis*, which then leads to a new thesis, antithesis, and so on. This process is exactly what is occurring on a global scale today. In the midst of great social upheaval, a union is emerging, in which the traditional, metaphysical orientation is being combined with the modern, scientific understanding. This consolidation of ancient and modern, and Eastern and Western thought, of wisdom and knowledge, offers humanity not only the key to solve the problems of our age, but will form the foundation of a new civilization on this planet.

The Three Emperors of China

Most, and perhaps all, countries have their foundation mythologies and their founding figures. This is as true of modern nations as it is for societies many thousands of years old. According to legend, the first emperor of China was named Fu-Hi. While leading his people along the Yellow River, the responsibilities of leadership prompted Fu-Hi to reflect on the patterns of human interaction and upon the design of individual development. Living close to nature, he began to see that the myriad cycles unfolding everywhere were reflections of movement between two great poles.

Eventually, Fu-Hi realized that the oneness of infinity differentiates into two opposite and supporting motions in nature. He called one tendency yin and the other yang, and symbolized them as a broken line (– –), yin, and a solid line (—), yang. Fu-Hi gave the name yin to the expansive, centrifugal tendency, and yang to the contracting, centripetal tendency. He theorized that the interplay of these two forces was accountable for the life cycles of all things in the universe, both the animate and inanimate.

He further saw that from this initial differentiation of one into two—great yin and great yang—the two divide into four, which he called large yin and small yin, and large yang and small yang. These four again divide, creating eight stages of change.

The progression of this sequence is thus:

- One Infinity polarizes into great yin and great yang.
- These poles divide into great yin and small yin, and great yang and small yang.
- These four again divide into eight distinct stages.

Fu-Hi depicted these categories graphically as eight, three-line combinations of yin (broken) and yang (solid) lines, representing heaven, earth, and humanity. These three-line sets are called *trigrams*. The trigram for great yin was symbolized by three broken lines (☷), while great yang was drawn as three solid lines (☰). In between these two poles, there are six possible combinations, each with a name

Fig. 12 Fu-Hi's Eight Trigrams

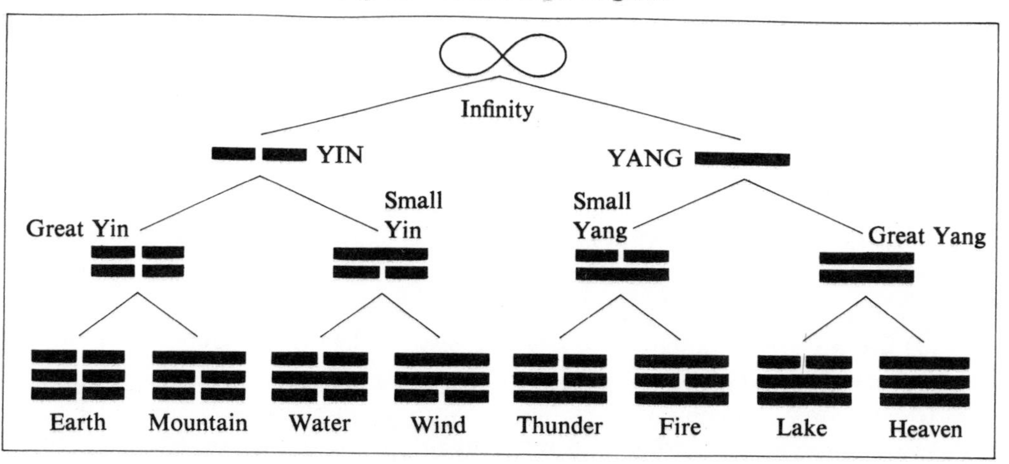

In this illustration: (1) Infinity divides into opposite and complementary tendencies, yin and yang. (2) These primary poles then divide into large yin and small yin, and large yang and small yang. (3) Each of these four categories again divides into the energetic qualities depicted under the individual trigrams.

of a natural phenomenon that reflects the particular trigram's energetic quality. These are illustrated in Figure 12.

By way of example, the trigram for water is composed of a central yang line enclosed by two yin lines (☵). This wonderfully unadorned symbol reveals the inherent nature of water, which on the surface is soft and yielding (yin qualities), but which has the power to dissolve even the hardest rock (a yang characteristic). The trigram for fire consists of two yang lines surrounding a central yin line (☲). This implies that fire, which is very yang on the surface—hot and active—is actually unstable and easily extinguished.

Fu-Hi called the pattern of interaction between these eight stages of development the Laws of Change, or the Principles of the Universe. As such, the trigrams were used to depict and explain the existence of all physical and psychological, natural and social manifestations.

The second legendary Emperor of China was Shin-No, or Divine Agriculture. Shin-No is credited with applying the principles of change to produce a system of agriculture, food production, and dietary principles. He developed the art of using food for personal well-being and development.

The third Emperor, Ko-Tei, or the Yellow Emperor, applied the principles of change to the realm of medicine and healing. Several thousands of years after his death, his ideas were recorded in the book, *Huang-ti Ching*, or *The Yellow Emperor's Classic of Internal Medicine*. The first part of this work, *So-Mon* (素問), is a general discussion of sickness. The second part, *Rei-Su* (靈樞), or spiritual structure, deals with the body's meridians and points, and explains their uses in healing.

Fu-Hi's principles of change were eventually used to develop spiritual practices, arts and crafts, technology and science, and in fact, all aspects of personal, community, and national life. In other words, it was upon the particular cosmology based on complementary opposites that society was built. The development of Chinese and Far-Eastern civilization thus mirrors one-half of the universal cycle of growth, moving as it does from the Infinite to the individual, or from the general to the specific. That is to say, starting with the universal principles of life, it went on to develop the complexities of a thriving social organization.

In our time, society is following the second half of this cycle, proceeding from the specific to the general. Beginning with the particular application of the laws of change to medicine and healing, we are now extending our attention to the broader fields of dietary practice, food production, and agriculture. Eventually, scientific discoveries and growing public acceptance will lead us to the recognition of the general applicability of these principles.

In the Chou Dynasty, about 1100 B.C., the historical record becomes clear. Because their culture had grown more complex, people began to feel that Fu-Hi's eight trigrams were too simple to explain the various interactions in society. The eight trigrams were thus combined with the same eight to create sixty-four *hexagrams* of six lines each. These hexagrams, representing various combinations of yin and yang, were compiled into the *I Ching*, or the *Book of Changes*, the most important book in China. Representing the order and pattern of nature, all reflections of Chinese civilization were subsequently based on the *I-Ching*.

Scholars and statesmen throughout Chinese history studied this work, as they have continued to do even into the twentieth century. Confucius, after many years of contemplation, wrote commentaries for each hexagram, and these have become a vital part of the *Book of Changes*. Confucianism is built on the precepts of the *I-Ching*, or the Unifying Principles. The term for the Order of the Universe in Confucianism is *Ten-Mei* (天命), or the Heavenly Order. Lao-Tzu also studied these laws of change, and his teachings, known as Taoism, are also founded on the principles of yin and yang.

Confucianism and Taoism, the two poles of Chinese philosophy, can be seen to exist in a complementary relationship. Confucianism teaches the ordering of society, and the individual's role within it. Taoism is concerned with the individual's relationship to the order of life and with personal development.

Ancient Teachings

Based on a worldview complementary to our own, the achievements of traditional societies are often disregarded, and their significance misinterpreted or ignored. As long as we insist on judging in terms of our own specific value system, the depth of traditional understanding and the practicality of its application will too easily be overlooked. When our studies are based on a similar perspective, namely, the concept of yin and yang, we can readily appreciate the clarity and precision of the insight our ancestors recorded for future generations.

The universal principles of change and harmony are expressed in all traditional civilizations, East and West. In Japan, the most sacred books are the *Kojiki* (古事記), the *Book of Ancient Events*, and the *Nihon Shoki* (日本書紀), or *Book of Japanese History*. These works record creation in the same terms as the *I-Ching*. From the one Heavenly Central God of Infinity, came centrifugality, Takami-Musubi, and centripetality, Kami-Musubi. Through the interaction of these polar forces, all phenomena appeared.

In the ancient Indian philosophy of Vedanta, which is the foundation of Buddhism and Hinduism, the principle of antagonistic complements is clearly depicted. Brahman, or Infinity, differentiates into Shiva and Parvati, Krishna and Radha, and other pairs of complementary divinities.

In the Christian Bible, the very first lines of *Genesis* explain creation this way: In the beginning, God [one infinity] created heaven [centripetality] and earth [centrifugality]. From these two all things came into existence.

The new testament contains many examples of this principle. There are numerous references to the first and the last, alpha and omega, light and dark, right and wrong, good and bad, and so on. In *The Gospel According to Thomas*, discovered shortly after World War II in an Egyptian cave, and representing the most direct record we have of the teachings of Jesus, Christ is quoted as saying, "If they ask you, 'What is the sign of your Father in you?' say to them, 'it is movement and repose.' " When his disciples asked how they shall enter the kingdom of Heaven, Jesus replied with as clear an explanation of the importance of yin and yang as we are likely to find:

> When you make the two one, and when you make the inside like the outside, and the outside like the inside, and the above like the below, and when you make the male and the female one and the same, so that the male not be male nor the female female . . . then will you enter the Kingdom.

The principles of life are the same in all places and at all times. It should come as no surprise, then, that traditional peoples comprehended, taught, and sought to live in harmony with them. Within this sameness, however, specific circumstances vary. The challenge for the modern world is twofold: (1) to acknowledge the universal principles of life, and (2) to flexibly apply them to conditions as they exist in the late twentieth century.

Yin and Yang in the Body

The interaction of the forces of yin and yang is reflected in the form and motion of all things. In the vegetable kingdom, for example, the roots of a plant grow downward under the influence of the yang or contracting force, while the leaves

Fig. 13 Energetics in the Plant Kingdom

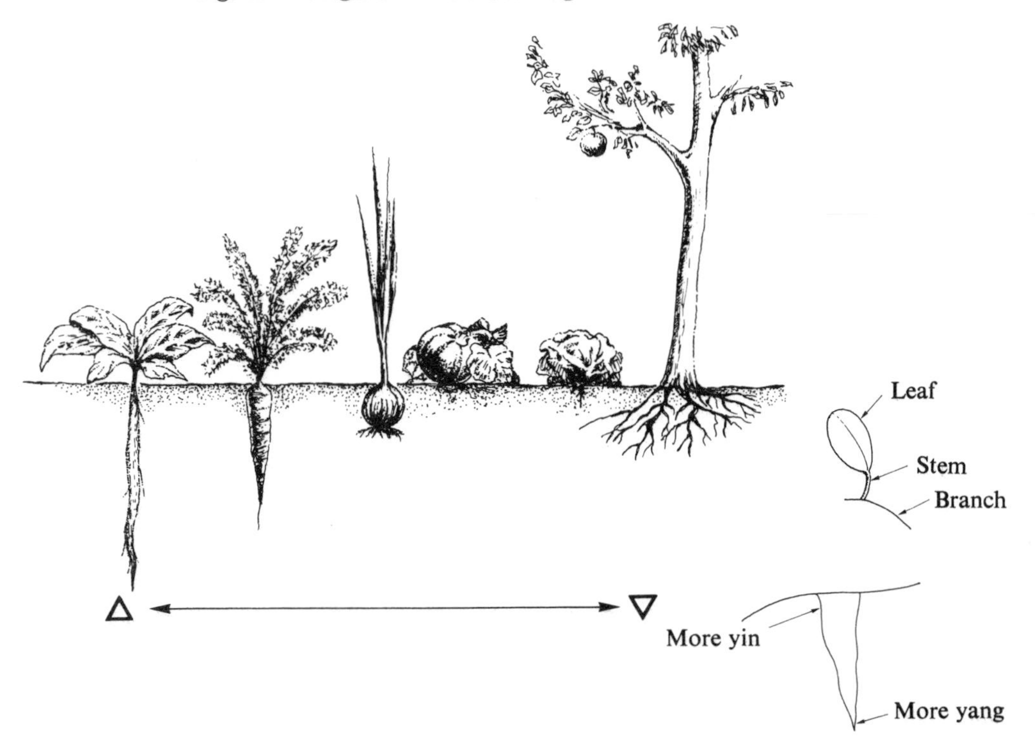

In the plant kingdom, Heaven's force causes vertical growth underground and horizontal growth above ground. Earth's force produces vertical growth above ground and horizontal growth below ground.

In a single plant, the moister, softer, expanded leaves are more yin than the drier, harder, contracted stems and branches. Underground, the more expanded, moister, upper section of the root is yin in comparison to the drier and harder root tip.

grow upward and outward under the expanding influence of the yin force. In addition, within any section of an individual plant, divisions of yin and yang can be distinguished. In the upper segment, the more expanded and moist leaves are yin in comparison to the compact, harder and drier branches and stems. In the lower section, the condensed root tip is yang in comparison to the more expanded upper portions.

The structure and function of the human body is fashioned and nourished in the same way. For instance, the head grows upward under the rising influence of the yin force, while the trunk grows downward under the descending influence of the yang force. Other examples include the relationship between the nervous system, which has a more yang, solid structure and a more yin, less active function, and the digestive system, with its more yin, hollow structure and more yang, active function.

The bodily organs can be divided into two general categories of yin and yang, with the hollow organs being more yin in terms of structure and more yang in terms of activity, and the solid organs being more yang in structure and more yin in activity. The blood and lymph system, the para- and orthosympathetic branches of the autonomic nervous systems, the right and left hemispheres of the brain, and the head and the trunk, are other pairs representing the complementary tendencies of yin and yang. The outer and inner, the center and periphery, the front and back, the left and right, and the upper and lower all represent antagonistic and complementary relationships within the body.

Metabolic processes are animated in a similar way. Examples include: the peristaltic (waving) motion of the intestines, the contraction and expansion of the heart and lungs, the secretion of insulin (a yang hormone) and anti-insulin (a more yin hormone), the alkaline saliva and the acidic stomach fluids, and the production of sperm and egg.

A complete book could be devoted just to listing the myriad complementary functions within the body, and an entire lifetime could be spent exploring their implications. For the moment, the above examples will suffice to convey the influence of yin and yang within the human body.

Five Transformations

We have seen that yin and yang continuously change into each other: at their extreme, yin changes into yang and yang changes into yin. Traditional peoples recognized that this alternating cycle, rather than occurring abruptly, unfolds in an orderly and gradual way. The transition from summer to winter, for instance, is an almost imperceptible progression on a day-to-day basis, as is the moment-to-moment journey from day to night, and the gentle passage from youth to old age. It is only when these courses reach specific levels of contrast that distinctions can be made.

On the basis of this perception, our ancestors realized that the cycle of energy between opposite poles could be further developed into five phases of transformation, providing a more detailed explanation of the interpay of yin and yang, and enhancing the potential to practically apply it in daily life.

In modern Chinese medicine, this five-staged cycle is translated into English as *The Five Elements Theory*. However, the idea of elements creates the notion of solid, steady states. The actual Oriental term is *Yin Yang Go Gyo* (陰陽五行), which literally means "the five goings of yin and yang." We now commonly refer to this process as the "five stages of energy transformation," or "the five stages of energy change." The image is of energy, or Ki, undergoing five distinguishable stages of transformation as it moves from one pole (centrifugality) to its opposite (centripetality) and back again.

Fig. 14 The Five Stages of Energy Transformation

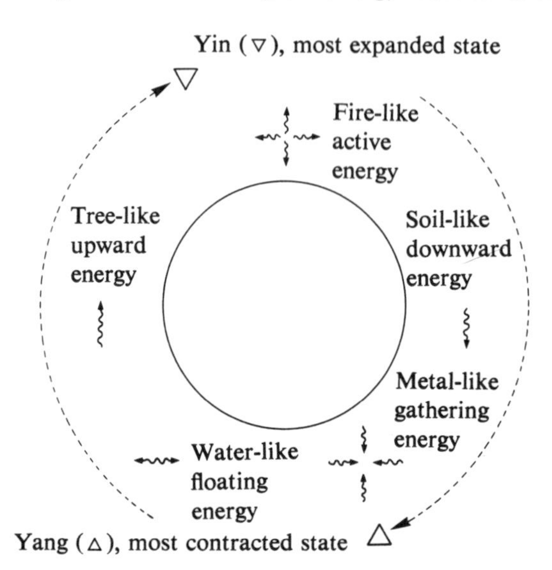

These stages were given names of objects commonly found in nature to illustrate the relationship between the physical and the energetic world. In their sequence of movement, they were called water, wood, fire, soil, and metal. These labels should not be taken literally, however. Rather than static objects, they represent transitory phases or convenient landmarks in an ever-moving process. Think of them as being identifiable peaks cresting along a continuous, wave-like sequence of energy. As commonly explained, the relationship between these stages is depicted as follows:

- Water produces wood, or vegetation.
- Wood provides the fuel for fire.
- Fire generates soil or ash.
- Soil condenses into metal.
- Metal melts or rusts into water.

The progressive nature of these phases was meant to convey the dynamic and cyclical character of the interaction between yin and yang. Their spiralic nature is illustrated in the shift from the metal to water stage. It is at this point that a loop occurs in the circuit, leading either inward or outward to a new dimension of influence.

A more accurate picture of these five stages is conveyed by the terms: water-like energy, tree-like energy, fire-like energy, soil-like energy, and metal-like energy. In our time, it is perhaps clearer to employ the energetic or atmospheric point of view and use the expressions:

- Floating energy (water-like): Energy that is beginning to expand in a horizontal direction
- Upward energy (tree-like): A more animated, rising and expanding state of energy
- Active energy (fire-like): Very active energy moving in all directions
- Downward energy (soil-like): Energy that is beginning to condense
- Gathering energy (metal-like): Energy in its most condensed state

Fig. 15 Natural Cycles and the Five Transformations

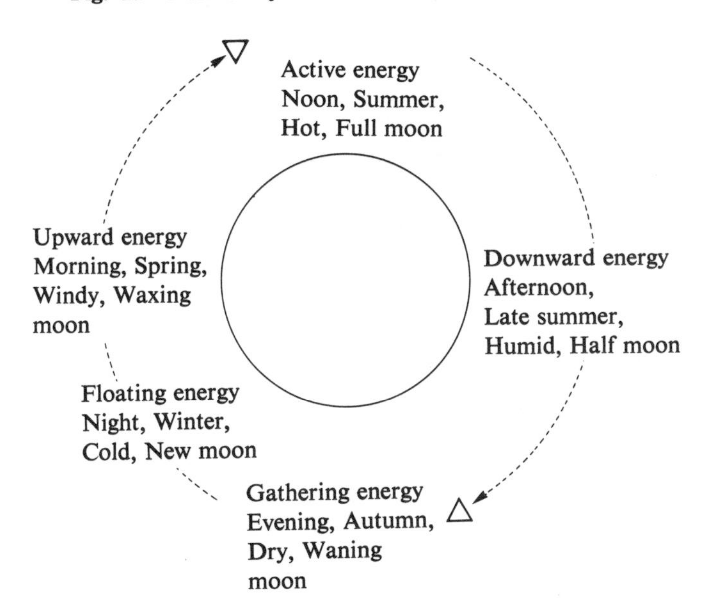

Recognizing the universal nature of the process of change, ancient peoples were able to classify numerous processes and phenomena according to the Five Transformations of Energy. Examples include:

- The changes in atmospheric energy over the course of a twenty-four hour day
- The progression of the twenty-eight day lunar cycle
- The unfolding of the solar year
- Various weather-related conditions associated with, but not limited to, the seasons

As explained earlier, Oriental-medicine practitioners view the physical body in a way that is opposite to modern medical and scientific theory. The traditional approach to physiology was based on the recognition that the source of matter

Fig. 16 Bodily Organs and the Five Transformations

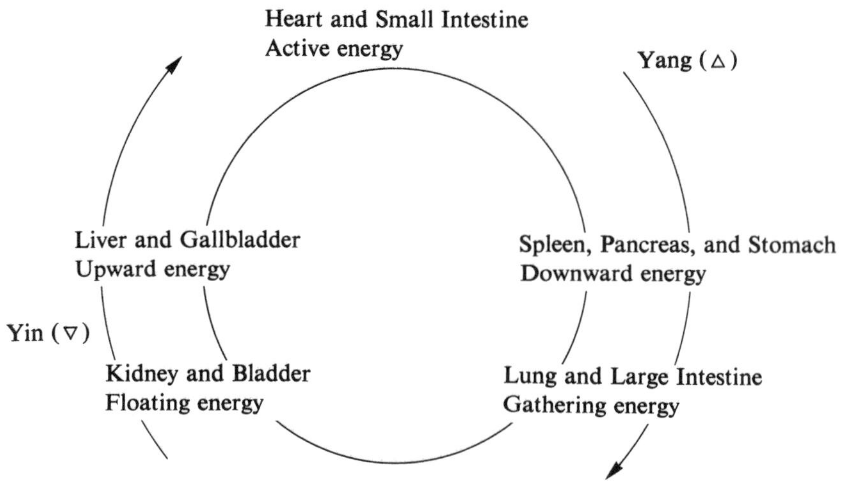

was energy. The concept of bodily organs—their structure and function—is thus energetically rather than physically oriented. We will discuss this in detail in the next chapter. For our present purposes we simply need to realize that this distinction in approaches exists. The classification of organs according to the Five Transformations of Energy is illustrated in Figure 16.

With the information in the above figures, we already know a great deal about the energetics of the body. For instance, the organs were grouped in pairs, according to their complemental energetic nature. Each organ pair is associated with a particular quality of energy. The kidneys and bladder, for example, are related to the floating type of energy, and the liver and gallbladder to the upward-moving type of energy. In additon, each organ pair is part of either the yin or yang half of the energetic cycle.

From the twenty-four-hour cycle we can see the time of day each organ pair is activated; from the lunar cycle, the time of the month; and from the yearly cycle, the season each is most active. The atmospheric classification explains the energetic quality of different weather conditions, and their relationship to the organs.

An extensive list of correspondences was created to show the energetic relationship existing between various phenomena. These classifications illustrate the macrocosmic and the microcosmic correlation of life. From the smallest to the largest listing, the diverse phenomena within each category reflect a similar energetic basis.

It is easy to see, for instance, why the color green represents the spring season. Going a step further, the influence of the color green is often described as cool and soothing, relaxing and refreshing. The energy is yin, and within this category, its specific nature is raising and expanding, as reflected in the characteristic growth pattern of vegetation in the spring of the year.

The information provided in Table 4 provides insights into the basic nature of life. In the realm of healing, it establishes the basis for diagnosis and treatment. For diagnostic purposes, the chart can be used in the following way:

Table 4 List of Correspondences within the Five Transformations

	A	B	C	D	E
Energy:	Upward	Very active	Downward	Solidified	Floating
Examples:	Gas	Plasma	Condensation	Solid	Liquid
	Tree	Fire	Soil	Metal	Water
Organ energy:	Liver, gall-bladder	Heart, small intestine	Spleen-pancreas, stomach	Lungs, large intestine	Kidneys, bladder
Direction:	East	South	Center	West	North
Season:	Spring	Summer	Late summer	Autumn	Winter
Time of month:	Increasing half-moon	Full moon	Obscured moon	Decreasing half-moon	New moon
Time of day:	Morning	Noon	Afternoon	Evening	Night
Environment:	Windy	Hot	Humid	Dry	Cold
Grain:	Wheat, barley	Corn	Millet	Rice	Beans
Vegetables:	Sprouts and upward-growing plants	Enlarged leafy plants	Round plants	Contracted, small plants	Root plants
Fruits:	Spring fruits	Summer fruits	Late summer fruits	Autumn fruits	Winter and dried fruits
Odor:	Oily, greasy	Burning	Fragrant	Fishy	Putrefying
Tastes:	Sour	Bitter	Sweet	Pungent	Salty
Physical parts:	Tissues	Blood vessels	Muscles	Skin	Bones
Physical branches:	Nails	Body hair and facial color	Breast, lips	Breath	Head hair
Skin color:	Blue, gray	Red	Yellow, milky	Pale	Black, dark
Physical liquids:	Tears	Sweat	Slaver	Snivel	Saliva
Physical changes:	Gripping	Anxious	Sobbing	Coughing	Shivering
5 Voices:	Shouting	Talking	Singing	Crying	Groaning
5 Functions:	Color	Odor	Taste	Voice	Fluid
Psychological reaction:	Anger, excitement	Laughing, talkative	Indecisive, suspicious	Sadness, depression	Fear, insecurity

- Troubles with the kidneys and/or bladder will appear in the ears, bones, and head hair. There may be a distinctive putrefying odor, a dark facial color, and the saliva may be excessive or deficient.
- Troubles with the liver and/or gallbladder will appear in the eyes, tissues, and nails. There may be an oily or rancid odor, a blue or gray facial color, and the eyes may be watery or too dry.
- Troubles with the heart and/or small intestine will appear in the blood vessels, tongue, and body hair. There may be a bitter odor, a red facial color, and excessive or deficient perspiration.
- Troubles with the spleen-pancreas and/or stomach will appear in the lips and breasts. There may be a sweet odor, a yellow facial color, and drooling.
- Troubles with the lungs and/or large intestine will appear in the throat and nose, and the skin. There may be a fishy odor, a pale facial color, and a runny nose.

When considering a course of treatment, the following are some of the factors to consider:

- The types of grains, vegetables, and other food categories associated with each energy phase represent the same type of energy that created the related organs. These foods consequently nourish the functions of the organs and their associated psychological characteristics. In excess or deficiency, the energy of these foods may produce imbalances within the associated category of characteristics that will show up on the various levels of the Self.
- The particular taste associated with each energy phase enhances the functions of the organs and psychological tendencies. In excess or deficiency, it can cause imbalances. Craving for certain tastes can give a cue as to the source of the problem.
- The color identified with each organ generates the same quality of vibration as its associated organ and psychological states. Colors can thus be used to enhance the functions of particular organs and psychological qualities. This is also the basis of the use of various gem stones both in healing and to accentuate certain psychological and spiritual qualities. Individual gems resonate at certain frequencies that augment the qualities they are associated with.

Examples of Application

According to the information in Table 4, if a problem arises at a certain time of day, during a distinct phase of the moon, in a particular season, or under specific weather conditions, the organ pair within the same energy category may be related to, and perhaps is the source of the problem. If, for instance, an illness regularly arises in the early morning, especially on windy days, and/or in the spring, the involvement of the liver and gallbladder can be suspected.

To relieve problems related to specific organ pairs, we first determine in what way the energy is out of balance. For instance, is it excessive or deficient. Once this is determined, appropriate steps can be taken, using the information provided in the list of correspondences.

To enhance the energy flow within a certain organ pair, we can include food items from the same category. In the case of liver troubles, we could thus take wheat and barley, scallions, leeks, and other upward-growing vegetables. We may want to occasionally eat some spring-type fruit as well.

In addition, we could include the sour taste from time to time, in the form of rice or *umeboshi* vinegar, or sauerkraut. If fish is desired, we would take small amounts of coastal fish like cod or halibut.

Of course, these items would be consumed in small, medicinal amounts, and, for this purpose, only for a short period of time. It would not be necessary to eat all foods listed.

Depending on the circumstances, we may also want to temporarily reduce items in the opposite side of the yin/yang energetic cycle mentioned earlier (see Figure 14). In this case, the liver is nourished by the yin, rising energy. An excess of more yang, downward energy will create or aggravate problems.

In the opposite case, we may find that the energy of a certain organ pair is excessive. Then we may want to reduce foods and other elements in the same category, and place a light emphasis on those from the complementary half of the yin and yang cycle. (Refinements in the approach to both excessive and deficient energy will be discussed shortly.)

Emotions, Mind, and Spirit

The nonphysical aspects of the Self are directly related to the condition of the physical body. Characteristics of each reflect, influence, and are influenced by, the others. As mentioned earlier, a physical problem immediately creates emotional and mental imbalances, and emotional or mental disorders have a direct impact on the physical condition.

Figure 17 represents the emotional qualities associated with each of the five stages of energy transformation. If the energy represented by each stage flows smoothly within the body, one's emotional expression will be healthy and appropriate. If the energy is disrupted, the emotional expression will likewise be distorted in some way, either exaggerated or repressed, for instance. The approach to such a problem is to balance the energy flow, and the method is the same as for physical disorders.

In other words, we can try to encourage the positive emotional states that support the category affected, and diminish emotional states that inhibit it. Obviously, this is easier said than done. Because the energy of the emotional body is more refined, the effort to regulate it can be a demanding task. We would thus also make use of the physical qualities—foods, tastes, colors, and so on—to enhance our applications.

Mental and spiritual characteristics can be classified in the same way, as shown in Figure 18. In health, the positive aspects of each is manifested, in sickness, when the body's energy flow is disrupted, the negative aspects will be expressed.

Fig. 17 Emotional Characteristics and the Five Transformations

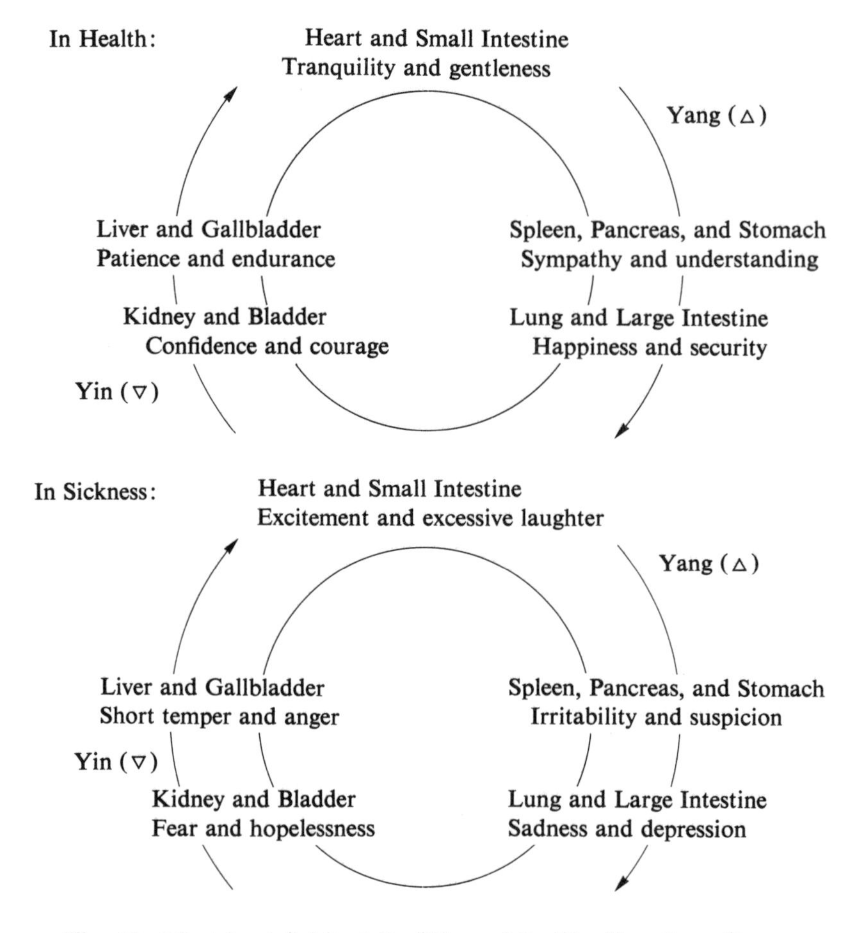

Fig. 18 Mental and Spiritual Qualities and the Five Transformations

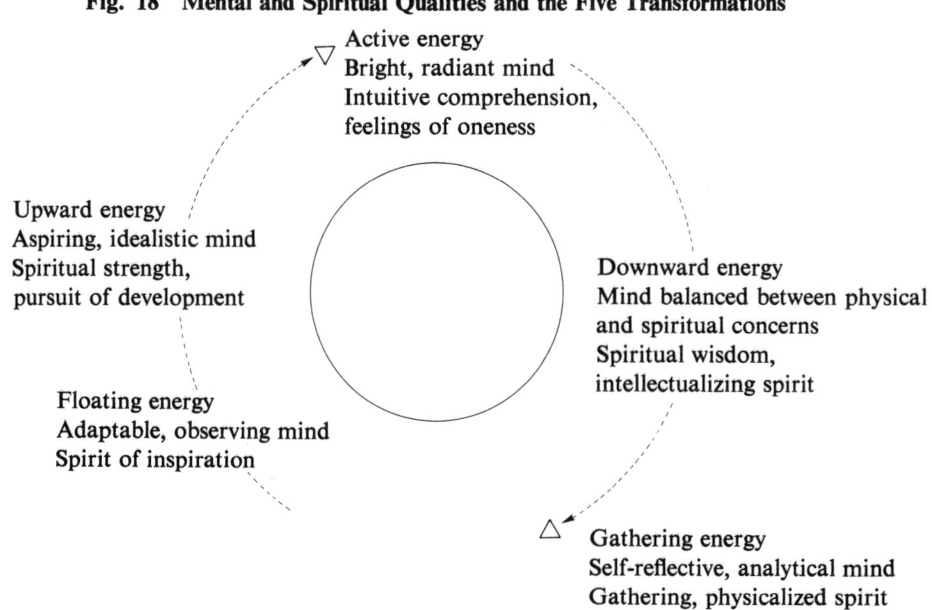

A summation of the correspondences of the nonphysical qualities of the Self follows:

- *Kidney/Bladder:* In health these organs are related to courage, confidence, curiosity, ambition, and inspiration. An unbalanced condition produces fear, a sense of hopelessness, and a loss of self-esteem.
- *Liver/Gallbladder:* In health, these organs are related to patience and endurance. If unbalanced, they produce impatience, short temper, and anger.
- *Heart/Small Intestine:* In health, these organs are related to gentleness and tranquility. If umbalanced, these organs produce overexcitability, excessive laughter and talking.
- *Spleen-pancreas/Stomach:* In health, these organs produce understanding and wisdom, compassion and sympathy. If umbalanced, they produce worry, irritability, skepticism, and criticism.
- *Lungs/Large Intestine:* In health, these organs produce a sense of security and wholeness. If umbalanced, they produce feelings of sadness and depression.

With this panoramic relation of the individual and the larger forces of life in mind, we can treat any personal problem, whether it be physical or psychological. These categories are, after all, merely different states of individual energy quality. As discussed earlier, when treating, we can approach from the spirit, mind, or body. Influencing one level will have an immediate influence on all the others.

However, within this two-way relationship between physical and spiritual, a natural sequence presents itself. As human beings, the realm we have the most immediate control over is the material. The physical body is the foundation upon which our consciousness is based. Thus, when faced with a restraint of any sort, we naturally start from the beginning—with daily diet and lifestyle practices, which profoundly affect all aspects of our being. This point will be examined in detail as we continue our study.

Energy Cycles

Within the pattern of energy's five transformations, several key cycles operate. The first of these is the basic yin and yang cycle, sometimes referred to as the *Husband-Wife Relation*. The image reflects the idea that the relationship between the two halves of the cycle is a mutually sustaining one, with each partner having specific responsibilities and influences.

Representing the husband, the yin or expanding energy of water, wood, and *principal fire* (heart and small intestine) are balanced by the wife, the contracting energies of *secondary fire* (the heart governor and triple heater functions), soil, and metal. When properly balanced, the husband (expanding energy) should be slightly more active than that of the wife (contracting energy). If either force is too strong or too weak, the resulting imbalance will create disorder within the body just as it will in a relationship.

Fig. 19 The Husband-and-Wife Cycle

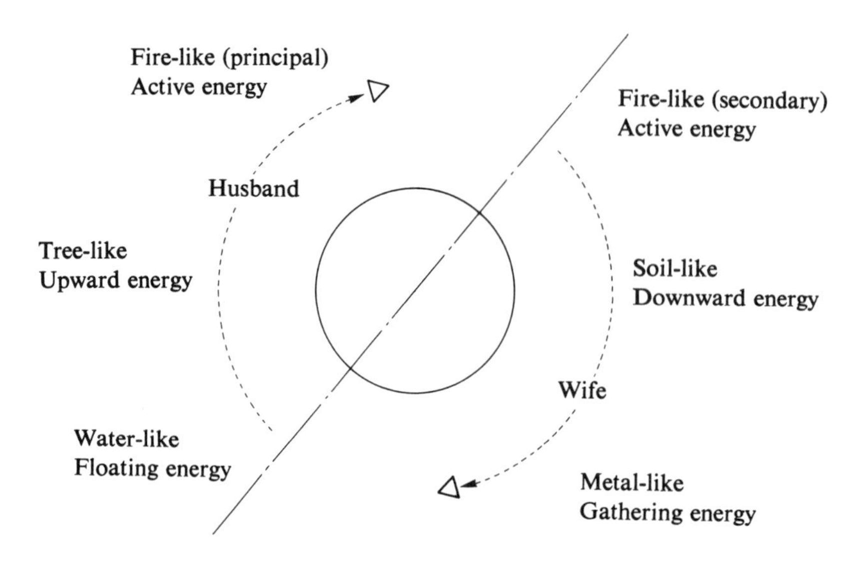

An additional pair of energy cycles operating within the five transformations exhibit complementary tendencies. One is a source of support or nourishment, and the second, operating in an opposite manner, works as a regulating or balancing influence.

The support cycle is sometimes referred to as the *Mother-Child or Parent-Child Relationship*. The significance of the name becomes clear when we examine the nature of this cycle. Proceeding clockwise around the spiral, each phase nourishes, or gives birth to, the one that follows. Thus:

- Floating energy supports (is the mother of) rising energy,
- Rising energy generates active energy,

Fig. 20 The Support and Regulating Cycles

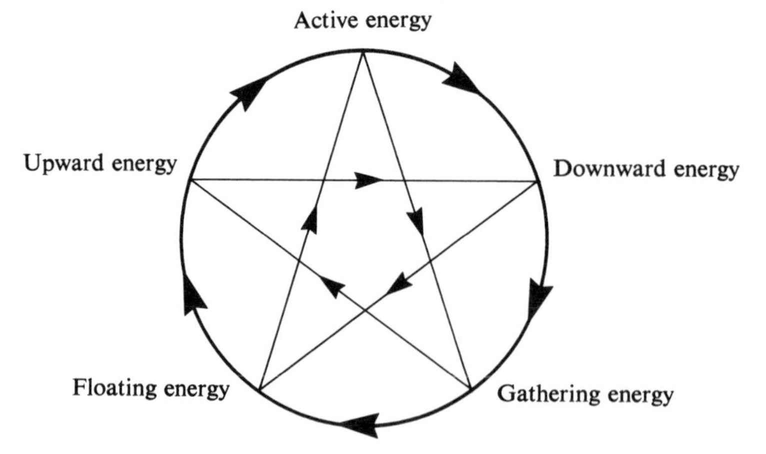

The outer, clockwise circle represents the Support Cycle.
The inner, star-like pattern is the course of the Regulating Cycle.

- Active energy produces downward energy,
- Downward energy begets gathering energy,
- Gathering energy supports floating energy.

As an example of how this support cycle can be applied to healing, let us suppose there is a problem with the kidneys. This can manifest as either excessive or deficient energy flow. If excessive, the symptoms will likely be apparent. There may be fever, sharp pain, or swelling, for instance. If deficient, the indications may not be readily noticeable, as the trouble tends to remain inside. Also, in cases where the energy is excessive, acute symptoms generally appear, and when the energy is deficient, the symptoms are more likely to be chronic.

If excess energy is causing the problem, the body's natural impulse is to drain it via urination and sweating. In cases where these responses are insufficient, a fever may develop to discharge the energy, in the form of heat, through the skin. Using an understanding of the support cycle, we can assist this process.

We could treat the kidney directly by draining energy from the organ and its meridian. However, the kidney's floating-type of energy naturally flows to the liver. If the floating energy is excessive, it is most likely overflowing and pouring into the liver and gallbladder, the next organ pair. Depending on the individual's overall condition, under certain circumstances it would be more efficient to reduce or drain energy from the liver and its meridian rather than directly from the kidneys.

In the same way, if there is a deficiency of energy in the kidneys, we can stimulate the kidney meridian directly, or we can stimulate the organ preceding it (the parent), thus nourishing the affected organ (the child). In this case, the gathering energy of the lung and large intestine organ pair serve as the mother of the floating energy of the kidneys. To activate the kidneys, we can follow the natural pattern of energy flow and give energy to the lung and its meridian.

The Regulating Cycle

The second cycle, illustrated in Figure 20, works in a complemental way. Commonly called the *Regulating Cycle*, this process refers to the regulation that one stage, the "grandparent," will have on its "grandchild," or the second stage from the original phase. Problems arise if:

1. The controlling influence of one stage becomes too great, thus inhibiting the function of the organ pair of its grandchild, or
2. The controlling partner is too weak, thus allowing the function of its grandchild organ-pair to become excessive.

If, for example, we stimulate the kidneys, the liver, or child, will also be nourished. However, the active energy of the heart and small intestine, the grandchild, may be inhibited if the floating energy of the kidney becomes excessive.

In this cycle:

- Upward energy controls downward energy,
- Downward energy regulates floating energy,
- Floating energy monitors active energy,
- Active energy oversees gathering energy,
- Gathering energy controls upward energy.

A word of caution is called for here. These are general examples. When deciding whether it is appropriate to use either of these two cycles, the condition of all of the meridians and organs, and of the person as a whole, must first be determined. Treating problems with rote prescriptions violates the principles of traditional and Oriental medicine outlined earlier.

When used wisely, the five transfomations and the various energetic cycles at work within them are serviceable tools in the field of healing. And yet, the concepts of simplicity and practicality should regulate our therapies.

Also, do not make the mistake of assuming that the application of these energetic cycles is limited to the area of health care. Being universal principles, they apply to all creation. Study and use them for personal growth, and to realize your goals in life.

Now that we have examined the roots and trunk of Far-Eastern civilization, we are just about ready to sample the fruits, or the practical application of the traditional worldview to the realm of healing. Before we do, however, the branch of this tree that deals with the body's energy system needs to be outlined in more detail. In chapter 4 we examine the forces that form and activate the human body.

4. Meridians and Points

Our exploration of traditional and Oriental medicine has already taken us a considerable distance. The major landmarks thus far include:

1. The concept of the nonphysical world of Ki underlying and producing material existence.
2. The vision of Ki moving constantly between the universal poles of yin and yang, or expansion and contraction.
3. The recognition that the alternating movement of Ki between opposites unfolds in a progressive pattern through five identifiable phases—a process which traditional peoples called the Five Stages of Energy Transformation.

In addition, we have seen how the forces of yin and yang, interacting in the solar system, create an immense, human-like energy form that surrounds the planet and extends toward the periphery of the solar system. The human body is a materialized replica of this energy pattern.

The planet itself—including the successive layers of core, mantle, crust, oceans, atmosphere, and radiation belts—is produced by the interaction of the motions of contraction and expansion, which our ancestors called Heaven's force and Earth's force. The human structure is generated by the same energies, and shares many similarities with the earth. For instance, Heaven's and Earth's forces create the primary channel in the human body just as they generate the intensely charged line that runs through the center of planet—the earth's primary channel. Humans have seven energy centers, called chakras, which correlate to the planet's single energy center, the magnetic core.

Meridians

From the chakras, Ki circulates to all areas of the body, charging each of its billions of cells. These currents of energy are called *meridians* in Chinese medicine. If we use the image of a swiftly flowing river to portray the primary channel, the chakras can be likened to whirlpools arising within this powerful current. The meridians are tributaries of this river. Branching off from the primary channel, they divide and subdivide into increasingly smaller streams which finally join with the cells. In this way, each cell is continually supplied with energy via the meridians, which in turn receive energy from the chakras, the primary channel and ultimately from the universe itself in the form of Heaven's and Earth's forces.

The meridians are often described as channels along which Ki flows, but this is somewhat misleading. Actually, there are no channels that direct or confine the flow of Ki. Think instead of streams of energy flowing actively from one of the centrally located chakras out to the body's periphery and then back again to one of the chakras. The meridians are these energy currents rather than any particular tubes or vessels that carry Ki.

This mechanism parallels the activity of the earth's streams and rivers. It is not the river banks that determine the course of a river. Rather, it is the amount of water and the rate of flow that produce the banks. If and when these two factors change, new embankments are formed.

On the earth, the discharge of energy from lines comparable to the body's meridians creates mountain ranges like the Andes, the Rockies, the Himalayas, and the great mountain ranges rising from the floor of the oceans. Divisions of these energy streams branch out across the planet. Prehistoric sacred sites, and later, settlements, towns, and cities grew up at points along these lines, with each having a different nature depending on the energetic quality of the particular spot. For instance, some cities are more business oriented or are famous for their arts and crafts. Others become known as university towns, as centers of technology, as places devoted to spiritual practices, and so on. In each case, the emphasis comes from the characteristic energy of the area, which in turn stimulates specific physical and psychological attributes of the inhabitants.

Traditional peoples were well aware of these lines and the influence they exerted on their surroundings. In China, they are called *dragon lines*, and a sophisticated art, known as *Feng-shui*, was developed to locate and utilize the energy generated along them. For instance, the quality of the energy at a particular site could be subtly altered in various ways to make it more harmonious with the activities being pursued there. Locations for distinctive types of buildings, such as a temple, school, government office, or personal residence, were selected according to the nature of the energy deemed appropriate for the intended activity.

In the Western world, the earth's energy lines have been called by various names since ancient times. They are now generally referred to as *ley lines* in English. In this century a steady body of information has been accumulating, and there are now a number of books available, both on the Chinese art of Feng-shui and on the Western study of ley lines. It is sufficient for our purposes to realize that the meridians of the human body correspond to these highly charged energy lines that run across the planet.

The meridians represent our connection with the larger forces of creation. They are important not only to our study of Oriental medicine, but to every aspect of human activity. On a larger scale, they can help put us in touch with the basic nature of life. To properly understand the human meridian system, an explanation of embryonic development, from the energetic perspective, will be helpful.

Meridians in the Embryo

Although not physically detectable, the inside surface of the uterus is lined with a series of twelve ridges, each of which carries a strong charge of energy. In addition, the uterus is aligned directly along a woman's primary channel, and is located in the area of the abdominal chakra, known as the *Ki-Kai*, or the "sea of Ki," in Japanese. It is interesting to note that a human life begins in this sea of energy just as life on this planet began long ago in the primeval seas.

It is no coincidence that fertilization, implantation, and fetal development take place in this highly charged region. The human body is fundamentally a pattern of energy. The guidelines and nourishment necessary for fetal growth are provided by: (1) the strong concentration of energy coming directly from a mother's primary channel, (2) the abdominal chakra, and (3) the energy transmitted through a woman's womb via the twelve uterine meridians.

This active energy charge causes the ovum to spin on its axis, which in turn generates an aura of energy around the ovum. In much the same way, the earth itself rotates on its axis and is surrounded by highly charged belts of radiation. Fetal growth unfolds by rapid cell division, so that, in just 280 days, the original fertilized ovum develops into an infant composed of trillions of cells, working in a coordinated way, and with organs and systems ready to sustain independent life.

Fig. 21 Energetics of Cell Division

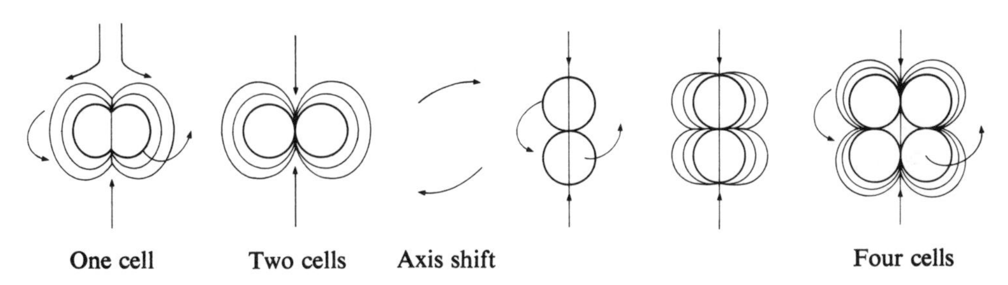

Heaven's force pushes down and in on the fertilized ovum, causing it to spin on its axis. The resulting expansive force of this rotation causes the ovum to bulge along its center. Earth's force pushes up and outward on the ovum, accelerating cell division.

Cell division, like all motion and growth, is stimulated by the interaction of yin and yang, or Earth's and Heaven's forces. As we have seen, Heaven's force is stronger, in the approximate ratio of about 1: 7, Earth's force to Heaven's force. This means that the amount of incoming energy received by the earth is approximately seven times greater than the energy generated outward by the planet. During cell division, Heaven's force, being stronger, pushes down upon the ovum, causing it to spin on its axis just like a toy top does when its handle is depressed. This gyration generates a centrifugal or expansive force which causes the ovum to protrude at its center much as the planet itself bulges along the equator. The downward motion of Heaven's force also tends to compress the circular form of the ovum, that is, it pushes the ovum down on either side. The rising motion of Earth's force pushes upward, thus supplementing the centrifugal motion needed for separation of the new cells.

With the completion of the initial division of cells, the ovum's *center of gravity* (the central point where the inward motion of Heaven's force ends and the outward motion of Earth's force begins) changes position, causing a shift of its axis—a process that occurs periodically on the earth as well. As these first two cells begin to spin on their new axis, the process of cell division is quickly repeated, and soon another axis shift takes place. This mechanism unfolds rapidly in the early stages of fetal development, as the cells divide from one to two, four, eight, sixteen, and so on.

Fig. 22 Formation of the Meridians and Organ and Limb Spirals

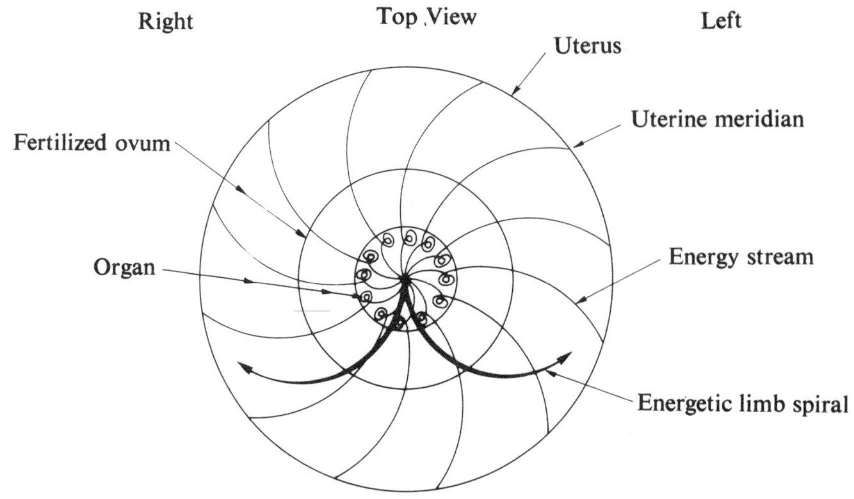

The energy from the twelve uterine meridians travels in a spiral motion. It penetrates the surface of the ovum at a dozen points. Then, because of the rotation, or spin, of the ovum, this energy continues coiling as it moves inward toward the center (see Figure 22). Deep inside, these energy currents culminate in dense, tightly compacted spirals which later develop into the body's internal organs.

Having reached their most concentrated point, the twelve energy streams then reverse direction and discharge to the periphery in two pairs of spiralic currents. One pair moves upward and later differentiates into the arms, hands, and fingers. The other pair moves downward, and subsequently produces the legs, feet, and toes.

The meridians represent this entire course of energy flow, as it enters the body, creates and activates the organs, then discharges upward and downward to form and activate the limbs. In other words, the organs are not distinct from the meridians, but are rather the most dense, physicalized part of the entire meridian course. This is one reason why, when diagnosing or treating a patient, traditional physicians never thought in terms of separate, isolated body parts. From an energetic point of view, separation does not exist.

Yin and Yang Meridians

The meridians, or streams of energy, are classified into two basic categories, reflecting the complementary nature of Heaven's and Earth's forces. One type of energy flow is more yang, strong and rapid, and the other is more yin, mild and slow. As they reach the center of the ovum, these distinct complementary forces generate opposite types of central spirals:

- Yang energy produces yin or outward-moving spirals.
- Yin energy produces yang or inward-moving spirals.

During fetal growth, the coils of yang energy create the opposite, or structurally yin organs, which are more expanded and hollow. The helixes of yin energy

Table 5 Zang and Fu Organs

Zang Organs (compact structure)	Fu Organs (hollow structure)
Lungs	Large Intestine
Heart	Small Intestine
Kidneys	Bladder
Spleen/Pancreas	Stomach
Liver	Gallbladder

generate structurally yang organs, which are more compact and solid. In Oriental medicine, the structurally yang organs are grouped into the category called *Zang*(臓), and the structurally yin organs are called *Fu* (腑). The motion or activity of the more yang, or Zang, organs is slower or more yin. The movement or action of the more yin, or Fu, organs is faster or more yang. For reference, the organs in each classification are listed in Table 5.

Since we can classify by either energy quality, organ structure, or organ function, these categories can be a source of confusion. Depending on which attribute we are discussing, the meridian or organ can accurately be said to be either yin or yang. The following sequence may be helpful in keeping this distinction in mind.

- Yang meridians represent the flow of yang energy.
  Yang energy creates structurally yin (hollow) organs.
  Structurally yin organs have a yang (active) motion.
- Yin meridians represent the flow of yin energy.
  Yin energy creates structurally yang (solid) organs.
  Structurally yang organs have a yin (less active) motion.

The yin and yang meridians and organs complement and balance each other. Using the kidneys and bladder organ-pair as an example, we see that the physical structure of the kidneys is comparatively more compact or yang, while the bladder is more expanded or yin. From an energy standpoint, the kidneys were created and are activated more by yin energy, thus the kidneys and the kidney meridian are classified as being yin. The hollow bladder was created and is activated more by yang energy, and thus the bladder and the bladder meridian are labeled yang.

Compared to the bladder, the kidneys' motion and activity are more yin, or inactive. The physical—as opposed to the energetic—function of the kidneys is to act as a filter. They do not move much. Complementing the kidneys, the bladder expands and contracts in an active way. Its function is thus more yang.

This relationship can be further simplified as follows:

- Yang energy (meridian)—yin structure—yang function
- Yin energy (meridian)—yang structure—yin function

Table 6 provides a summary classification of the meridians, the physical structure of their related organs, and the function of their organs.

When considering how to explain this complementary relationship between

Table 6 Organs Classified by Structure and Function

Yand Meridians	Yin Meridians
Yin Structure	Yang Structure
Yang Function	Yin Function
Large Intestine	Lungs
Stomach	Spleen/Pancreas
Small Intestine	Heart
Bladder	Kidney
Gallbladder	Liver
Triple Heater	Heart Governor

energy and structure, George Ohsawa realized that the outlook of twentieth-century civilization is materially oriented. He thus chose physical structure as the criterion for identification. Consequently, in macrobiotic teaching, the structurally more compact organs, such as the kidneys, lungs and liver, are judged to be yang. The structurally more hollow organs, including the bladder, large intestine and gallbladder, are considered to be yin.

This seems to contradict the classification system of Oriental medicine in which the structurally more compact organs are labeled yin, and the structurally more hollow organs are called yang. In reality, this apparent contradiction highlights the paradoxical nature of existence: the opposite and complementary nature of structure and function within a single phenomenon. To avoid confusion, one simply must clarify which outlook is being used, the material or the energetic.

Meridian Pairs

As mentioned earlier, the ten organ meridians are grouped into five pairs. The energetic nature and function of these paired meridians and their organs are complementary. Thus, each pair consists of a yin and a yang organ and meridian. In some cases, this relationship is clear, as in the case of the kidneys and bladder, or the liver and gallbladder. The close proximity and functional association are apparent. Other times the correlation is less apparent, as in the case of the heart and small intestine, and the lungs and the large intestine.

In *Acupuncture and the Philosophy of the Far East*, George Ohsawa summarized the physical relationship between individual organ pairs in this way:

- The large intestine influences the venous blood by absorbing water.
  The lungs operate on venous blood by supplying it with oxygen.
- The small intestine initiates the process of transforming digested food into blood.
  The heart circulates blood to all of the cells.
- The bladder stores excess liquid for discharge via urination.
  The kidneys remove excess water from the blood and help to maintain the blood's mineral balance.
- The stomach separates sugars from food.

The spleen/pancreas condenses these sugars into body tissue by the secretion of insulin and anti-insulin or glycogen.
- The gallbladder stores the bile, which is then used for emulsifying fats. The liver extracts excess yin from the blood and transforms it into bile.

The intimate connection between the paired meridians is reflected in the fact that if there is a disturbance in the energy of one meridian, or a problem with one organ in the pair, the other meridian and/or organ will also be affected.

In Table 6 the meridian and organ pairs are listed in descending order of their complementary-and-antagonistic nature. The first pair, the lungs and the large intestine, represent the greatest polarity, and the final pair, the Heart Governor and Triple Heater functions, the least. The difference in the degree of polarity within organ pairs is determined by each partner's structure and function, and by its location in the body. These factors are in turn reflections of the quality of Ki that governs respective meridians/organs.

The last pair of meridians in Table 6 are not associated with particular organs. They are functions, working in a comprehensive way, to regulate the body's complete flow of energy. Together, they govern the absorption, circulation, and release of Ki from the body. The triple heater deals with the discharge of energy, in the form of calorie or heat, that is generated by the activity of the organs.

In health, the body maintains a generally constant temperature of about 36.5 degrees centigrade. It is the function of the triple heater to control this homeostatic process by regulating caloric discharge toward the body's surface. If organ activity is faster than normal, the triple heater accelerates the release of energy. If metabolic processes are unusually slow, the triple heater diminishes the emission of heat.

The triple heater consists of the fourth or heart chakra, the third or stomach chakra, and the second or abdominal chakra. These are respectively called the upper, middle, and lower heaters. The triple heater meridian handles energy from the particular organs related to each of these three energy centers. In the upper heater, the controlling point is located about the width of two to three fingers above the base of the sternum (see Figure 23). The control point for the middle

Fig. 23 The Triple Heater

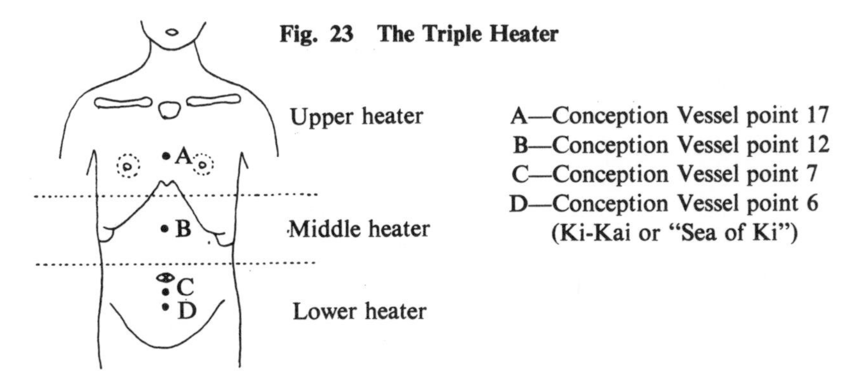

The control point for each of the three heaters is used for diagnosis and treatment in acupuncture, moxibustion, massage and palm healing.

heater is situated in the center of the solar plexus. The lower heater's control point is found approximately three-fingers width below the navel.

The basic meridian system consists of these twelve streams of energy, which correspond to the five yin and five yang organ meridians, plus the pair of yin and yang functions. It must be noted, however, that individual meridians do not operate independently of the others. At both its beginning and end, each meridian is connected to another. As a group, the meridians constitute a single energy current. The nature of this stream varies from meridian to meridian, much as the flow of water differs as it cycles from mountain to sea, evaporates, and then condenses to fall back to earth as rain.

Fig. 24 The Conception and Governing Vessels

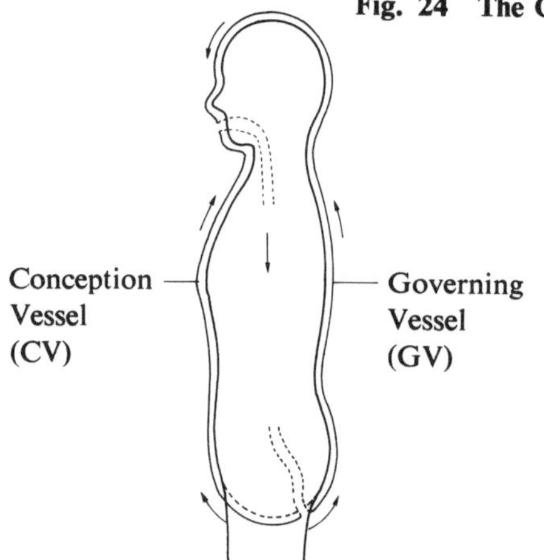

The Conception and Governing Vessels—actually complementary halves of a single energy circuit—correspond to and overlap the heart governor and triple heater meridians. Together, these four meridans have a comprehensive influence on all physical, mental and spiritual activities. Each of the other ten meridians has a specific and partial influence.

There are other meridians, collectively known as the *eight extra meridians*. A pair of these, the *Governing Vessel* and the *Conception Vessel*, are considered major meridians, while the other six are seen as extensions of the basic twelve. These two major meridians actually constitute the body's original meridian: together they form the primary channel, and represent the principal flow of Heaven's and Earth's forces within the body. Working together, they have a comprehensive influence on all physical, psychological and spiritual activities. It is from the governing and conception vessels that the other meridians differentiate, each exerting a partial direction over the various aspects of the Self.

Both of these meridians move upward on the surface of the body, then enter the mouth, and spiral downward in a half-twist, crossing at the junction of the Hara. This twist marks the turning point from one half of the complementary cycle into its opposite. The course of each of these two meridians is as follows:

- The governing vessel begins at the coccyx, the small triangular bone at the base of the spine. It flows upward on the surface of the back, along the spinal cord, over the head and down the face to the mouth. Entering the mouth, the governing vessel descends internally to the genital area, and exits at the perineum, the area between the anus and the genitals.
- The conception vessel begins at the perineum, and streams upward on the front surface of the body. It moves along the center of the trunk to the

mouth. Entering the mouth, the conception vessel moves down the center of the body, deep inside. It exits in the area of the coccyx, where the cycle begins once more.

Course of Energy Flow

The meridians, with the exception of the conception and governing vessels, flow symmetrically on both sides of the body. That is to say, there are identical segments on the right and left sides. They run in a helical pattern from the center to the periphery and then back to the center, so that each organ pair describes one complete cycle. The path of each of the meridian pairs resembles the petal of a flower and the entire meridian system can be likened to a six-petal energy blossom.

Table 7 Energy Cycle along the Meridians

1.	Lung (Yin)	7.	Bladder (Yang)
2.	Large Intestine (Yang)	8.	Kidney (Yin)
3.	Stomach (Yang)	9.	Heart Governor (Yin)
4.	Spleen/Pancreas (Yin)	10.	Triple Heater (Yang)
5.	Heart (Yin)	11.	Gallbladder (Yang)
6.	Small Intestine (Yang)	12.	Liver (Yin)

We have already mentioned that instead of being separate streams, the meridians are actually one continuous flow along which distinct qualities of energy can be recognized. Traditional peoples recognized a surge or wave-like pattern along the meridians. The course of this swell of energy follows a specific order, starting with the lungs and ending with the liver. The complete sequence is depicted in Table 7. This cycle is repeated approximately fifty times per day, depending on one's age (more frequently in the young, less often as we age), activity level, and general state of health.

While this cycle is repeated numerous times during the course of the day, there are particular times when individual merdians/organs are especially active. This occurs because there is a larger 24-hour cycle that influences the earth's Ki.

The time of day that each meridian/organ is expressly active is listed below:

3–5 A.M.	Lungs
5–7 A.M.	Large Intestine
7–9 A.M.	Stomach
9–11 A.M.	Spleen/Pancreas
11 A.M.–1 P.M.	Heart
1–3 P.M.	Small Intestine
3–5 P.M.	Bladder
5–7 P.M.	Kidneys
7–9 P.M.	Heart Governor
9–11 P.M.	Triple Heater
11 P.M.–1 A.M.	Gallbladder
1–3 A.M.	Liver

Although perhaps appearing complicated at first, the path of the meridians is not difficult to learn, and knowing where each meridian runs can be a tremendous aid in understanding changes and symptoms that may develop at various locations on the body.

Following is an illustration and a general description of the course of each meridian through the body. They are presented in succession, according to the order of energy flow as described above. With the assumption that most readers are not familiar with the anatomical terms for various locations and parts of the body, the less precise but more easily understood everyday terms are used.

- *Lung Meridian:* Begins at the stomach chakra and descends to connect with

Fig. 25 Lung Meridian

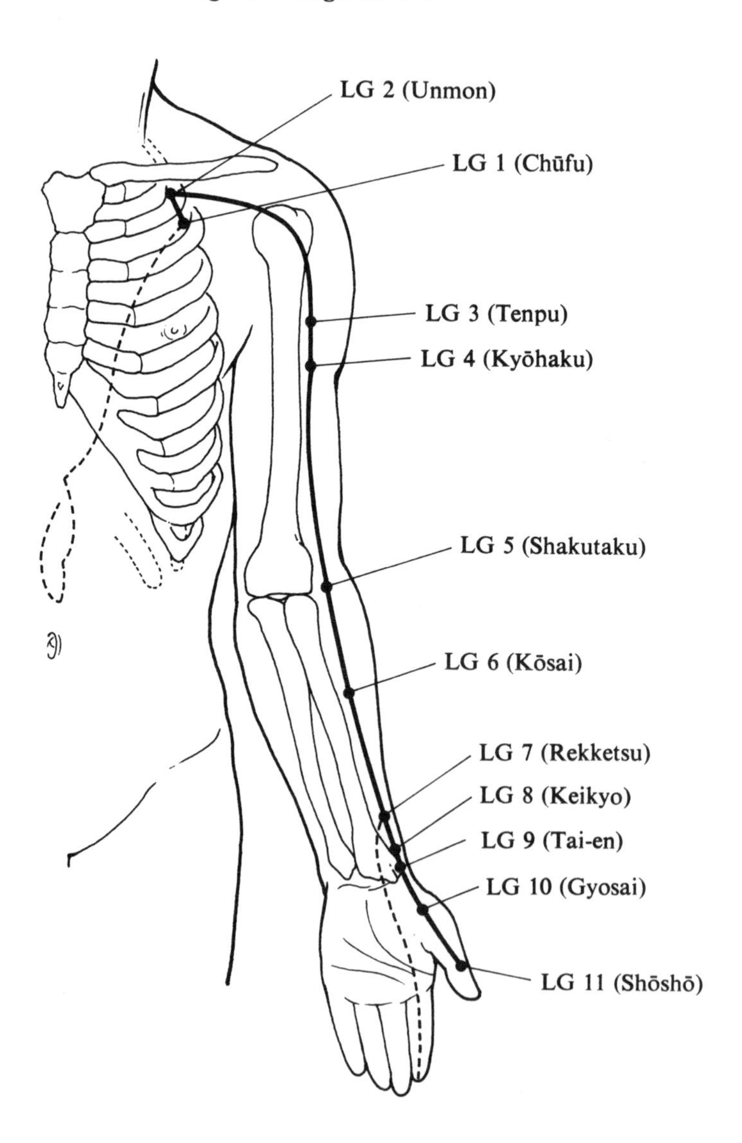

its partner organ, the large intestine. It then reverses direction, passes through the lungs, ascends to the throat, and moves out to the shoulder. From there, it runs down the inner arm to the outer corner of the thumb nail. Several inches above the wrist, a branch of the lung meridian descends directly to the index finger, where the large intestine meridian begins.

• *Large Intestine Meridian:* Begins at the thumb-side corner of the index finger and runs up the finger, hand, and the thumb side of the arm to the top of the shoulder. From here, one branch enters the body and descends to the large intestine and the Hara chakra. Another branch goes from the shoulder up the side of the neck to the face, crosses between the mouth and the nose, and ends at the outside corner of the nostril. At the end of the nostril this branch connects to the stomach meridian.

Fig. 26 Large Intestine Meridian

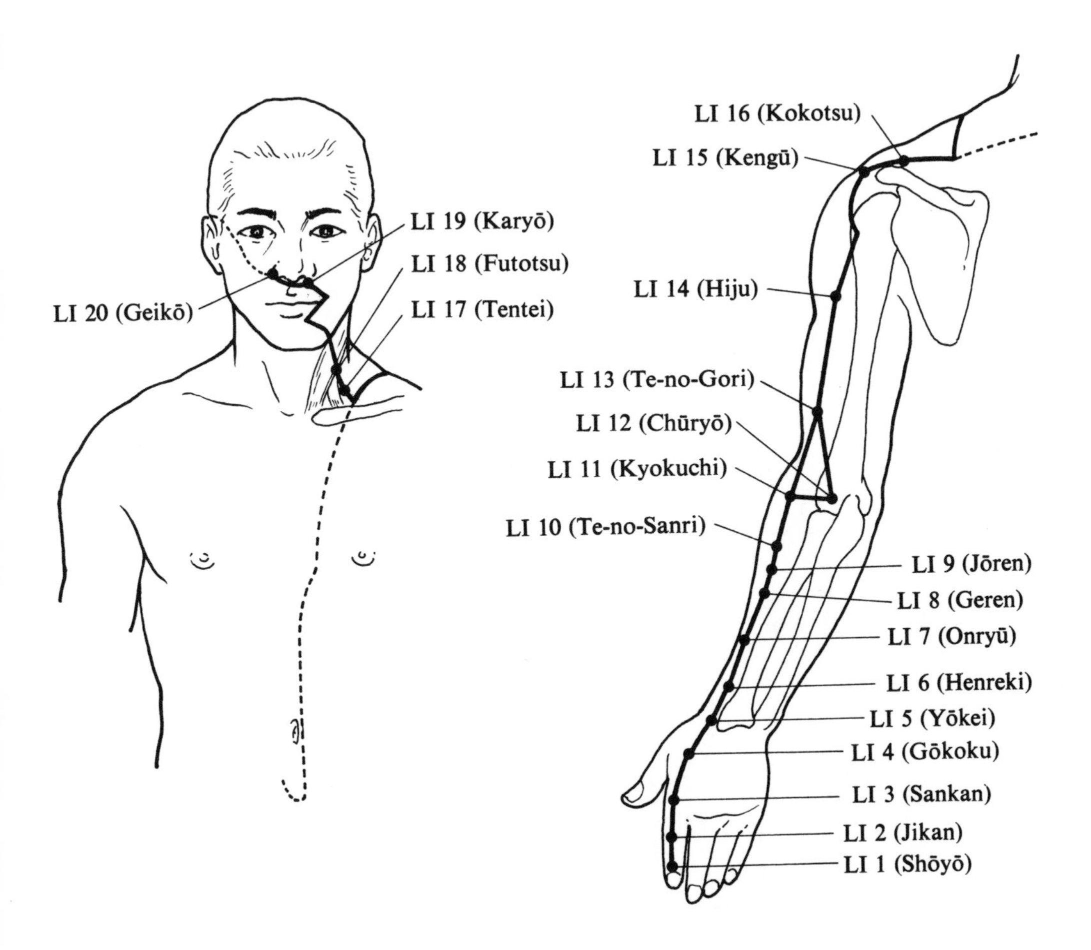

• *Stomach Meridian:* Beginning at the corner of the nose, a branch of the stomach meridian goes to the head, while another branch enters the body and descends to the stomach. It continues down the trunk, over the front of the thigh to the outside of the knee. Continuing downward, it runs on the outside of the lower leg over the top of the foot to the second and third toes. From the top of the foot, a branch diverts to the outside corner of the first toe. It is here that the spleen meridian begins.

Fig. 27 Stomach Meridian

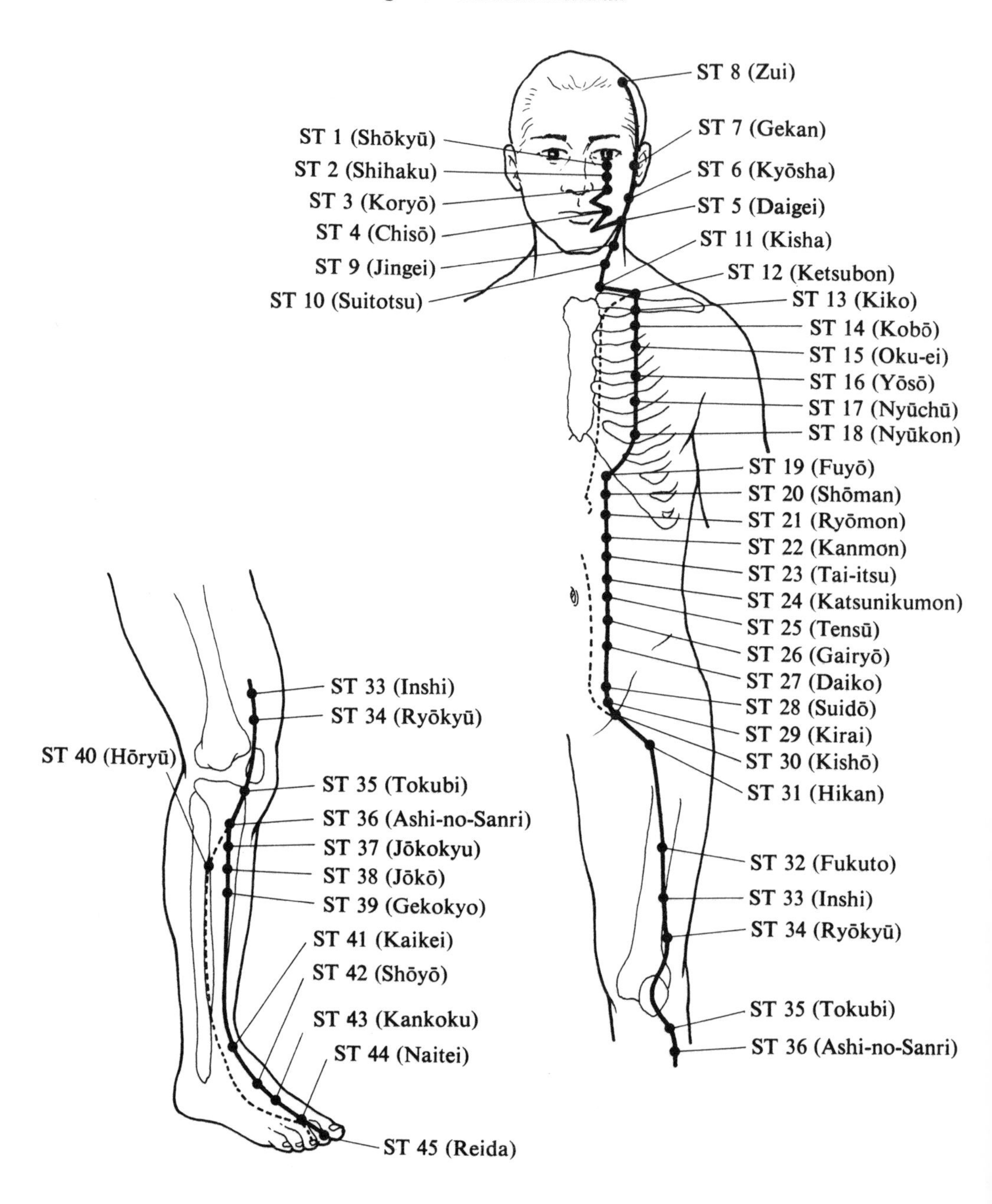

• *Spleen Meridian:* Beginning at the outside corner of the first, or large, toe, the spleen meridian rises along the inside of the foot above the arch, and around the ankle bone. It ascends along the inner leg, enters the trunk and connects with the spleen.

A branch of the spleen meridian goes to the three chakras in the trunk of the body, the Hara chakra, the stomach chakra, and the heart chakra. At the heart chakra it connects with the heart meridian.

Fig. 28 Spleen Meridian

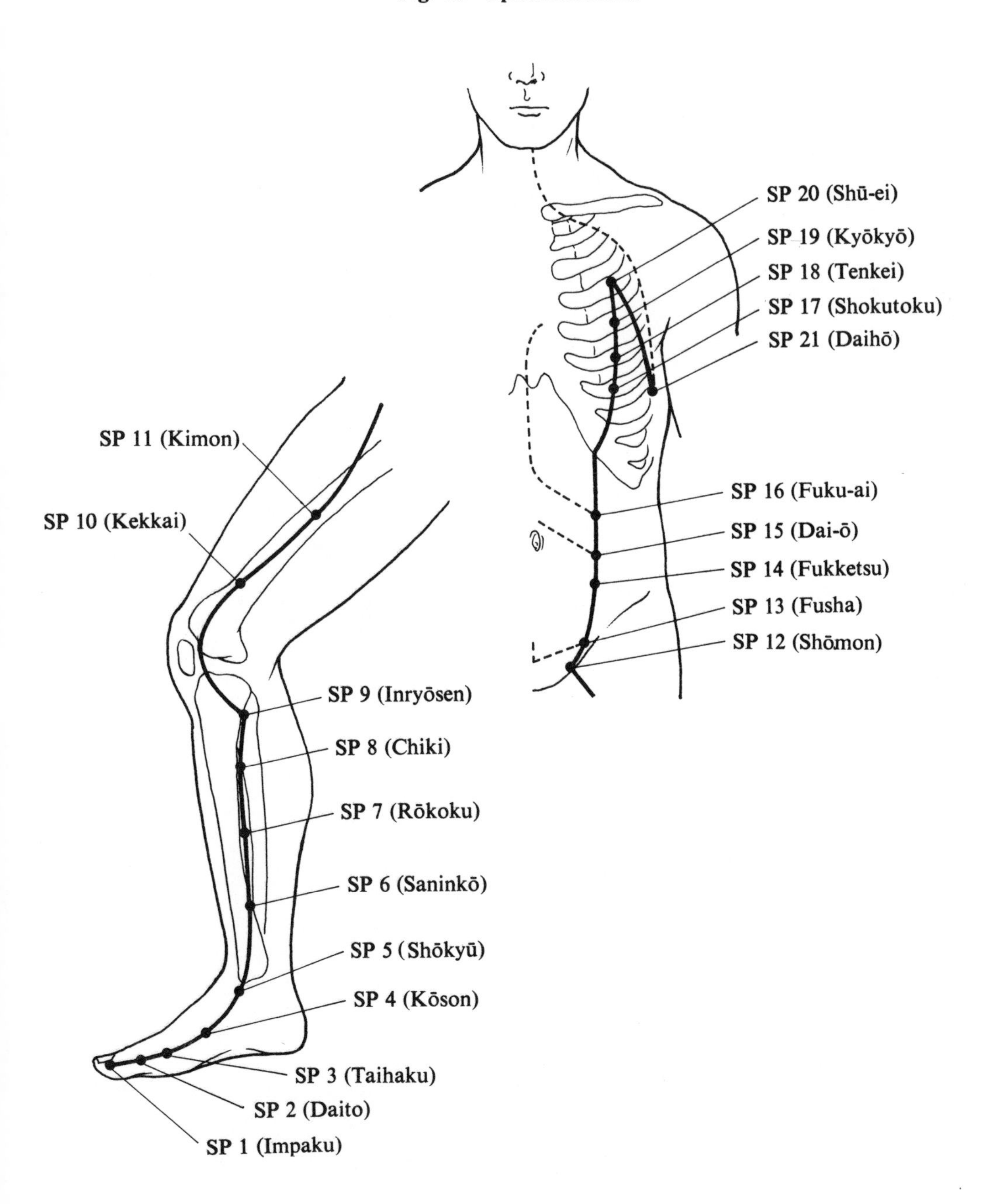

• *Heart Meridian:* Beginning at the heart chakra, one branch of this meridian moves upward across the chest, the side of the throat and face, to the eye. Another branch goes to the armpit and down the middle of the inside of the arm to the end of the little finger on the inside. The heart meridian connects to the small intestine meridian at the end of the little finger.

Fig. 29 Heart Meridian

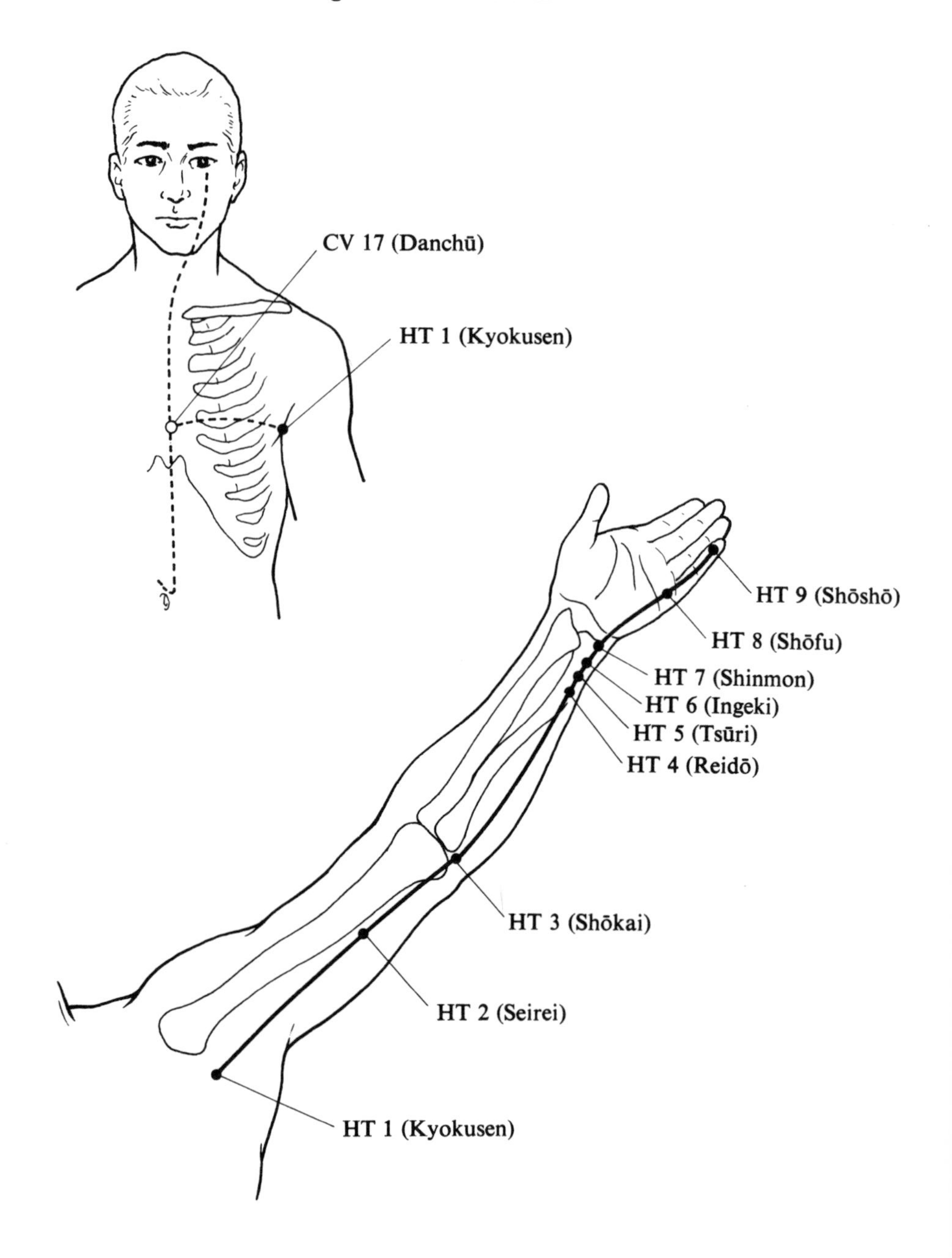

• *Small Intestine Meridian:* Begins on the outside tip of the little finger and goes back along the outside of the arm to the shoulder, where it divides into two branches. One branch goes internally down the front of the body to the small intestines. Another branch runs up the side of the neck to the inner corner of the eye where it connects with the bladder meridian.

Fig. 30 Small Intestine Meridian

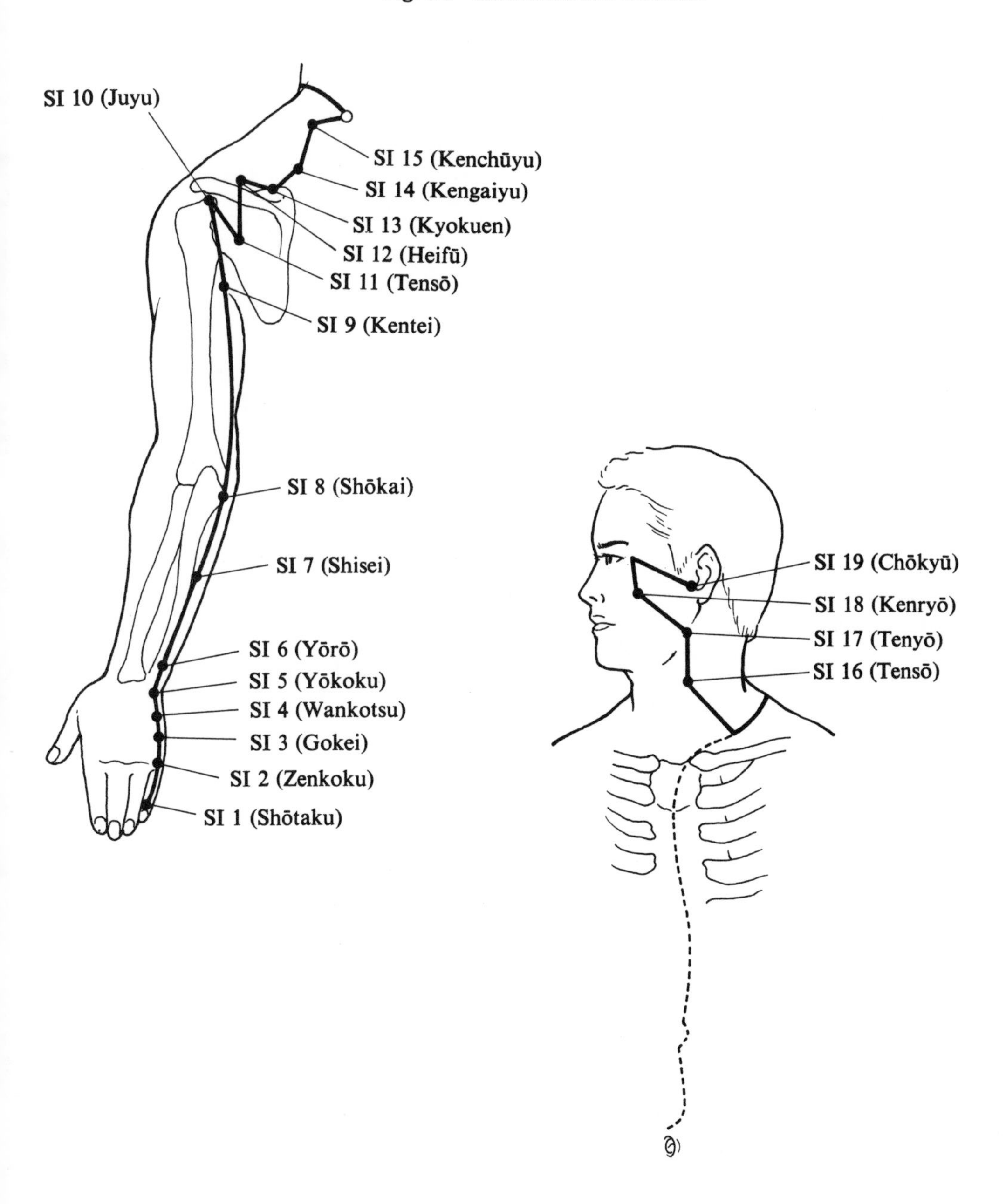

• *Bladder Meridian:* Begins at the inner corner of the eye and runs up across the forehead, over the head and down the neck and back. The bladder meridian connects all Yu points (discussed below) on the back. Thus it is an important meridian in diagnosis and treatment. At the lumber region, a branch connects to the kidney and the bladder.

The meridian runs down the buttocks and the back of the legs, over the

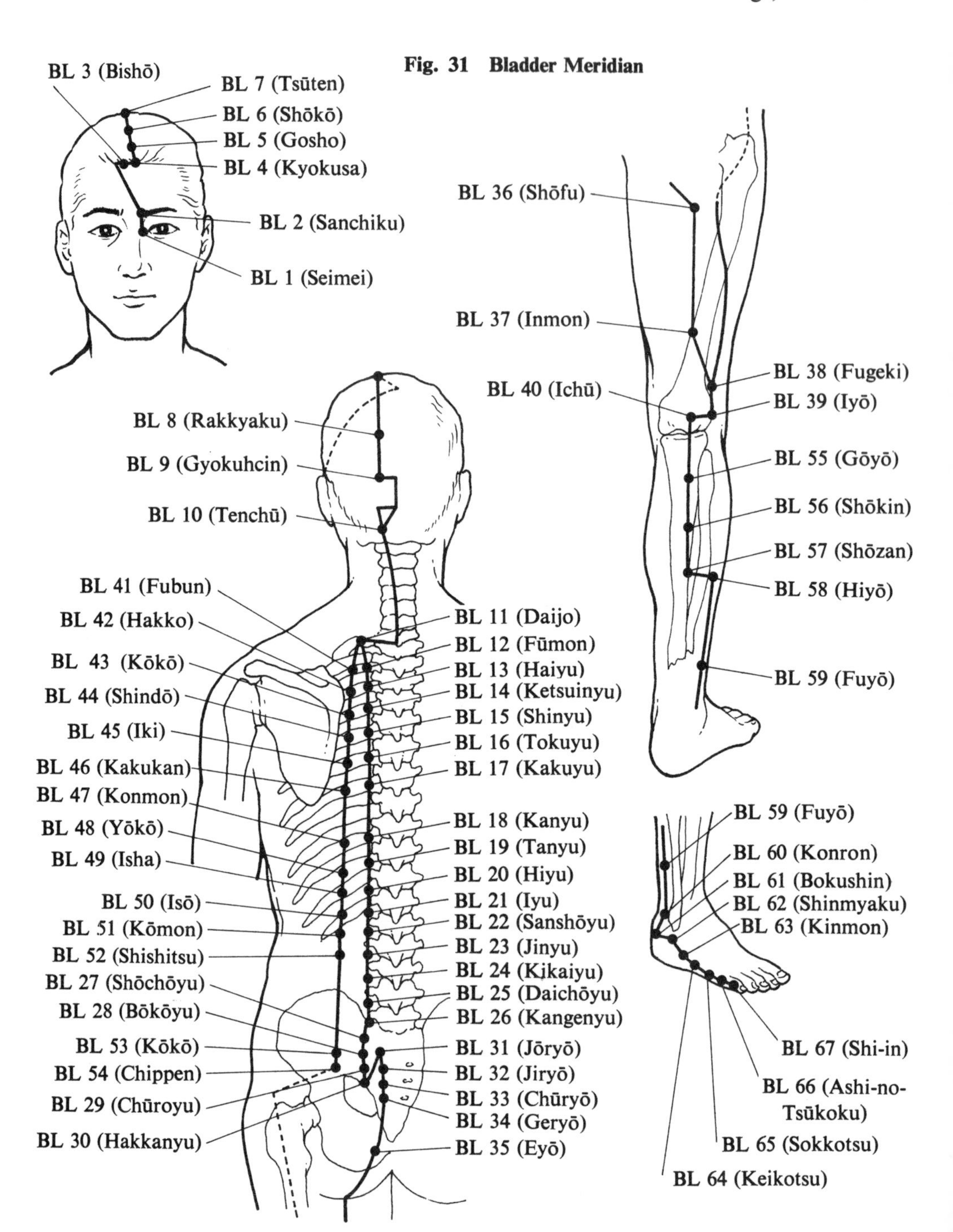

Fig. 31 Bladder Meridian

outside of the Achilles tendon, around the outside of the ankle and over the foot to the outside of the little toe. From the little toe it runs to the bottom of the foot where the kidney meridian begins.

• *Kidney Meridian:* Begins on the sole of the foot toward the front, in the indentation between the pads formed at the base of the toes. This meridian runs along the arch of the foot, circles the inner ankle bone, ascends the inside of the leg, and moves through the trunk where it connects with the kidney.

The meridian then continues upward to the throat. A branch of the kidney meridian goes to the heart chakra where it connects to the heart governor meridian.

Fig. 32 Kidney Meridian

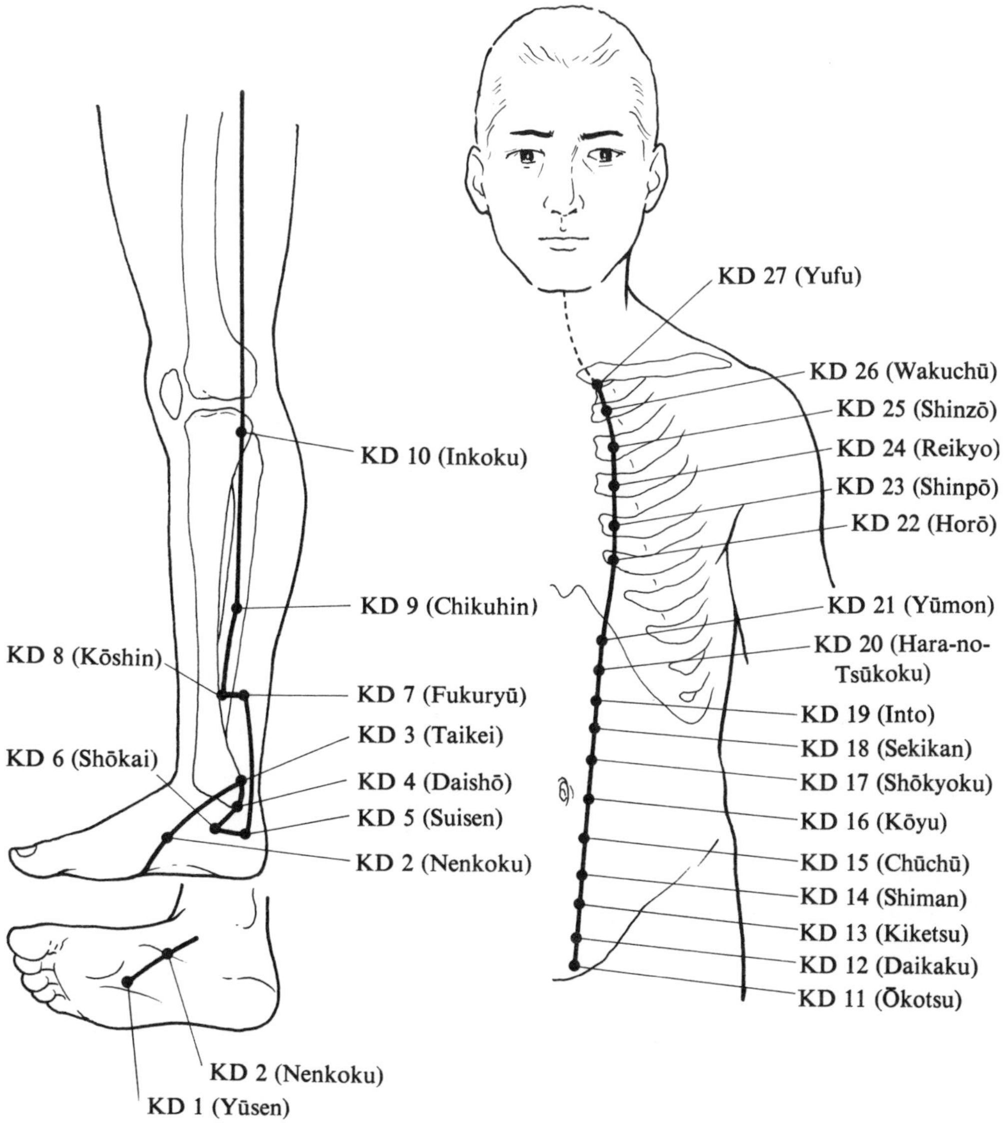

KD 10 (Inkoku)
KD 9 (Chikuhin)
KD 8 (Kōshin)
KD 7 (Fukuryū)
KD 3 (Taikei)
KD 6 (Shōkai)
KD 4 (Daishō)
KD 5 (Suisen)
KD 2 (Nenkoku)
KD 2 (Nenkoku)
KD 1 (Yūsen)
KD 27 (Yufu)
KD 26 (Wakuchū)
KD 25 (Shinzō)
KD 24 (Reikyo)
KD 23 (Shinpō)
KD 22 (Horō)
KD 21 (Yūmon)
KD 20 (Hara-no-Tsūkoku)
KD 19 (Into)
KD 18 (Sekikan)
KD 17 (Shōkyoku)
KD 16 (Kōyu)
KD 15 (Chūchū)
KD 14 (Shiman)
KD 13 (Kiketsu)
KD 12 (Daikaku)
KD 11 (Ōkotsu)

• *Heart Governor Meridian:* Beginning in the pericardium, this meridian runs across the chest and down the inside of the arm, over the center of the palm to the tip of the middle finger. A branch extends from the center of the palm to the fourth or ring finger where the triple heater meridian begins.

Fig. 33 Heart Governor Meridian

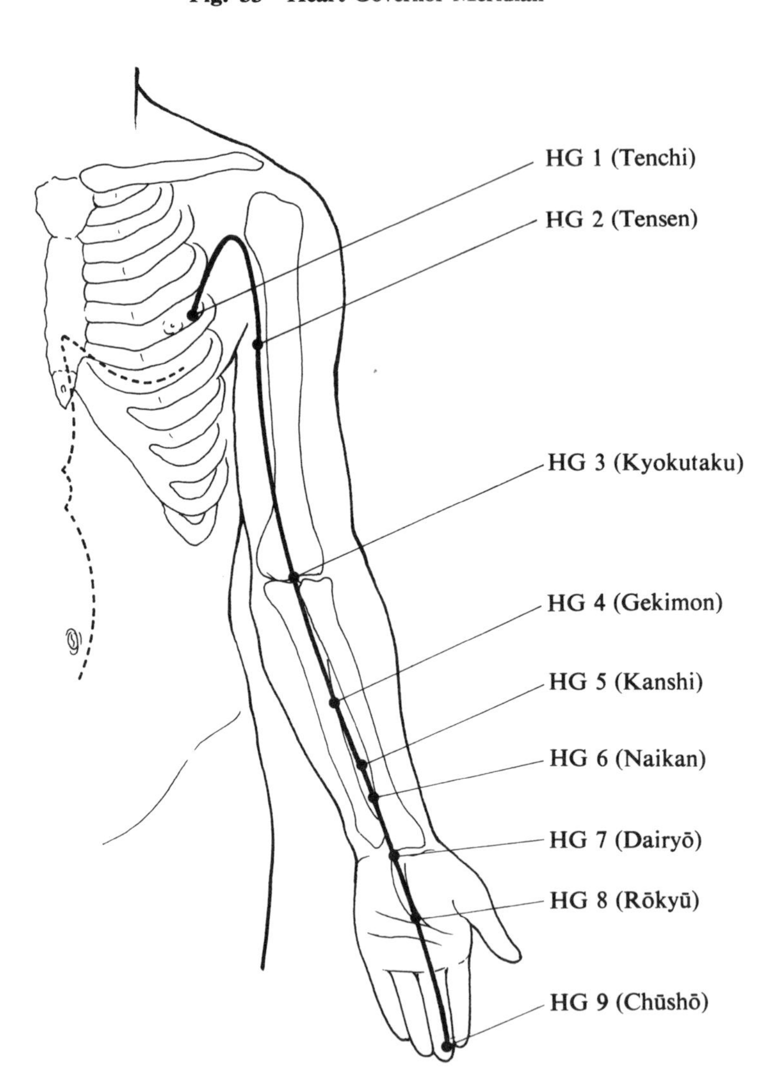

• *Triple Heater Meridian:* Begins at the outside tip of the fourth finger and runs up the outside of the arm to the shoulder. One branch continues upward over the side of the head. Another branch goes to the trunk and connects the three chakras collectively known as the triple heater—the heart, stomach, and lower abdominal chakras.

The branch of the triple heater meridian that goes to the face, connects with the gallbladder meridian at the end of the eyebrow.

Fig. 34 Triple Heater Meridian

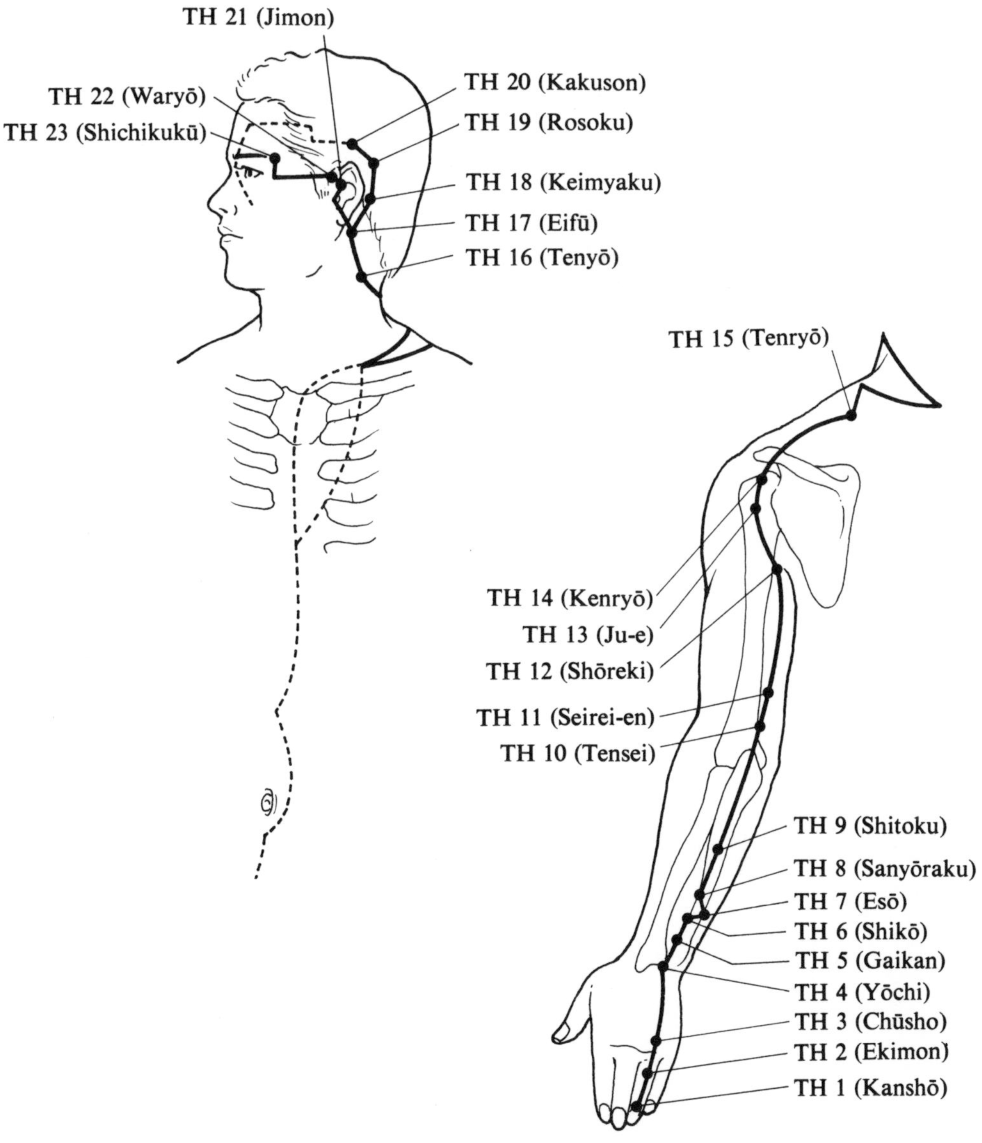

• *Gallbladder Meridian:* One branch starts at the face and passes downward through the neck and chest to the gallbladder. It connects with the main branch at the hip.

The main branch begins at the outside of the eyebrow and rises across the side of the head where it spirals or zigzags several times before going down the side of the neck to the top of the shoulders. It runs down the side of the

Fig. 35 Gallbladder Meridian

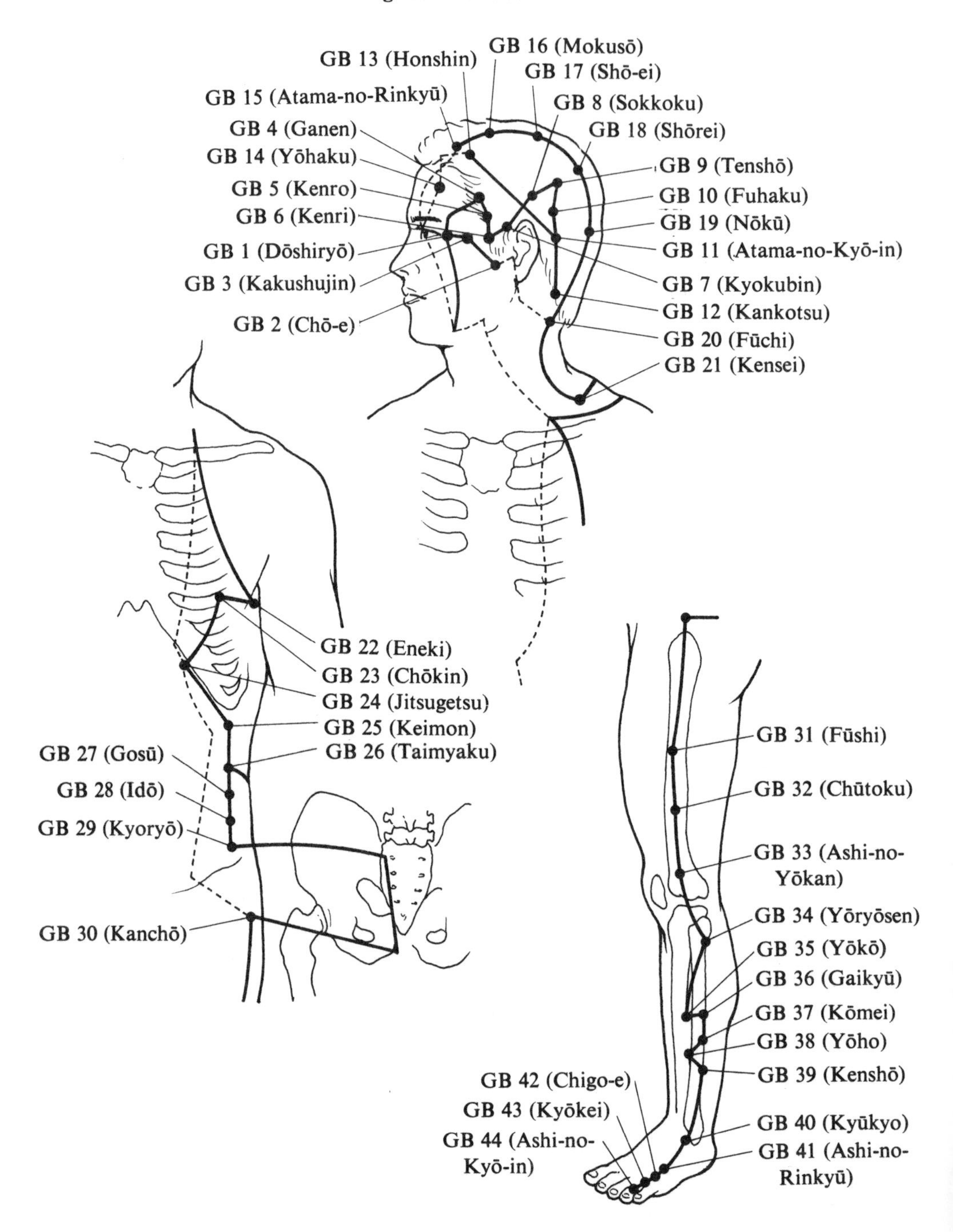

trunk to the hip. From here the meridian goes down the outside of the leg. It crosses above the ankle bone, and runs to the fourth toe. A branch goes to the inside of the large toe, where the liver meridian begins.

• *Liver Meridian:* Begins at the inside corner of the large toe and travels up the inside of the leg, enters the trunk, and moves to the liver. This meridian continues up the trunk to the eyes, and on to the top of the head. From here, a branch goes to the stomach chakra where it connects to the first meridian, the lung meridian.

Fig. 36 Liver Meridian

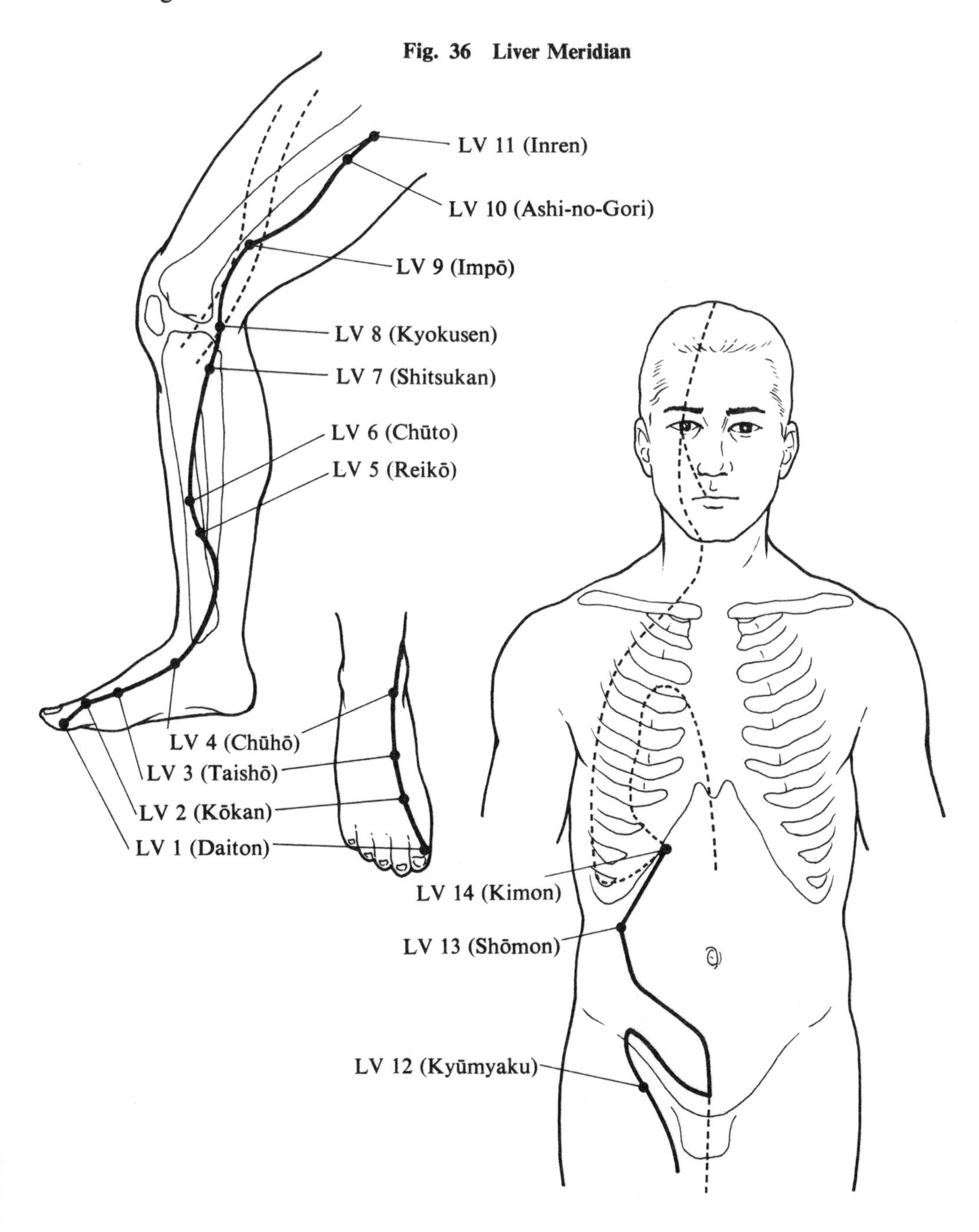

Origin of the Meridians

As we have seen, the uterus has twelve currents of energy, or meridians, that provide a strong charge in the female's Hara region. Each of these uterine meridians corresponds to the twelve basic or surface meridians found in both women and men. These in turn are activated by the distinct qualities of energy that influence the planet. What then, is the source of these twelve discrete aspects of energy?

The answer to this question is to be found in the concept of the macrocosm and microcosm, the individual and the infinite, that is echoed throughout the ancient world. The human constitution is a reflection of far-larger forces in the universe. Variations in the quality of Ki running through the human body originate in the constellations that revolve in deep space along the earth's ecliptic.

Throughout our life, the functions of the meridians, and their most condensed sections, the organs, are directly influenced by these twelve constellations. This is why each meridian is particularly active at certain times of day, certain times during the year, and certain times during longer cycles of time, depending on which constellation is most actively influencing the earth at that specific time.

The relationship between the meridians and the constellations is described in Table 8.

Table 8 Correlation between the Meridians and Constellations

Meridians	Constellations
Lungs	Aries
Large Intestine	Taurus
Stomach	Gemini
Spleen	Cancer
Heart	Leo
Small Intestine	Virgo
Bladder	Libra
Kidneys	Scorpio
Heart Governor	Sagittarius
Triple Heater	Capricorn
Gallbladder	Aquarius
Liver	Pisces

An understanding of the planet's movement through space will help clarify the constellation's energetic influence on the earth. The planet is tipped at an approximate 23.5 degree angle from the perpendicular with respect to the plane of the sun and earth. This is why, as the earth revolves, the sun appears to rise in a slightly different part of the sky each day.

The sun's farthest point north, over the *Tropic of Cancer* (23.5 degrees north latitude), is reached at the summer solstice. It crosses the equator at the autumn equinox, reaches the *Tropic of Capricorn* (23.5 degrees south latitude) at the winter solstice, and then turns north, crossing the equator at the spring equinox. The sun's

Fig. 37 Celestial Origin of the Meridians

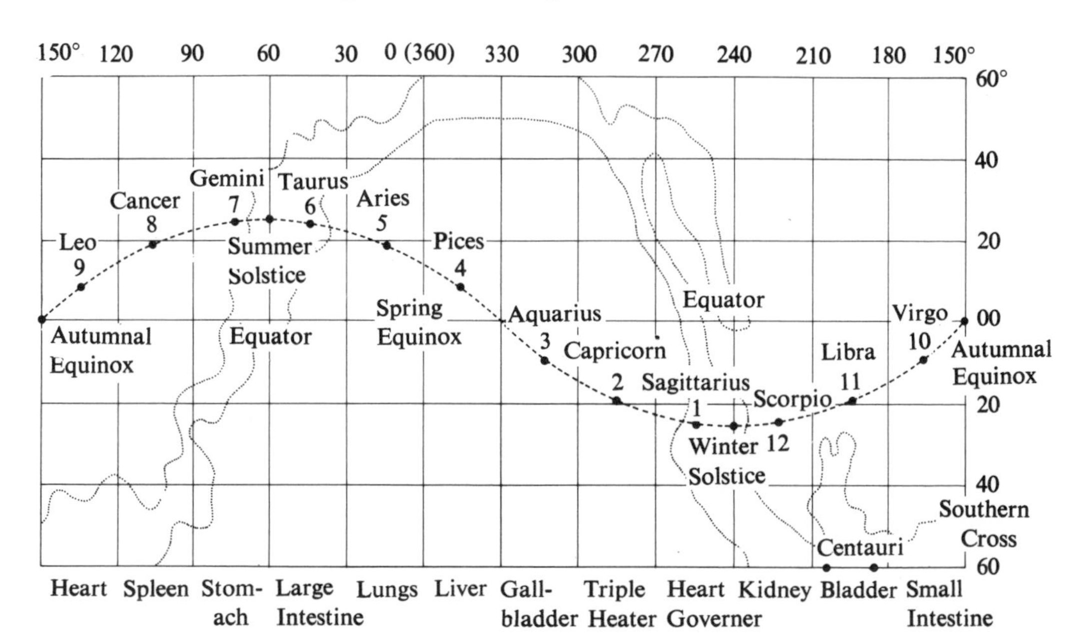

apparent movement is thus within a belt of sky directly over the band of the earth between the Tropics. This path is known as the *ecliptic*.

The constellations are also in this belt, called the zodiac. Thus, for example, charts currently in use list the sun passing through the constellation Libra during most of the month of October. This is another way of saying that this particular constellation is most directly in line with the earth during this period. Figure 37 presents a year-long map of this motion, starting with the autumn equinox. Please note, however, that the chart has been adjusted to reflect the present positions of the constellations. It is slightly different from the version commonly used, which is now several thousands of years old.

As each of the twelve constellations faces the earth in turn, its particular quality of energy is most strongly received. This energy activates its related meridian and associated organ. It also generates those psychological and spiritual qualities associated with the meridian.

The information provided in Figure 37 includes the seasonal influences, and can provide useful insights concerning the functions of the meridians. In addition, because development in the womb covers only nine months (or only three-quarters of the complete cycle), an individual's least developed organs and personality traits tend to be those associated with the months the baby was not in the womb. For a child born in September, the kidneys, bladder, and small intestine may not be as strong as the other organs, and perhaps will be more susceptible to abuse. The character traits related to these meridians and organs may be the ones the individual will work to cultivate as he matures.

Points of Energy

Along the energy lines running over the surface of the earth, various natural phenomenon occur representing differing qualities of Ki. These include hills and valleys, springs and streams, wooded and open areas, swamps and deserts. Each of these is produced by, and in turn generates, certain energetic qualities. The meridians of the human body share similar characteristics. Along the meridians, points of various natures exist on the body's surface which correspond to those on the surface of the planet. In Oriental medicine, these points are called *tsubo* (壺).

Although the usual translation of the Japanese word *tsubo* is "point," a more accurate rendering would be "hole." Tsubo are places along the meridians where energy is pouring out, although energy can be absorbed at these points, depending on the needs of the body. Because changes in the quality of the meridian's energy quickly show up at these points, the tsubo are commonly employed for diagnosis. They are also manipulated, in various ways, in treatment to either give or drain energy. This is typically done with needles, moxibustion, or massage.

The number of tsubo on the fourteen surface meridians is approximately 365 (scholars differ slightly in their count of tsubo along the bladder, gallbladder, and liver meridians and the conception vessel), although many more tsubo are identified throughout the body. In the ear alone, there are points to treat most areas of the body. Individual meridians have different numbers of tsubo, as can be seen on the meridian charts. The heart and heart governor meridians have the least number of points, nine, while the bladder meridian has by far the most, sixty-three. These numbers should actually be doubled, as the meridians and their points run bilaterally on the left and right sides of the body. The exception, as already mentioned, is the conception vessel and the governing vessel, located along the center of the body. In the section that follows, we will discuss some of the more important points.

Yu and Bo Points

We have seen that energy from a mother's twelve uterine meridians penetrates the surface of the fertilized ovum and spirals in toward its central region. These entry points are the body's first tsubo. Early in its development, the embryo begins to change from a spherical to a crescent form by folding in on itself. As this happens, the original surface or outside becomes the back. From that point on, the corresponding tsubo are located on the back of the body. The new front surface is formed from what formally was the central part of the embryo.

From the time the fetal shape emerges, Ki enters the body from the back, through twelve major pairs of points, called *Yu* points, located along the bladder meridian. *Yu* (兪) means "pouring in" or "entering," and it is at these points that the twelve basic meridians actually begin. From the Yu points, energy coils inward, creating and energizing the tightly bound spirals of energy that we call organs.

Each of the twelve Yu points is related to a specific meridian and organ or function. Individual Yu points are thus named after their respective meridians, for example, the Lung Yu point, the Heart Governor Yu point, and so on (see

Fig. 38 Yu and Bo Points

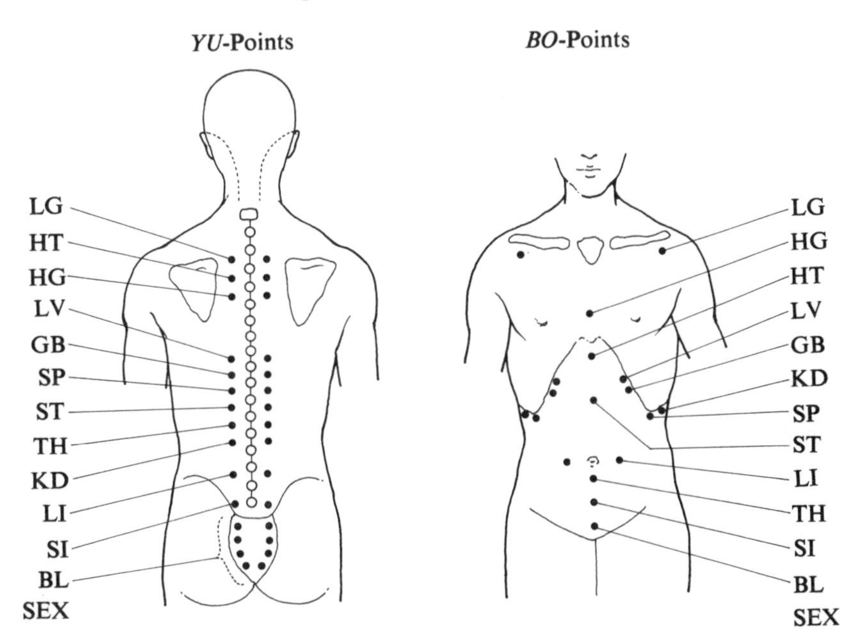

LG—Lungs
HT—Heart
HG—Heart Governor (Energy Circulation)
LV—Liver
GB—Gallbladder
SP—Spleen and Pancreas
ST—Stomach
TH—Triple Heater (Energy and Heat Metabolism)
KD—Kidneys
LI—Large Intestine
SI—Small Intestine
BL-SEX—Bladder and Sexual functions

Figure 38). Note that because the bladder meridian is bilateral, there are two Yu points for each meridian, one on each side of the spine.

From the center of the spirals that the Yu point's energy create deep inside the body, Ki spirals out to a series of points on the surface of the body at the front. These tsubo are called *Bo* points. *Bo* (募) means "assimilation" or "gathering." Unlike the Yu points, the Bo points are not associated with one particular meridian. They are spread out across the front of the trunk, from just below the collarbone to well below the navel. Half of the twelve Bo points are bilateral, appearing on the left and right sides. The other six appear only once. This is because they are situated along the conception vessel, which runs up the center of the trunk.

Energy flows out from the Bo points to the body's periphery, forming and energizing the limbs. Ki from the organs in the central region (yang position) of the trunk moves downward from the Bo points, creating the legs, feet and toes. Ki from the organs and functions in the more peripheral (yin position) upper and lower regions of the trunk, moves upward from the Bo points, producing the arms, hands and fingers. (The bladder meridian is an exception. Located in the pelvic region, the bladder meridian flows downward to the little toe.)

Because of the strong polar relationship between the Yu and Bo points—entry and exit, front and back, and sending inward and gathering on the surface—they are very important in many types of treatment. By stimulating a Yu point, for instance, the Ki flowing to its related organ or function can be increased. This is called for when a deficiency is detected. If the energy is excessive, the related Bo point can be stimulated to draw out the excess. These tsubo are also primary points for diagnosis.

A simple example will help illustrate the role these points play in the healing process, and the significance they offer to medical practitioners. A student who had been following the macrobiotic approach to diet for several months received a massage from an experienced practitioner. Two days later, a large boil developed on the spleen's Yu point, and continued to issue for a number of days. The relationship in this case was obvious. The combination of a balanced diet and the stimulus of a massage activated the function of the spleen, which discharged its excess via the Yu point.

It is unlikely that a Western-oriented doctor would have identified the connection between the discharge and the organ from which it originated. Nor would he be apt to appreciate the therapeutic effect of this symptom. As a result, any treatment would likely be designed to stop the discharge, and would be directed to the effect, the boil, while the cause, a buildup of excess in the spleen, went unrecognized.

The locations of the Yu and Bo points for each meridian and organ are given in Figure 38.

Sei, Gen, and Go Points

To understand this next set of points, a clearer understanding of the formation of the arms and legs is necessary. As we have seen, the structure of the universe is spiralic. All things are formed, move in, and decompose in a logarithmic spiral.

Fig. 39 Correlation between Arm and Organ Spirals

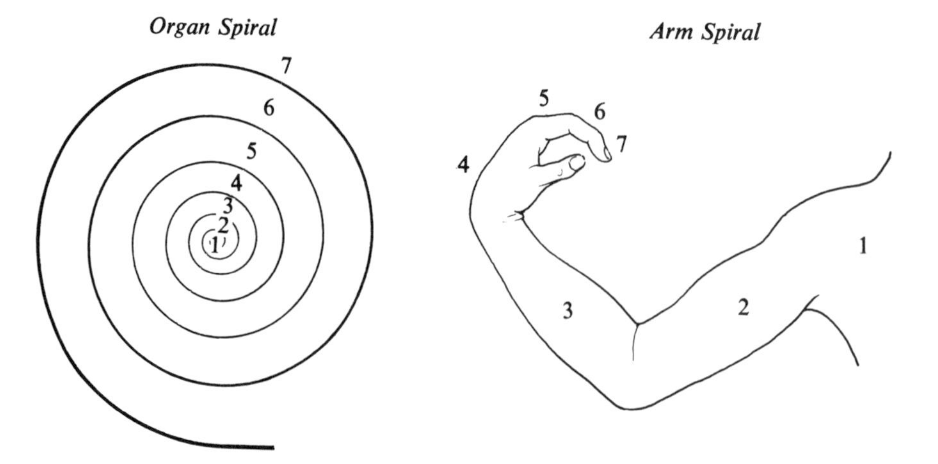

The body organs are mature spirals, each one having seven orbits or layers of structure. The arms and legs have a corresponding seven-orbit spiralic structure.

Reflecting this pattern, each of our organs forms a seven-orbited spiral of energy. Similarly, each arm and each leg is a seven-orbited spiral. Taking the arm as an example, the orbits of the arm spiral are: (1) the region that includes the shoulder blade and the collarbone, (2) the upper arm, (3) the forearm, (4) the hand, (5) the first finger bone, (6) the second finger bone, and (7) the last finger bone.

With this association in mind, we can appreciate the important connection between the points on the periphery of the body—the arms and legs—and the internal organs. Moving inward from the most peripheral point on the meridian (usually near the tip of the finger or toe) are a series of points that serve a vital function in the polar relation between the organ spirals and the spirals that form the limbs. In sequence from the periphery toward the center, these points are known as the *Sei*, *Ei*, *Yu* (different from the Yu points on the back), *Gen*, *Kei*, and *Go* points. Ancient Chinese philosophers/physicians used the image of the various natures of flowing water to describe the character of Ki at these points.

- The Sei point is like a spring, or the beginning of a stream.
- At the Ei point, the spring has turned into a stream.
- The Yu point represents a more active flow of Ki.
- The Gen point is a place of gathering or pooling of Ki.
- The Kei point is like the tail of a pool, where energy is slowed.
- At the Go point, the energy has become a powerful river.

These tsubo enable a practitioner to make precise adjustments in the energy of specific meridians while taking into consideration the particular condition of the patient. To do this, the antagonistic relationship between the inner and outer, the center and periphery is used. This concept implies that the way to influence the inaccessible central region is to treat the related surface area farthest away from it. Thus, to stimulate the deepest part of an organ, the meridian's peripheral points are employed.

As already mentioned, these points are called *Sei* (井) points. Sei means "well" or "spring," and it is here that Ki pours up and out from the meridians much as water does from an underground spring. From the Sei points, energy flows from one meridian to the next in the sequence outlined earlier. By manipulating its Sei points, an organ's deepest regions can be affected.

To treat the peripheral area of an organ, we select a set of points that correspond to the inner sections of the limb spiral, and thus the outer orbit of the organ spiral. These tsubo, called *Go* (合) points, are generally located around the elbow or knee, or in some cases higher up. Go means "unified" or "joined," and the name is an indication of the important function of the Go points. They serve to concentrate (unify) and thus activate the flow of the meridians' energy.

To find the point corresponding to the mid-part of the organ—the fourth orbit of its seven-orbited spiral—we go to the fourth orbit of the arm or leg spiral, generally around the wrist or ankle. These points are called *Gen* (原) points.

The usual translation for Gen is "source" point, but this may be misleading. A clearer rendering would be "balancing" point. Whenever a certain organ or merid-

Fig. 40 Sei, Gen and Go Points

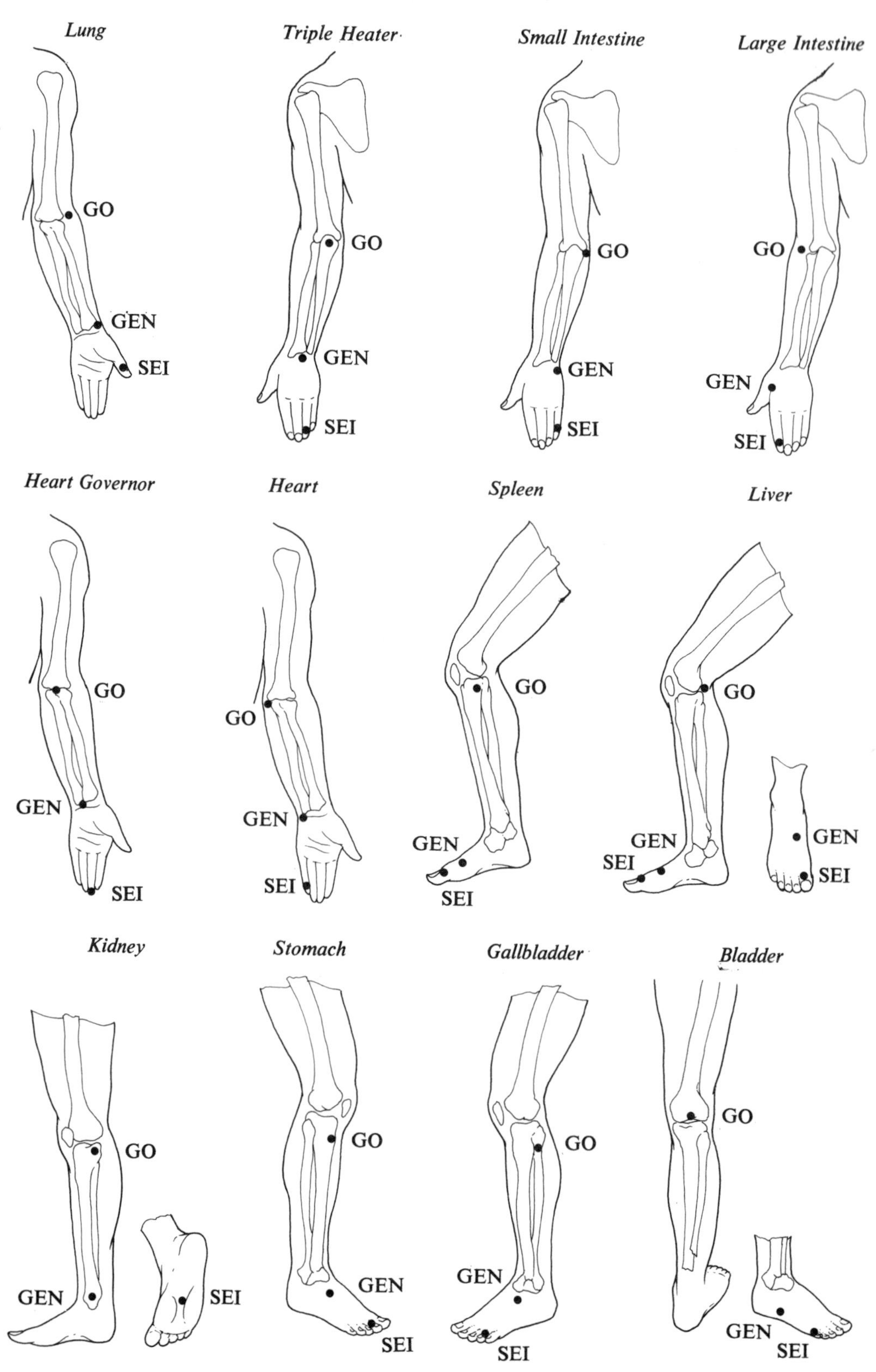

ian is troubled, whether from deficient or excessive energy, the trouble will show up immediately around the balancing or Gen point. By treating this tsubo, we can balance the entire meridian, including its related organ.

The Ei points are used to treat the organ's inner to central region, and the Kei points to influence the region encompassing the outer to middle section.

An illustration here will help to clarify the utility of this set of points. Using the large intestine meridian as an example, locate its Sei, Gen, and Go points (see Figure 40). If there is a problem with this organ-meridian, constipation for instance, a simple, effective treatment can be given with the hands. Hold the large-intestine Sei point between one thumb and finger, and the Go point with the other hand. Apply light pressure and pull away from the center, or away from the Gen point in opposite directions. In this simple way, we are drawing stagnated energy from the Gen point. Continue for three to five minutes to balance the meridian's Ki flow. Next, move to the partner organ, the lungs, and treat in the same manner. Then treat the other arm. For a general tonification, this process can be done on all the meridians.

Fig. 41 Treating the Large Intestine's Gen Point

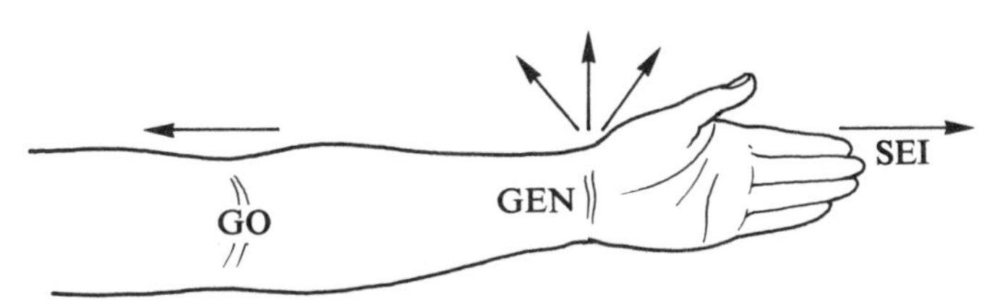

Stimulating the Sei and Go points relieves stagnation at the Gen point.

Five Transformation Points

Each organ and function in the body is influenced by a certain meridian. In addition, on each meridian, all the other meridians and their organs are represented. This concept of the part mirroring the whole is also true for distinct areas of the body. The ear, as already mentioned, contains tsubo for the entire body, and foot reflexology is a type of massage in which different regions of the sole of the foot are stimulated to influence specific organs and systems.

The link between meridians appears in the tsubo on each meridian that correspond to the five stages of energy transmutation—water or floating, wood or upward-moving, fire or active, soil or downward-moving, and metal or gathering energy. We have already examined the correlation between each of these phases and its associated meridians and organs. The lungs, for instance, are affiliated with gathering energy, or the metal stage. The points on the lung meridian will directly influence the lungs. In addition, if the metal point on any other meridian is stimulated, the lungs and their paired organ, the large intestine, will be affected.

The five transformation points are easy to locate. Actually, we have already reviewed some of them. Starting with the Sei point, they include the Ei, Yu, Kei

Fig. 42 The Five Transformation Points

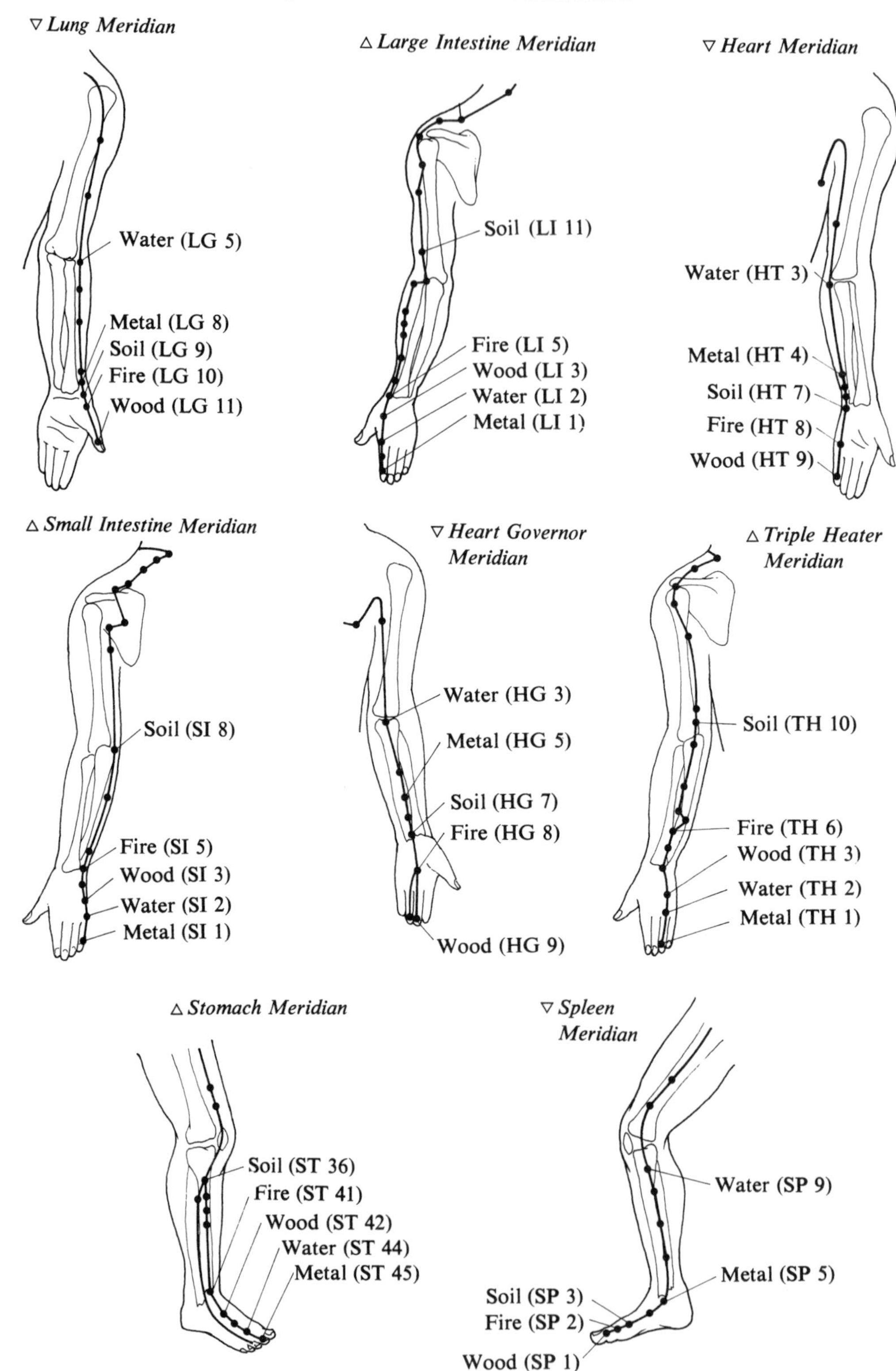

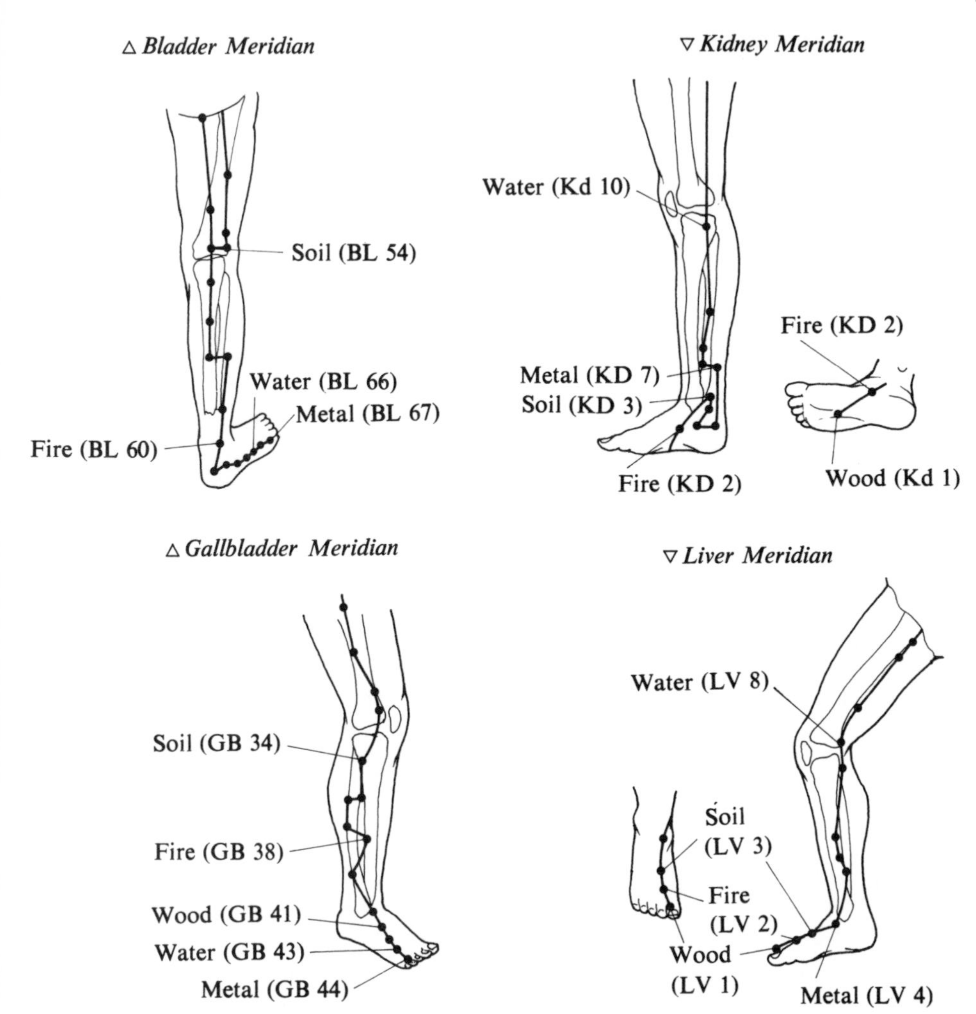

and Go points described above. On the yin meridians (the yang organs), the Sei point correlates to wood or rising energy, the Ei point to fire, the Yu point to soil, the Kei point to metal, and the Go point to water. On the yang meridians (yin organs) the Sei point corresponds to the metal or gathering energy, the Ei point to water, the Yu point to wood, the Kei point to fire, and the Go point to soil. The complete sequence is illustrated in Figure 42.

On both types of meridians, the cycle then starts over, and continues in sequence to include all points on the meridians. However, because of the polarity with the organs discussed above, these first five are the most effective. In fact, many problems can be treated with these five transformation points only.

Why not directly treat the meridian associated with the affected organ rather than a point on a different meridian? For the answer to this question, we must return to the cycles of Ki discussed in chapter 3. If there is a deficiency within the liver, and the liver meridian (rising energy) is activated, the heart (active energy) will also be activated according to the support cycle, or mother-child relationship. However, according to the control cycle, the spleen (downward energy) will be inhibited. If the stimulation to the liver is too strong, or if there is already a weakness in the spleen, this treatment will have undesirable effects.

In this case we must choose a different method for stimulating the liver. The liver meridian can be used, but to avoid a negative effect on the spleen, we could treat the soil point (associated with the spleen) on the liver meridian. This will reduce or nullify the overriding effect produced when the liver is activated. As an alternative, we could treat the wood point—which correlates to the liver—on the spleen meridian, or on another meridian, depending upon the individual's condition and the desired results.

Once again we see the principle of yin and yang at work. By making one organ yang, another becomes yin. By activating yin meridians we depress the yang meridians. Because of the numerous polar relationships within the body, no treatment can be good for all the organs, systems, and processes. If we strengthen one category, we may weaken the other.

Relationships such as the one above highlights, are the reason why it is essential to understand the overall condition of the patient before treating symptoms. It would be ineffective, and could be counterproductive to arbitrarily select points for treatment. Practitioners need a comprehensive understanding of energy, and a dynamic knowledge of the individual's condition to treat effectively. In addition, physicians should always seek to simplify their treatments.

The Importance of Names

Traditionally, a name was given to each of the points along the meridians. These labels reflect the particular energy quality of individual points, and contain insight into their uses. Unfortunately, in recent times the tsubo are identified by numbers, which give no indication of their energetic nature or their usefulness. (For example, Lung 1, Lung 2, and so on.) This again illustrates our modern, analytical approach. Numbers are convenient for cataloging and reference purposes. They also bypass the language barrier for both Western students and for individuals in various Oriental nations who wish to consult texts from neighboring countries.

On the other hand, the traditional names provided insight into both the nature of the points and their uses in healing and in the prevention of illness. They are valuable resources that should not be ignored. Perhaps the best solution would be to keep the numbering system, while offering a special course in schools of Oriental medicine to explain the meaning of the names.

Several examples of the significance of the names of meridian points are provided below. Each contains the sequential number of the tsubo, the Chinese name, the English translation, and a sampling of the recommended uses for the point. (For a complete listing, see *Acupuncture Medicine*, by Yoshiaki Omura, Japan Publications, Inc., 1982.)

- Lung 4, *Hsia Pai*, "pure lung." Recommended when experiencing coughing, a choking sensation, or shortness of breath.
- Large Intestine 20, *Ying Lsiang*, "welcoming of fragrance or smell." For a stuffy nose, rhinitis, and nasal sinusitis.

- Stomach 18, *Ju Ken*, "breast root" or "milk source." For inflammation of the mammary gland, and insufficient lactation.
- Spleen 14, *Fu Chieh*, "abdominal knot." For abdominal pain and colic.
- Heart 9, *Shao Chung*, "small rush." For emergency treatments of arrhythmia, coma, unconsciousness and fainting.
- Small Intestine 9, *Chien Chen*, "the virtue of the shoulder." For paralysis or pain of the upper arms, or diseases of the shoulder joint and surrounding tissue.
- Bladder 12, *Feng Men*, "gate of wind." For respiratory diseases including pneumonia, bronchitis, and the common cold.
- Kidney 7, *Fu Liu*, "back flow of trapped water." For kidney problems and night sweats.
- Gallbladder 2, *Ting Hui*, "gathering for listening." Deafness, ringing in the ears.
- Liver 3, *Tai Chung*, "big rush." Abdominal spasms and cramps.

One final aspect of Oriental medical theory remains to be examined before the practical applications and specific treatments are discussed. In chapter 5, traditional diagnostic techniques are introduced.

5. Diagnosis

The immediate task that any medical consultant faces is to identify the nature of a patient's problem so that appropriate action can be taken. Modern and traditionally oriented physicians go about their evaluation in opposite ways. This difference exists both in the information deemed important and in the means of gathering it.

Like all complementary pairs, both approaches have their unique strengths and weaknesses, uses and limitations. Contemporary medicine isolates, analyzes, and then categorizes. Its goal is to pinpoint the source of the complaint. The value of such an approach lies in this direct and exact ability to narrow in on a problem. The medical establishment excels at emergency-type situations. In cases of traumatic injuries and acute, life-threatening illness, the technology and the skills of specialists save lives. Like any overly developed strength, however, such sharply focused expertise obviously has its corresponding blind spots.

Wielding almost unimagined powers to probe and intervene, our medicine has lost its view of the body as a whole, and of the patient as a person, with a family, perhaps a career, and certainly a past and future: all factors traditional physicians regarded as essential to understanding an individual's state of health. In addition, modern medicine has forsaken its faith in the recuperative abilities of the human body, and of humanity's intimate relation with the natural world.

This was not always the case. Just several generations ago, the practice of Western medicine was as much an art as a science. Physicians combined their training, experience, and senses to assess a patient's condition. Diagnostic ability developed as the practitioner's skills matured. All this changed with the advances in technology made during and after Word War II. Clinical tests began to replace rather than supplement the physician's judgment. This period marks the practical divorce of the human element from the practice of medicine. Today, with the all but total dependence on technology, this trend is almost complete.

In contrast to this mechanical, highly specialized approach, the diagnostic methods employed in traditional medicine follow the same tenets as those set forth for medical practice in general, as described in chapter 1. In relation to diagnosis, these principles are:

1. A Holistic Orientation: The focus is on the entire Self, and its interaction with all realms of life. Approached from the dimension of space, this implies that the practitioner views the body as a whole, rather than trying to isolate body parts and symptoms. The individual is perceived as a matrix of interrelated processes, including the body, mind, and spirit. In addition, the individual's broader spatial relationships—to society and to the forces of nature—are considered to be essential influences on one's state of health.

From the dimension of time, the practitioner considers the inherited factors passed on from the individual's parents, grandparents, and so on. The character of the individual's early years—regarded as having a crucial influence on one's destiny—is assessed as well. The combined factors of inheritance and quality of life extending from conception through early childhood shape the individual's basic physical constitution and psychological orientation. By considering these past influences, along with present circumstances, a skilled practitioner can recognize the direction of the person's future.

2. *A Spiritual or Nonmaterial Orientation:* This principle acknowledges the fact that all manifestations of individual health and character are reflections of Ki, or invisible energy flow. Problems, whether physical or psychological, are seen as imbalances of Ki. The purpose of diagnosis is thus to discover where and in what ways imbalances exist, and to determine what has generated them. Only after these factors have been established, can proper steps be taken to establish harmony.

3. *Cause-oriented rather than Symptomatic:* The traditional practitioner moves from understanding the presenting symptoms to discovering the cause, and on to the source of a patient's problems. In the simple case of constipation, for instance, the symptoms may be related to a sluggish intestinal condition. While addressing this situation, the practitioner will seek the cause in the patient's diet and lifestyle. Furthermore, the physician will search for the source of the condition in the individual's view of life, which created the day-to-day patterns of living that in turn produced the sluggish intestines.

4. *Intuitive as Compared to Conceptual:* According to this principle, the practitioner will use the dynamic interplay of knowledge, experience, and judgment to evaluate the individual's condition. Along the same lines, only the simplest diagnostic methods are employed. Because of this, it is essential that the physician's own condition be clear and healthy. A deep understanding of the order of life, as expressed in the principles of yin and yang, is a further requirement.

5. *Practical rather than Theoretical:* Instead of trying to rigidly fit symptoms into established guidelines, and then make formula-type recommendations, the practitioner recognizes the uniqueness of the individual, even when the problem matches a clearly defined category.

Returning to the example of constipation, although the gross symptoms may appear similar, the general cause can actually be one of two opposite factors—an excessively yin or excessively yang intestinal condition. In the former case, the intestines are loose and swollen, and the contractive partner of peristaltic motion is deficient. In the latter case, the intestines are tight and constricted, and the expanding partner of peristaltic motion is deficient.

The source of the problem may be originating in the intestines themselves, or another, apparently unrelated factor may be inhibiting the function of the intestines, as illustrated in the support and regulating cycles discussed earlier. Recognizing this complexity, the practitioner approaches diagnosis with a flexible mind.

Purpose of Diagnosis

Based on these five principles, Oriental and traditional physicians developed profoundly accurate, safe, and simple methods of diagnosis. Practitioners were not satisfied, however, with a system which, after problems arose, simply aimed at identifying a symptom or set of symptoms so that the proper treatments could be recommended for temporary relief. This was of course important, but it was considered of rather limited use, and was employed as a preliminary step only. Nor was diagnosis restricted to the evaluation of an individual's condition after a complaint became serious enough to seek help.

Of greater significance was the use of diagnosis for the early detection of a developing problem. In this way, diagnosis served as a preventive measure. Physical problems generally do not begin suddenly and without warning. They progress gradually and over time, and usually the more serious the condition, in cases of degenerative disease, for example, the longer the disease process has been going on. This often means many years.

During this period, the Self—the body, emotions, mind, and spirit—undergoes change and continually presents feedback in the form of various signs or symptoms that reflect these alterations. Appearing at first as minor complaints, these early warning signs are often ignored, self-medicated—with pain killers for instance—or treated symptomatically by a doctor. If disorders emerge on the emotional or mental level, individuals may seek counseling, take mood-altering medications, or develop addictions to socially acceptable substances such as coffee, cigarettes, or chocolate, to dull the discomfort. Or, individuals may simply try to cope, accepting such impediments as an inevitable part of modern life.

Traditional physicians recognized that even lesser complaints reflected the early stages of what could eventually become a serious problem. This is why seemingly minor discomforts and signs were regarded seriously. Practitioners sought to redress the underlying imbalances such symptoms indicated before the ailments developed into full-blown illnesses.

A further goal of diagnosis was to determine if the individual's outlook and lifestyle were appropriate with his natural and social environment. In other words, was the patient a truly happy and healthy individual, and was his day-to-day behavior leading to personal growth. The answers to these questions indicated the type of future the individual's present circumstances were creating. From this point, steps could be taken to change an individual's future if his current direction was inappropriate to his long-term well-being.

Diagnosis thus takes in the total Self as we go from symptom to cause to origin of a particular complaint, and from past way of life to present condition to future potential for health and happiness.

Methods of Diagnosis

With the unifying principles of yin and yang, the applications of traditional diagnosis are innumerable. Any aspect of individual expression can be used to understand one's past way of life, present condition, and future direction. Until one gains an understanding of such methods, this idea may sound improbable. Once one has encountered them, such practices may seem mysterious, even magical. These reactions simply indicate how far we are removed from the natural order of life.

Actually, traditional diagnostic methods are based on the relation of the macrocosm to the microcosm, or of the Infinite to the individual. The implication is that we can know the whole by seeing the part, and understand the part by viewing the whole. In practical application, this means that any particular area of the body can be examined to determine the health of any other specific area, or, of the body as a whole.

The hands and feet exemplify the dynamics of this principle. *Hand* and *foot reflexology* are practices based on the complementary relation of the body's periphery to its center. That is to say, the internal organs and their related systems can be both diagnosed and treated at specific spots on the feet and hands. The widely used and often belittled art of palm reading is based on the same principles. We have seen how psychological characteristics are related to the functions of the internal organs. By determining the strength and weakness of various organs—and their related systems—via examination of their corresponding areas of the palm, one's character can similarly be assessed.

This type of appraisal requires sensitivity and perception. Shunning specialized equipment, traditional diagnostic techniques were based on the use of the physician's senses, combined with experience and training, to develop an intuitive understanding of the relationship between the individual and the larger forces of life.

Following is an introduction to the major categories of diagnostic methods used in Oriental medicine. Our purpose here is to illustrate the principles upon which each method is based and to provide an overview of their application. For a detailed study, readers are referred to the comprehensive book, *How to See Your Health: The Book of Oriental Diagnosis* (Michio Kushi, Japan Publications, Inc., 1978).

Four general methods of diagnosis are used in Oriental medicine. The Chinese and Japanese names, along with a brief description, are given below.

1. Visual examination, *Wang Chen* (Japanese: *Bo Shin*) (望診).
2. Diagnosis by the sense of sound, or listening diagnosis, *Wen Chen* (*Bun Shin*) (聞診). This category also includes appraisal of the body odor, *Wu Hsiang* (*Go Kou*) (五香).
3. Examination by the sense of touch, *Chieh Chen* (*Setsu Shin*) (切診). This category includes but is not limited to the techniques of:
   Examination of the tsubo along the meridians
   Abdominal palpation
   Diagnosis of the back
   Pulse diagnosis
4. Examination of the tongue, *She Chen* (*Zetsu Shin*) (舌診).

Each of these techniques represents the application of the principles of yin and yang to respective dimensions of the Self. Without the perspective that these universal forces provide, it is impossible to recognize and interpret the myriad and sometimes subtle information the individual is presenting.

Modern medicine uses technology—X-rays, chemical analysis, optical and electronic microscopes, and so on—as extensions of the senses to isolate and examine what would otherwise be impossible to behold. Recently, Oriental doctors have started using electronic devices to locate points along the meridians and to measure Ki. Such information, however, is still confined to a relatively limited range within the immense field of influences upon our lives. Treatments based on findings gathered in this fashion are bound to be of limited value. Consequently, a permanent cure can never be achieved, and an effective strategy for prevention is impossible.

The medical profession's growing dependence on sophisticated equipment indicates that as a society, we have lost the understanding of nature, as reflected in the concepts of yin and yang. Perhaps more troublesome is the inference that our sensitivity and perception has been dulled by our worldview and way of life.

Diagnosis by Seeing

Bo-Shin, or diagnosis using the practitioner's sense of sight, is based on the myriad polar relationships existing within the body, including the internal and external, the left and right sides, the front and the back, the center and periphery, and the head and trunk. It also includes the relationship between the body and the mind. Simply stated, this means that the internal is reflected in the external; that we can know the inside by viewing the outside.

A main feature of visual diagnosis is *facial diagnosis*, in which facial features are observed for clues concerning the internal condition. Dividing the body into the trunk and head, the mouth and neck region represent the body's center. From this point the head grows upward under the influence of Earth's force and the trunk grows downward under the influence of Heaven's force, in a general ratio of 1: 7, head to body. If we received these two forces in equal amounts, the head and trunk would be similar in size, and if the interaction of these forces was in a different ratio, the proportions of the human form would be correspondingly different.

In this correlation, the head is the compact form of the trunk, and the trunk is the expanded form of the head. The head is more yang, solid and condensed, while the body is more yin, soft and elongated. Within this complementary relationship, organs and systems located internally in the lower body are mirrored externally on the face. Existing in expanded form in the trunk, the lower-body parts appear in contracted form in the head.

With this understanding, the following general correlations can be made:

- The upper region of the face corresponds to the lower area of the trunk.
- The middle area of the face reflects the middle region of the body.
- The lower portion of the face corresponds to the upper trunk.

Taking the mouth as the center, the following specific correspondences between the trunk and face exist:

Fig. 43 Correlation between the Face and Body Organs

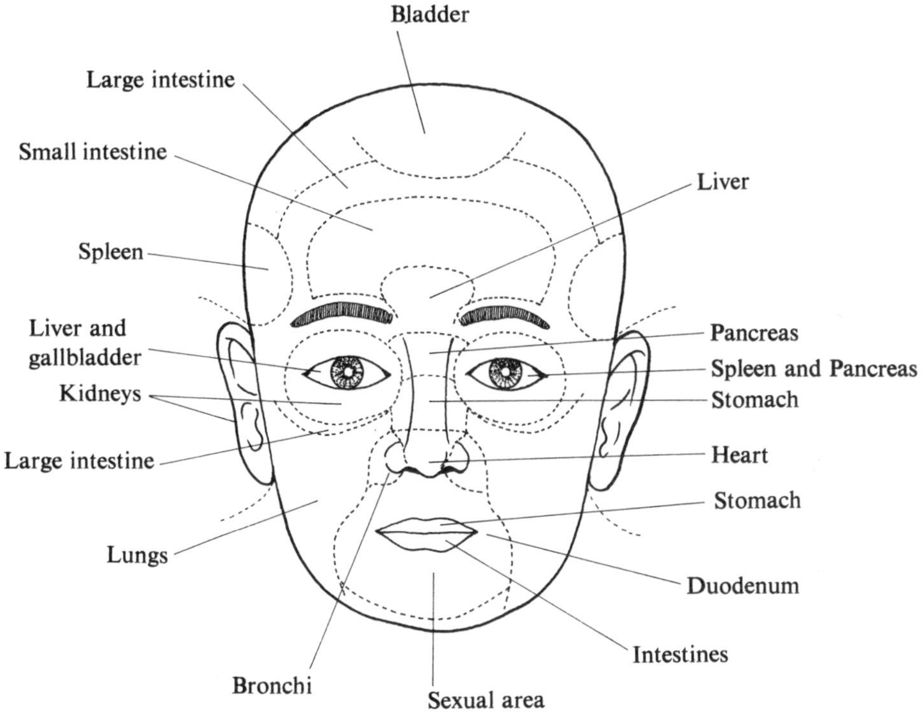

- Lungs and cheeks
- Large intestine and the upper and more peripheral portion of the forehead, and the outer section of the lower lip
- Heart and the tip of the nose
- Small intestine and the lower and more central portion of the forehead, and the inner section of the lower lip
- Kidneys and the ears, and a circular area encompassing the region above and below the eyes
- Bladder and the top portion of the forehead along the hair line
- Spleen and pancreas and the portion of the nose closest to the head, and the left eye. The spleen also correlates to the temples.
- Stomach and the central portion of the nose, and the upper lip
- Duodenum and the outer corners of the mouth
- Liver and the area of the forehead between the eyebrows, also the right eye
- Gallbladder and the area between the end of the eyebrows and the sideburns
- Sexual organs and the area encircling the mouth

The major organ systems of the body are also reflected in the face:

- The digestive and respiratory systems correspond to the area around the mouth, including the mouth cavity and tongue.
- The nervous system is reflected on the forehead, temples, and eyebrows.

Fig. 44 Correlation between the Face and Organ Systems

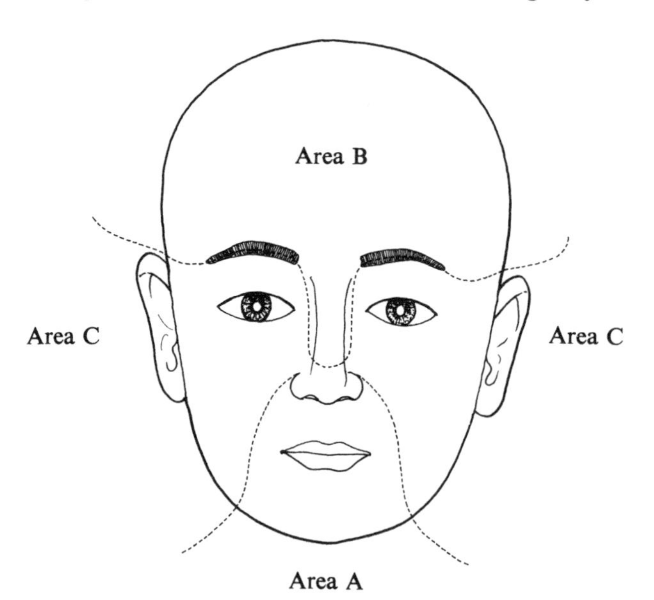

Area A: The conditions of the mouth, lips, tongue, mouth cavity, and area around the mouth, show the digestive functions as a whole. This area also relates partially to the respiratory function, especially at its peripheral area.
Area B: The condition of the forehead and its periphery, including the temples and eyebrows, represent the conditions of the nervous system as a whole.
Areas C and C′: The side facial areas, including both eyes, cheeks and ears, represent the conditions and functions of the circulatory and excretory systems as a whole.

- The circulatory and excretory systems correlate to the middle area of the face and head, including the cheeks, eyes, and ears.

These correspondences can be used in numerous ways. For instance, changes in facial skin color or texture; puffiness or tight, drawn areas; swollen or sunken areas; the appearance of broken capillaries on the surface of the skin; lines, pimples, freckles, or other marks; all reflect changes in the function and structure of the related organ. Using the cheeks as an example, we see that a pale color in the cheeks indicates a deficient energy flow and weak lung function. A red color denotes an excessive energy flow and inflammation. Pimples reflect the accumulation of mucus, and freckles reveal an acidic condition within the lungs. In this way, long before perceptible physical changes appear in the organs themselves, developing problems show up, in a variety of ways, in the face.

Facial diagnosis is not the only application of visual diagnosis, however. The traditional practitioner noted how the patient projected himself, how he dressed, his posture and movements. Each of these external factors reflect and provide valuable information concerning an individual's overall health, and the specific condition of various systems and organs.

Emotional, mental, and spiritual characteristics are revealed in the same way.

From the list of correspondences given in the Five Transformations chart (Table 4), we know that each organ pair is associated with particular qualities of the psyche. In health, these characteristics are expressed smoothly and appropriately. In sickness, some may be inhibited and others exaggerated. If, by visual diagnosis, we see that a particular organ is over- or underactive, we can expect a corresponding imbalance in the related psychological traits.

Although not discussed in detail here, we could also reverse this process and diagnose an individual's physical condition by his emotional expression, his intellectual orientation, and his spiritual qualities. In the same way, we can assess each of these more subtle factors by knowing the condition of the various organ pairs, which reflect the quality of the individual's energy flow.

Diagnosis by Listening

Diagnosing an individual through the sense of sound includes two complementary aspects. The first, more yang, method is by direct questioning to gain information about the symptoms and general condition. At the same time, the physician pays attention to the patient's manner of speaking. Is the individual bright and cheerful, confident and optimistic, depressed, fearful, hesitant. These and similar characteristics provide clues to the individual's strengths and weaknesses, and to the nature of the particular problem that prompted him to seek help.

The second, more yin, method involves assessing the quality of the patient's voice. From this alone, a skilled practitioner can determine not only the cause of a problem but an individual's overall state of mental and physical health. Listening diagnosis is based on the same principles as visual diagnosis. The difference being that listening deals with a different set of vibrations, or a different type of Ki. Visual diagnosis uses light, while listening diagnosis uses the vibration of sound. The application of this technique is as follows, based on the polar relationship between the paired organs, which tells us that if there is a problem with one organ in the pair, the other organ will also be affected:

- *Heart/Small Intestine:* Problems with either of these organs are reflected in irregular speech patterns. Speech does not flow smoothly, continuously, or rhythmically. It is punctuated by inappropriate breaks. The individual may often make mistakes in wording as well. If the heart is expanded, a yin condition, the pitch will be high, and interrupted with frequent pauses.

- *Lungs/Large Intestine:* If the energy of the lungs or large intestine is stagnated, the voice will be heavy and stuffy, especially when mucus deposits exist in either organ. In the case of a more yin condition, the voice will be thin or weak, as it is in the case of tuberculosis.

- *Kidneys/Bladder:* Problems in these organs are generally caused by imbalances of liquid or salt. This produces a watery voice, and a low vibration.

- *Spleen/Pancreas:* Troubles with these organs produce a whining, complaining voice. It fluctuates between fast and slow, high pitch and low pitch.

- *Liver/Gallbladder:* Troubles with these organs produce an impatient, often blunt speech pattern. The pitch is heavy, and the pattern is short and often brusque.

The Five Transformations chart (Table 4) also lists five distinct "voices," each of which relates to one of the five organ pairs. If one of these voices is characteristic of an individual's speech, we can suspect an imbalance in the energy of the related organ pair and meridians. By way of review, these correlations are as follows:

Table 9 "Voices" and the Five Transformations

Voice	Energy	Organ Pair
Shouting	Rising	Liver/Gallbladder
Talking (Excessive)	Active	Heart/Small Intestine
Singing	Downward	Spleen/Stomach
Crying	Gathering	Lung/Large Intestine
Groaning	Floating	Kidney/Bladder

Within the category of listening diagnosis, Oriental practitioners included the diagnostic technique that uses the sense of smell. A disorder with either member of an organ pair will often generate a particular telltale odor. The solid, physically yang organs are considered to be the source of these specific smells. However, the hollow, structurally yin, partner organ will be affected whenever imbalances develop within its complementary partner. The correlation between the organs and their related odors is listed in Table 10.

Table 10 Odors and the Five Transformations

Odor	Energy	Organ Pair
Oily, Fatty	Rising	Liver/Gallbladder
Burnt	Active	Heart/Small Intestine
Fragrant, Sweet	Downward	Spleen/Stomach
Fishy	Gathering	Lung/Large Intestine
Rotten, Putrefying	Floating	Kidney/Bladder

These two forms of diagnosis, by sound and odor, reveal precise information on the individual's state of health. They can be used to confirm and supplement information gained by visual diagnosis.

Diagnosis by Touching

A third application of traditional diagnosis involves the sense of touch. This method is divided into two categories: (1) the more yang or physical pressing of points to determine the state of Ki within the organ and along the meridian, and (2) the more yin method of palpitating of pulses for the same purpose.

Fig. 45 Examples of Diagnostic Points on Each Meridian

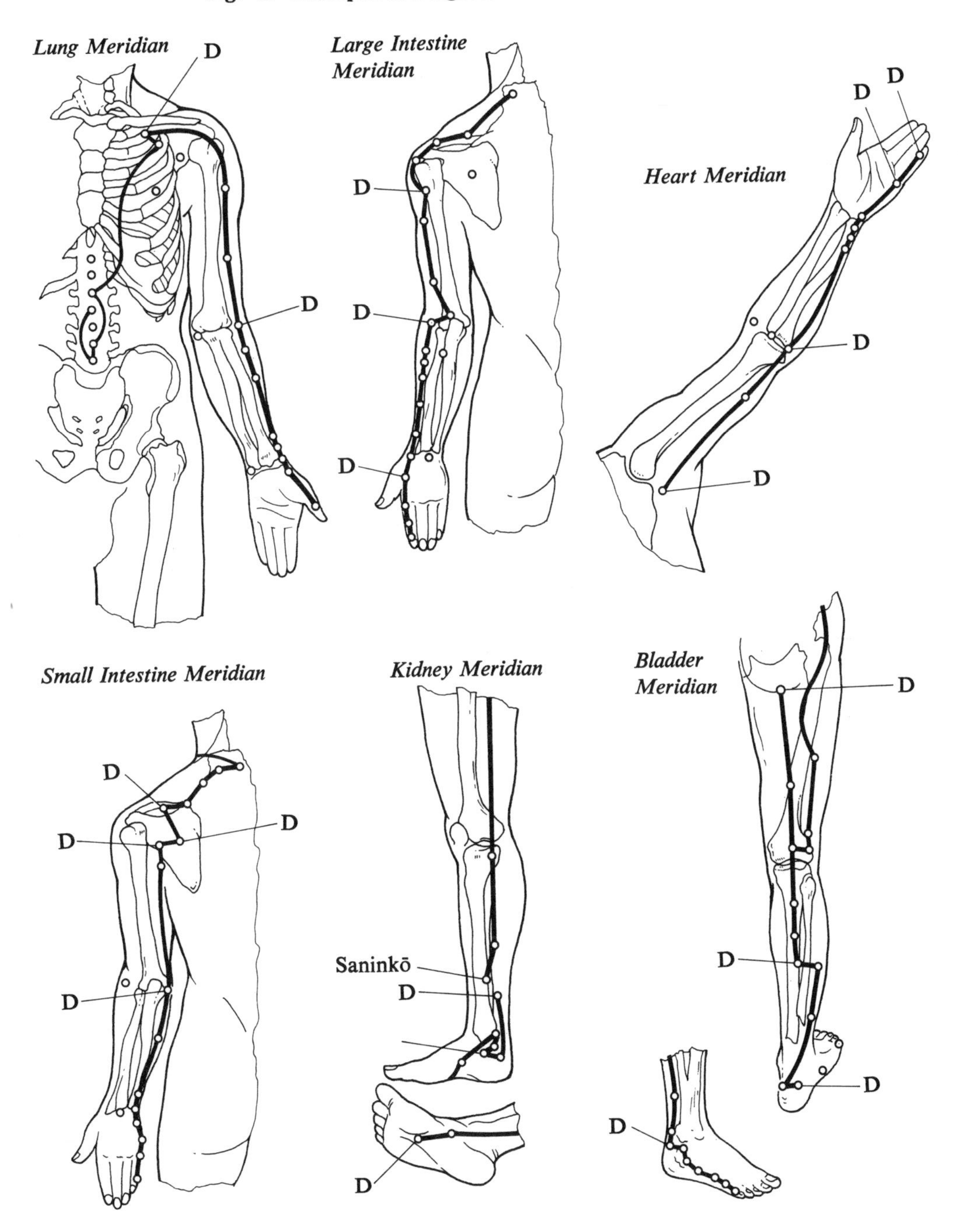

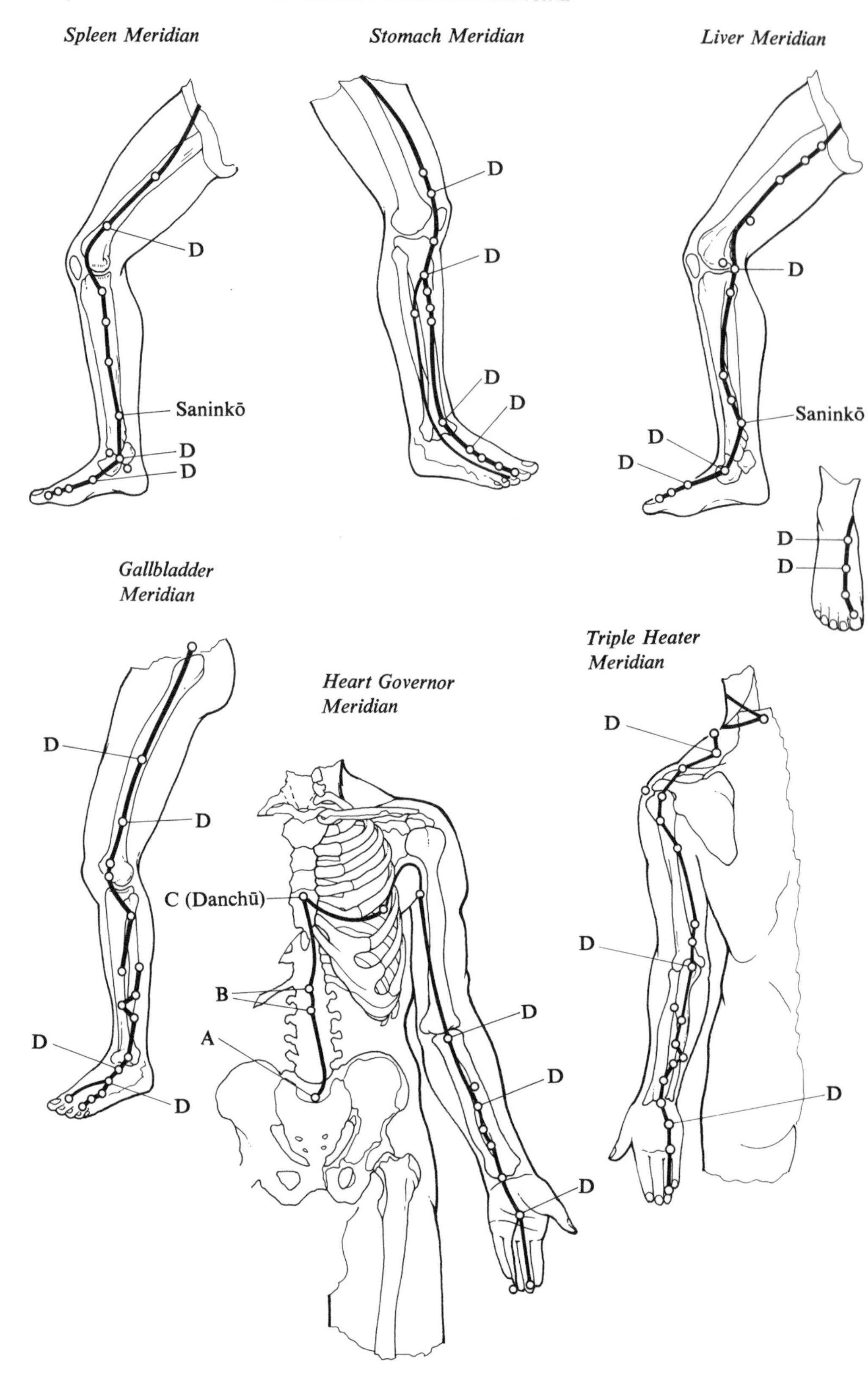
Spleen Meridian
D
Saninkō
D
D
Stomach Meridian
D
D
D
D
Liver Meridian
D
Saninkō
D
D
D
D
Gallbladder Meridian
D
D
D
D
Heart Governor Meridian
C (Danchū)
B
A
D
D
D
Triple Heater Meridian
D
D
D

Point or tsubo diagnosis is called *Shoku Shin* in Japanese. Points are pressed with the fingers to determine the Kyo (empty) and Jitsu (full) condition of the related meridian and organ pair. If, for example, when a diagnostic point along the liver meridian is pushed, the practitioner feels a surface softness and a deeper hardness, and the patient feels a dull pain, stagnation in the liver, and deficiency along the meridian is indicated. If the tsubo is swollen or "full," and a sharp pain or a surface hardness is felt, an excess of energy and an overactive condition is indicated.

Major diagnostic points exist at various locations along each of the meridians. There are additional points throughout the body that can also be used. The tsubo most commonly employed for diagnosis are illustrated in Figure 45.

Included within the category of diagnosis by touching is abdominal palpation. Specific areas of the abdomen correlate to individual internal organs (see Figure 46). Thus, the condition and function of the organs can be determined by pressure. Qualities to look for include: empty and full, and hardness and tenderness. In addition, the pulse from the abdominal aorta will be felt. A large and throbbing pulse indicates an imbalanced organ condition.

Fig. 46 Correlation between Abdominal Areas and Specific Organs

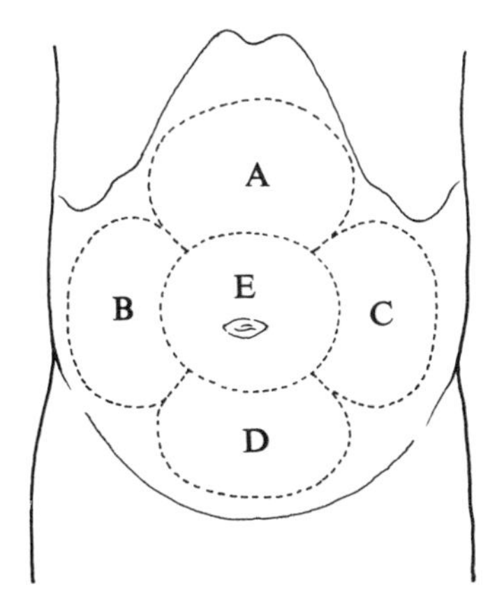

Area A: The upper abdominal region represents the condition of the heart and small intestine.
Area B: The right side of the abdominal region represents the condition of the lungs and large intestine.
Area C: The left side of the abdominal region represents the condition of the liver and gallbladder.
Area D: The lower abdominal region represents the condition of the kidneys and bladder.
Area E: The central part of the abdominal region represents the condition of the spleen, pancreas, and stomach.

In abdominal diagnosis, the person being examined lies on his back, with feet flat on the floor so that the knees are raised and leaning against each other. As the receiver exhales, the practitioner pushes deeply but gently with the extended fingers of one hand, into each area. The practitioner's free hand should rest on either the chest or abdomen to offset the pressure being applied.

Although discussed in *The Yellow Emperor's Classic of Internal Medicine*, abdominal diagnosis was not as widely used in China as the other diagnostic methods mentioned in this chapter. It was in Japan that this art was expanded and put into general practice. Readers who would like more information on abdominal diagnosis are referred to one of the shiatsu books in the bibliography.

The Pulses

Traditionally, the pulses were recognized as a vital source of information concerning a patient's condition. This was true of physicians in both the East and the West. Galen, the famous Greek physician who served at the court of the Roman emperor Marcus Aurelius, wrote in great detail about the qualities to be discerned from each pulse. It is in the Far East, however, where this practice has been preserved and refined into a highly accurate measure of an individual's physical and mental condition.

The pulses can be taken at numerous locations on the body, including: the temples, the sides of the neck, the groin area, under the arms, the inside of the elbows, the back of the knees, and at the ankles. However, the primary location for pulse taking is the inside of the wrists, along the lung meridian.

In modern medicine, the pulse is taken to gather information about the heart and blood circulation. Traditional medicine, in contrast, uses the pulses for detailed and precise information about specific meridians and their organs. The various characteristics that can be recognized at each of the pulses are reflections of the specific quality of energy along each meridian and within each organ.

Fig. 47 Location of the Wrist Pulses

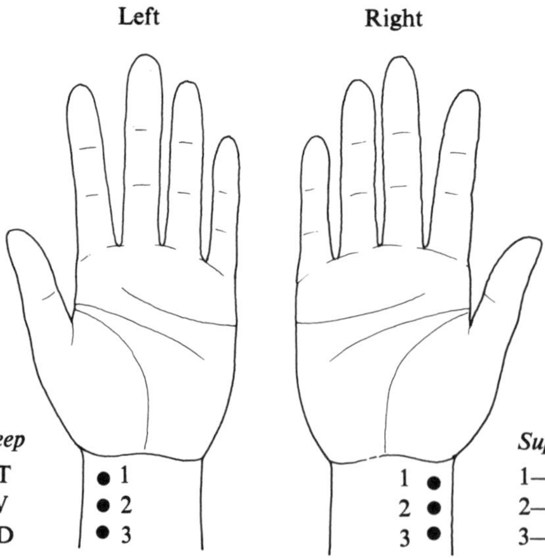

Left

Superficial	*Deep*
1—SI	HT
2—GB	LV
3—BL	KD

Right

Superficial	*Deep*
1—LI	LG
2—ST	SP/PAN
3—TH	HG

The pulses illustrated are for men. In women, the hands are reversed: the pulses shown on the left male wrist are found on the right wrist in females and the pulses shown on the right wrist appear on the left wrist in females.

The pulses are taken at three points on each wrist. Each point has two basic characters, a deep and a superficial "tone," for a total of twelve distinct pulses. Thus, the five pairs of meridians/organs and the comprehensive function of the triple hearter and heart governor can be assessed. A third, comprehensive pulse is found at the level between the deep and superficial pulses. It reflects the nutritional quality nourishing the paired meridians and their organs and functions.

Before listing the location of each pulse the complementary relation of the male and female in regards to the location of the pulses needs to be pointed out. We have already seen that the primary energy orientation of women is governed by Earth's force, and that of men, Heaven's force. This is to say that the energetic nature of the male and female exists in the same polar relationship found throughout creation.

Because of this energetic difference, the location of the pulses in males and females are also opposite. That is to say, the organs that are diagnosed on the right hand in men are found on the left hand in women. Table 11 gives the order of both the male and the female pulses. The point numbers refer to those listed in Figure 47.

Table 11 Order of the Pulses in Males and Females

	Left Wrist			Right Wrist	
Point	Superficial	Deep	Point	Superficial	Deep
Males					
1	Small Intestine	Heart	1	Large Intestine	Lung
2	Gallbladder	Liver	2	Stomach	Spleen/Pancreas
3	Bladder	Kidney	3	Triple Heater	Heart Governor
Females					
1	Large Intestine	Lung	1	Small Intestine	Heart
2	Stomach	Spleen/Pancreas	2	Gallbladder	Liver
3	Triple Heater	Heart Governor	3	Bladder	Kidneys

The more yang, compacted organs are created and nourished by a more yin, slower, less active energy. The yin, hollow organs are created and nourished by a more yang, faster, more active energy. The more active, surface pulses thus reflect the condition of the yang meridians and the structurally yin organs. The deeper pulses are more subtle, and reflect the yin meridians and the structurally yang organs.

The pulses are taken with the tips (not the pads) of the index, middle and ring fingers. The fingers are held vertically so that the tips touch the points, with the index finger resting on point number one in Figure 47. Pressing with a light touch detects the superficial pulse, and pressing deeply and rather hard, gives the deep pulse. Between the superficial and deep pulses, is the third pulse. It is felt by pressing deeply and then letting up slightly. As mentioned, this pulse reveals the quality of the nutritional factors nourishing the organs and their meridians.

The various pulses provide the following information:

- *Superficial Pulse:* Condition of the energetically yang meridians and the structurally yin (hollow) organs
- *Middle Pulse:* Nutritional quality nourishing the paired meridians and organs
- *Deep Pulse:* Condition of the energetically yin meridians and the structurally yang (solid) organs

Generally, the energy flow in the superficial pulses is more active, making these pulses distinct and easy to identify. The deep pulse is subtle and different qualities require more sensitivity to detect. Like its name, the middle pulse is between these two in degree of difficulty detect to.

A normal pulse is rhythmic, orderly, smooth, and peaceful. Traditionally, more than two hundred different qualities can be distinguished at each pulse. In general, however, the following characteristics, divided into complementary pairs, provide detailed information concerning meridian/organ condition. The numerous variations of these basic conditions provide supplementary information.

- *Strong Pulse:* Indicates an overactive or excessive state, often due to overconsumption of food and drink in general, or particular items that activate the specific meridian/organ, as discussed in the section on the Five Transformations in chapter 3.
- *Weak Pulse:* Indicates an underactive or deficient organ function and energy flow due to an insufficient nutritional state.
- *Rapid Pulse:* Indicates the active discharge of energy resulting from extreme yin items. A fever is an example, and if this condition is found in a certain organ, the organ can be considered to be feverish or inflamed.
- *Slow Pulse:* Indicates the stagnation of energy, possibly due to the consumption of extremely yang items. Accumulations of fat, cysts, and stones, can also be suspected.
- *Wide Pulse:* Indicates an expansion of the organ and an overactive condition due to excessive liquid and other yin items.
- *Narrow Pulse:* Indicates a contraction of the organ and an underactive condition due to the excessive intake of yang items such as salt and minerals.

Other Qualities of the Pulses:

- *Back-and-Forth Pulse:* Indicates hardness in the organ function and meridian flow due to excessive intake of yang items, such as salt and minerals along with excessive intake of yin items like liquid and fruit.
- *Irregular Pulse:* Indicates irregular organ function and energy flow due to the consumption of extremely yin and extremely yang items.
- *Rigid Pulse:* Indicates a hypo organ function and meridian flow due to the accumulation of fat, cholesterol, and mucus.
- *Jumpy Pulse:* Indicates a condition similar to an irregular pulse, with the addition of an excess of heavy fats.

- *Stagnated Pulse:* Indicates an underactive condition caused by the accumulation of fats and cholesterol, with a thick, sticky blood quality caused by protein-rich foods, and overeating in general.
- *Dead Pulse:* This manifests as an extremely underactive pulse caused by a tumor, stone, degeneration such as in cancer, or by malnutrition.

In addition, the following correlations between the pulses and the major systems in the body can be made:

- *Superficial Pulse:* Digestive and respiratory systems
- *Middle Pulse:* Circulatory and excretory systems
- *Deep Pulse:* Nervous system

On a psychological level, the pulses correlate to the following characteristics:

- *Superficial Pulse:* Sensory perception and ability
- *Middle Pulse:* Emotional perception and sensitivity
- *Deep Pulse:* Intellectual perception and qualities

An accurate practice of pulse diagnosis demands sensitivity, and a calm, peaceful mind on the part of the practitioner. The requirements for a traditional physician, discussed earlier, reflect this ability. Experience with hundreds of individuals is also necessary to provide a range for comparison.

Because of the wealth of information the pulses provide, and because of the perception taking the pulses engenders, students are encouraged to actively practice this art. With experience and a balanced way of life, a practitioner can use this form of diagnosis to gain a deep understanding of Ki within the human body.

Tongue Diagnosis

Like each particular area of the body, the tongue can be used to evaluate one's overall condition. *Zetsu Shin* as it is called in Japanese, is one of the most important forms of diagnosis used in Chinese medicine. Two main aspects are considered. First is the structure of the tongue. Is it wide or narrow, thick or thin, pointed or rounded. Such qualities convey information concerning the individual's basic constitution and overall strengths and weaknesses of body and mind. Structural characteristics to look for include:

Width:

- A wide tongue reflects an overall balanced physical and psychological disposition.
- A narrow tongue reflects a lack of physical adaptability with pronounced strengths and weaknesses. Mentally, thinking may be sharp but tend toward seeing a narrow view.
- A very wide tongue reflects a generally loose and expanded physical condition and a tendency toward more psychological concerns.

Fig. 48 Structural Features of the Tongue

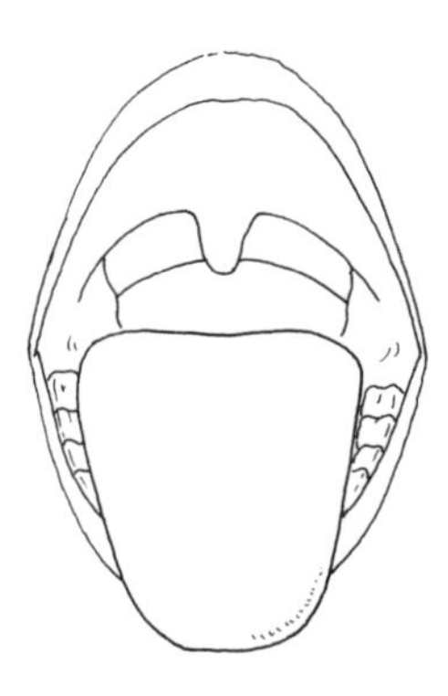

A. Wide tongue with a round tip

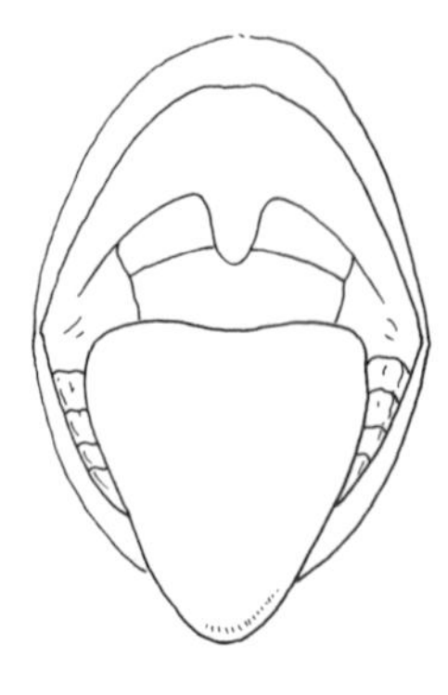

B. Narrow tongue with a sharp, pointed tip

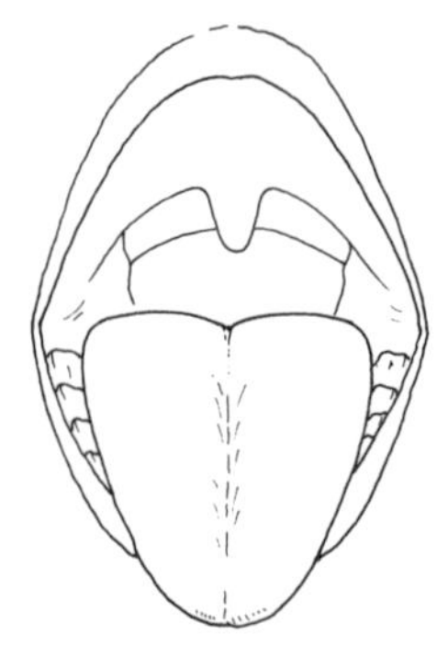

C. Tongue with a divided tip

Tip:

- A rounded tip reflects a flexible yet firm physical and mental condition.
- A pointed tip reflects a tight, perhaps even rigid physical condition and an aggressive or even offensive mentality.
- A very wide tip reflects an overall weakness of the physical body and a flaccid or even "spaced out" mental condition.
- A divided tip reflects a tendency toward physical and mental imbalances with the possibility for sharp fluctuations in thinking and mood.

Thickness:

- A flat tongue reflects a balanced condition and the ability to flexibly adapt to circumstances.
- A thin tongue reflects a more mental orientation, with a tendency to be more gentle and easy going.
- A thick tongue reflects a more physical orientation, with the tendency to be assertive or even aggressive.

As a whole, the tongue reflects the condition of the digestive system. Specific sections of the tongue mirror the condition of particular parts of the digestive system. The following correspondences exist in this relationship:

- The tip reflects the rectum and the descending colon.
- The front, side area reflects the large intestine.
- The back area relates to the liver, gallbladder, duodenum, and pancreas.
- The front, middle region reflects the small intestine.
- The middle region reflects the stomach.
- The far back area reflects the esophagus.
- The underside of the tongue reflects the quality of blood and lymph circulation in the corresponding area of the upper side.

Fig. 49 Correlation between Areas of the Tongue and the Digestive System

Top and Underside of the Tongue

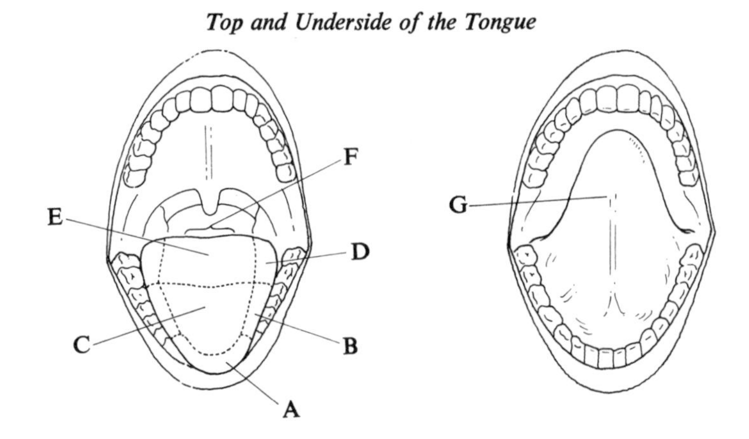

A—The tip area corresponds to the rectum and descending colon of the large intestine.
B—The peripheral area corresponds to the large intestine.
C—The middle region corresponds to the small intestine.
D—The back edge region corresponds to the duodenum, liver, gallbladder, and pancreas.
E—The near back region corresponds to the stomach.
F—The back region (the "root of the tongue") corresponds to the esophagus.
G—The underside reflects the condition of the blood and lymph circulation in each corresponding area.

In comparison to structure, the condition of the tongue is influenced more by daily lifestyle and provides information about an individual's current state of health. Qualities to look for include:

Color:

- *Dark Red:* Indicates inflammation; lesions or ulceration; and sometimes a degeneration of the related organ.
- *White:* Indicates stagnation of blood; fat and mucus deposits; or a weakness in the blood leading to such conditions as anemia.
- *Yellow:* Indicates a disorder of the liver and gallbladder, resulting in an excess secretion of bile; deposits of animal fats, especially in the middle organs of the body; and possible inflammation.
- *Blue or Purple:* Indicates stagnation of blood circulation and a serious weakening of the part of the digestive system that corresponds to the area of the tongue where the color appears.

The color on the underside of the tongue can also be used to determine the internal condition. In general, the colors and their indications listed above are the same, with the following exceptions:

- *Blue or Green:* In excess, either of these colors reflect disorders in the blood vessels and in blood quality and circulation.

- *Purple:* In excess, this color reflects disorders of the lymphatic and circulatory system. It indicates a weakening of immune ability and of the blood vessels.

Texture:
- A swollen or enlarged tongue: indicates a Jitsu, or full state.
- A shriveled or withered-looking tongue: indicates a Kyo, or empty state.

Movement: The flexibility of the tongue also reflects the condition of the digestive system. Characteristics to look for include:

- A flexible, supple, smoothly moving tongue
- A stiff, tense, or inflexible tongue
- A loose or lolling tongue
- A tongue with a pronounced slant to the left or right when it is extended

Pimples or projections on the tongue's surface indicate the discharge of fat, protein, and sugar. Where in the body this discharge is coming from can be determined by the specific area of the tongue on which it appears. See Figure 49 for the correlation between areas of the tongue and the digestive tract.

The second major aspect considered in tongue diagnosis is the coating, or moss, as it is called in Chinese medicine, on the tongue's surface. This category provides information related to an individual's more recent condition. Qualities are again divided into antagonistic pairs, and include moist and dry, excessive or deficient, thick or thin. The color of the coating reveals precise information concerning specific internal conditions.

The guidelines explained above, particularly concerning the aspects of location and color, can be used for a general understanding of the different qualities of coating found on the tongue.

Meridian Diagnosis

The twelve major meridians running through the body can also be used for purposes of diagnosis using the senses of sight and touch. Changes in the flow of Ki and in the structure and function of organs show up along the related meridians, often long before overt symptoms manifest. For instance, the clean, clear skin color along the meridians can change, indicating an imbalanced condition of the related organs, glands, systems, and energy flow. These color changes arise most often on the periphery of the meridian—at the arms and hands, the legs and feet, and on the face.

In this form of diagnosis, the practitioner examines the meridian, especially the periphery, noting variations in color, texture, and various marks such as pimples, moles, and callouses. Often, the meridian may be seen to be either sunken or swollen in certain areas or along its entire surface course. The swollen condition reflects an excess of energy and the sunken condition a deficiency. These and other factors signify changes in the quality and amount of energy of the involved meridian system.

Several colors are specifically related to abnormal conditions of the meridian and its organ pair.

- *Red:* Indicates an excessive energy flow along the meridian and charging the related organ, thus producing abnormally active organ functions.
- *White:* Indicates stagnation or blockage of energy, and a weak quality of blood and Ki.
- *Green*: Indicates structural degeneration and disordered energy. This most often appears along the Gen, or balancing points, on the meridians, and along the periphery of the meridian.
- *Blue and Purple:* Indicates a serious malfunctioning of the related organs and systems caused by the consumption of extremely yin items, including chemicals, medications, and drugs.

Because they are connected to a meridian, and exist in a periphery-and-central polar relationship, each toe and finger can be examined to determine the condition of the related meridian and its organ. Structural features, including the width and length, inward or outward curving, straight or twisted, reflect constitutional traits. Functional changes, including swelling, the presence of callouses and other qualities of skin texture, color, and marks provide detailed information concerning an individual's condition.

Value of Traditional Diagnosis

In addition to these basic methods of diagnosis, practically any aspect of individual expression—physical, emotional/mental and spiritual—can be used to evaluate basic strengths and weaknesses, past way of life, present state of health, and future expectations.

All that is needed is a dynamic understanding of the principles of yin and yang, a balanced condition, experience, and reflection on the relationship of the individual with the larger Self. This includes environmental conditions, social influences, and ancestral background.

A dynamic understanding of these factors develop our intuition, or consciousness, which is far more perceptive than any machine, no matter how complex and technologically advanced it may be. The benefits of such simple practices are many:

- They are safe and inexpensive.
- Anyone can learn to use them.
- They provide valuable information about one's personal condition and basic strengths and weaknesses.
- They enable one to recognize the influence of day-to-day lifestyle on physical and mental well-being.

- They orient one's thinking toward a more holistic and dynamic vision of one's connection with the process of life.
- They help one experience the reality of Ki.
- They engender a sense of personal responsibility for one's state of health. By extension, this gives a sense of freedom to both change one's condition, and to create the qualities we desire.

This concludes our general examination of the principles and theory of traditional and Oriental medicine. With this background, we are now ready to explore specific applications of these principles to the field of healing. Assuredly, there are refinements and additional concepts that a professional health-care practitioner must be conversant with. Such details go beyond the scope of this book, however, and interested readers are encouraged to review the more technical texts now available in English.

Part Two: Applying the Principles

INTRODUCTION TO PART 2

It has been said on more than one occasion that practice without theory is dangerous, and that theory without practice is useless. Part 1 was devoted to the principles of traditional and Oriental medicine. With the perspective that these precepts provide, we are now ready to explore the applications that make the traditional healing arts a practical complement to modern medicine.

As will be seen, when dealing with an illness, practitioners had a wide assortment of therapies at their disposal. In fact, the range of treatments used in different cultures is remarkable. Within this diversity, however, a hierarchy of preference emerges. The continuum of care moves from simple alterations in daily lifestyle to complex remedies; from ministrations involving full personal participation to procedures requiring the services of a professional.

The following chapters are arranged in this order. Starting with the preventative and restorative properties of daily diet, we go on to explore the specific medicinal uses of food. A variety of additional methods for manipulating Ki energy are introduced in subsequent chapters. Supporting the holistic nature of traditional medicine, each of these applications can also be employed to enhance physical and mental well-being and to foster personal growth. It is only in the last chapter of Part 2 that we turn to acupuncture and moxibustion, the two treatments that commonly come to mind when Oriental medicine is mentioned.

Readers may be surprised at some of the applications utilized as medical treatments. But perhaps not. We have already explored the dynamics of Ki, and the entirely new possibilities for healing and growth that this subtle energy makes available for us.

1. Food as Medicine

The earliest relationship we form in life is with food. After fertilization, our first foods are the forces of Heaven and Earth, which we receive via the mother's meridians and directly from her primary channel. Within a few days, the ovum implants itself in the wall of the uterus and we begin to consume a more physical food directly from the mother's bloodstream. From this nourishment, our bodies, including our brain and nervous system, are fashioned. Eating precedes emotional response, thinking, and even the most basic automatic physical activities.

Although slowly beginning to change, our concept of food is still narrow, and the profound influence of dietary habits on every aspect of our lives is seldom recognized. Too often, food is dealt with as a commodity, in which growers, manufacturers, distributors, and retailers, with the services of the advertising industry, seek the highest profit for their merchandise. Consumers value convenience in preparation and low prices over whole foods and items grown or produced with quality. Seldom do the dynamics of daily diet in an individual's or a society's welfare reach the forum of public consideration. To properly assess the value and medicinal uses of dietary practice, the traditional attitude toward food needs to be clarified.

The Infinite Range of Food

We have already seen that humanity comes from, is sustained by, and returns to Infinity by way of a seven-orbited logarithmic spiral. This was depicted in Figure 4, Complementary Spirals of Life. The implication of this spiralic process of development is that, moment to moment, we are a part of Infinity itself, and, simultaneously, of each of the levels of its manifestation. Individual human beings continuously interact with every stage of life through the ceaseless interchange of various forms of energy. From the large view, this entire process can be called "eating," in which our nourishment consists of the energy served from each and every dimension of existence.

Food is any substance that we ingest, digest, assimilate or internalize, and then make part of ourselves. The additional considerations of eliminating those factors that cannot be used, and the storing of any excess, must also be included. The digestive system takes care of the first part of this process, and the circulatory system is involved with distributing food particles throughout the body. The eliminatory system either discharges the factors that we cannot use or stores them for later release.

Clearly, the concept of eating involves the solids and liquids that we consume at meal and snack times. It can be easily expanded to include the gases that we inhale. They too are taken in, digested or broken down into their usable parts, assimilated into the bloodstream, circulated to each cell in the body, and gaseous wastes are eliminated.

Once we acknowledge these general characteristics, it is not such a big jump to the recognition that food also includes all the stimulations and vibrations that we are exposed to throughout the day. This includes the colors, tastes, textures, temperatures, sounds, and odors we absorb from our nearby environment, and the finer energy, in the form of waves or vibrations, that we receive from distant space.

The systems that digest food in this more refined form are the meridian and nervous systems. Stimulations from the periphery of the long- and short-wave range of the vibrational spectrum either activate cells directly, or become part of the meridian flow. Energy from the central portions of the long- and short-wave scale is received via the five senses. Such stimulations are channeled from the periphery to the central nervous system, and on to the brain, its main processor, much as the small intestine plays the central role in the digestive system. From the brain, this more subtle nourishment is distributed to all parts of the body, and to each aspect of our consciousness—physical, as well as psychological.

Like solid food, this nonmaterial aspect of nutrition becomes a part of our being. It influences the quality of our emotions, thoughts, and spirituality, as well as our physical structure, much as physical food influences both body and mind. We eliminate this subtle type of food through the energies of emotion, thought, character, and day-to-day consciousness. For example, an angry outburst discharges a great deal of energy, which is why people often feel more relaxed and calm after expressing anger. Walking into a room where there has recently been a quarrel, one can often sense or feel the strong vibrations.

Each of the emotions is similarly an expression of various types of energy. In health, our emotions are suitable responses to particular situations. In sickness, they are either exaggerated or repressed. Our thoughts are the same. Dark, heavy thoughts, bright, cheerful thoughts, thoughts of love or of hate, of worry or optimism, all reflect the discharge of different energetic qualities. In this way, the emotions are one means that we return energy to our environment. Depending on the state of health of the meridians and organs, this process can be either smooth or hypo- or hyperactive.

Too often, we mistakenly assume that emotional traits are inherent aspects of our personality. In reality, they are the long-term or temporary expression of one's energy quality. By changing the nature of the energies we consume and generate, we have the ability to alter the qualities of thought and emotion.

Excess or imbalanced nourishment on this level is stored in the various bodies, including the physical body, in the same way excess or imbalanced material nutrition is stored throughout the physical and the finer bodies. It is eliminated gradually or suddenly, in both psychological and physical ways.

Reflecting on the natural order of life, food can thus be classified into complementary categories. One consists of the physical aspects of our environment—solids, liquids, and gasses—the other involves the nonphysical factors, or the more refined forms of our environment. The first category is processed primarily by the digestive and respiratory systems, while the second is handled by the meridian and nervous systems. Figure 50 illustrates this relationship.

It bears repeating that each aspect of our Self is continually affected by all the others: thus physical food influences the health of our nonphysical body, and

Fig. 50 Complementary Relation of the Digestive and Nervous Systems

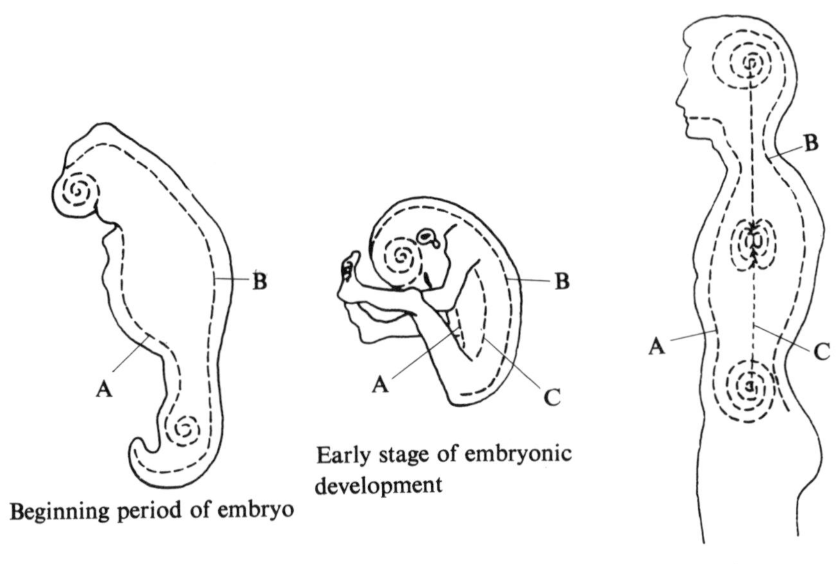

Beginning period of embryo

Early stage of embryonic development

Fully-grown adult

A: Digestive system—Physical food
B: Nervous system—Vibrational food
C: Circulatory system—Transports both types of food

nonphysical food affects or nourishes the physical body. As a simple example, anyone who has ever had a cup of coffee or an alcoholic drink knows the influence these beverages have on thoughts and emotions. On the other hand, eagerly anticipating a pleasant experience releases a plentiful supply of vitality that washes away fatigue and worries.

Seven Stages of Food

The types of food that we use as nourishment can be further divided into seven categories that reflect the seven stages of existence discussed in Part 1. In this scenario, each level in the centripetal spiral of individualization is progressively more concentrated than the one it emerges from, with the fertilized human ovum representing the most condensed form, or the microcosm of the macrocosm. In the reverse journey—the centrifugal spiral in which consciousness moves from individual to universal awareness—each stage is progressively more expanded than the one it emerges from. From the start of embryonic life, our development mirrors this opposite course, moving from individual to Infinite consciousness.

Depending on the perspective we take, our pattern of food consumption can consequently be seen as either a sequentially contracting or expanding one. From the view of Infinity, this starts with an extremely refined nourishment of short-wave vibrations and culminates with the consumption of an extremely concentrated form of energy—the fetus takes its nourishment from mother's blood. For a human being, however, this consumption pattern is reversed. In this centrifugal spiral, each major food category represents an enlargement and refinement of the realm it develops from. The successive orbits of both spirals unfold in logarithmic fashion, in the 1 to 7 ratio discussed earlier.

For human beings, the successive stages of food are listed below. Note that this pattern is reversed as we journey from the state of universal to individual consciousness—our food categories become progressively more condensed.

- *Minerals:* The most condensed or yang food we consume comes from the category of minerals.
- *Protein:* Our consumption of protein is approximately seven times greater than minerals.
- *Carbohydrates:* We take in seven times the amount of carbohydrates as we do protein.
- *Water:* Again, water is needed in a ratio of seven times the amount of carbohydrates.
- *Air:* At this point we depart from the common definition of food. We take in air in a proportion seven times greater than the amount of water.
- *Vibrations:* Our next category of food is vibrations, in the form of light, sound, heat, and so on. We ingest these constantly, and if they could be measured, we would find that the amount is approximately seven times the amount of air.
- *Extremely Fine Short-wave Vibrations:* The final stage of nourishment on this expanding scale is the more refined vibrations of extremely short-waves that connect us directly with infinity.

Fig. 51 Progressive Categories of Food Intake

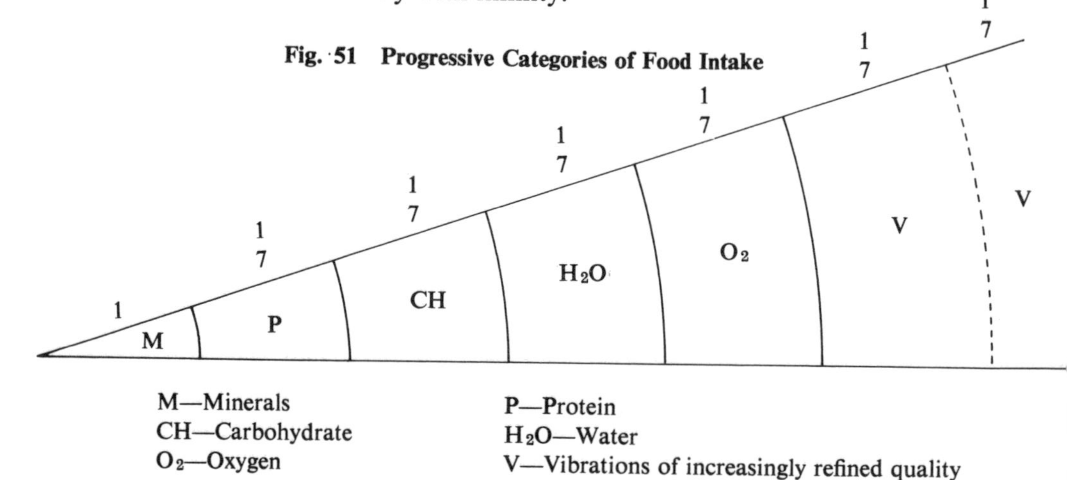

M—Minerals
P—Protein
CH—Carbohydrate
H_2O—Water
O_2—Oxygen
V—Vibrations of increasingly refined quality

As this relationship indicates, those types of nourishment that we exercise direct control over—groups one, two, and three above—are of crucial importance both to our well-being and to our continual personal growth. If our proportions are imbalanced on any of the more condensed levels, over which we have direct control, the consumption on all the others will be directly affected. By consuming the first three stages in an orderly and appropriate fashion, we influence both the quality and amount of the more refined vibrations we attract.

Complementary Views

In modern society, the approach to food is based on a general pair of complementary views of life. One recognizes only the physical aspects of existence, while ignoring or denying the spiritual. It is characterized by a more mechanical and analytical view, and consequently sees food as simply being fuel for the body machine. No recognition is given to the connection between our daily diet and the quality of our emotional, intellectual and spiritual natures. Food is analyzed and broken down into its component parts—the macronutrients of protein, carbohydrates, and fats, and the micronutrients of vitamins, minerals, enzymes, and so on—and recommended amounts are established for each. In its most extreme form, this view suggests that the body can best be nourished with tablets and supplements.

The opposite approach emphasizes the spiritual dimensions of the Self, while downplaying or actually ignoring the importance of the physical. It thus holds that food is exclusively related to the physical body, and has no influence on our mental and spiritual selves. This results in individuals trying to develop emotional stability, mental clarity, or spiritual consciousness in various ways, while totally ignoring the connection between mind and body, and the influence of food on both.

As human beings, the two poles of our existence are the physical body and spiritual consciousness. And yet, these are in no way separate. There is no place to which we can point and say here one ends and the other begins. The two halves of the Self constantly interact, with the quality of the one directly affecting the quality of the other. Ignoring either partner while trying to develop the other, clearly violates the principles of ecology and holism. In the long run, such a strategy creates imbalances and a one-sided participation in life.

Degrees of Control

Of all the aspects of our Self, the easiest to control is the more condensed, physical body. Those dimensions of the individual existing as more subtle forms of energy are proportionally more difficult to directly regulate. Even within the physical body, many processes take place automatically, such as heartbeat, respiration, digestion, and so on. Yes, to a certain extent we influence these functions by the quality of our emotions, thoughts, and spiritual consciousness, but, as we shall see, the most direct means we have for regulation comes from daily diet.

As most of us are probably aware, it is not so easy to govern our emotions. We may be able to suppress them, or learn how to express them, but in general, they seem to manifest quite independently, and often in spite of personal wishes. Thoughts, an even more subtle range of vibration, are more elusive. Even for a single minute, it is difficult to direct our thinking along one line. The most refined dimension of the Self, consciousness or spirituality, fluctuates instant by instant, and is almost impossible to intentionally influence for even the shortest period of time.

In the chapter on Ki, we discussed the importance of working from each aspect of our Self, not just for prevention or healing, but for continued personal development. Yet, we must start at the beginning. By eating a diet balanced according to individual circumstances, we automatically influence all aspects of our Self.

For example, according to the quality and quantity of our diet, changes occur in: the speed and depth of breathing; the strength and rate of heartbeats; blood pressure; hormone levels and blood sugar levels; frequency and amounts of urination, defecation, and perspiration; energy levels; moods; and the quality of our thinking. Food and drink control our destiny. Unless we take responsibility for our day-to-day eating, we will be unable, in the long run, to direct or influence the other aspects of our Self. Then, instead of being shaped by a consistent and natural pattern of growth, our physical and mental well-being will be subject to the extreme pressures that typify our modern way of life. In such a situation, it should come as no surprise that our moods, thoughts, and physical health fluctuate in a haphazard and uncontrollable manner.

Whatever our strengths and weaknesses, the tools to accentuate and compensate are as close as our kitchen. This understanding is concisely expressed in the following quote from the *Upanishads*, which are ancient Hindu scriptures thought to contain secret or mystical teachings. This particular passage accurately sums up the traditional view of food and its role in the spiral of life.

> From food are born all creatures, which live upon food and after death return to food. Food is the chief of all things. It is therefore said to be medicine for all diseases of the body. Those who worship food as Brahman gain all material objects. From food are born all beings which, being born, grow by food.

Medicinal Applications

Being the source of life, food is the primary cause of, and our basic tool for treating any type of imbalance. This includes symptoms of energy disharmony on both the physical and psychological levels. These are, after all, simply different dimensions that collectively, we call the Self.

When dealing with sickness, there are three primary aspects of food to consider.

1. Daily diet, which, in the case of illness, is out of balance and must be brought back into harmony with the individual's condition and circumstances.
2. The use of specific, short-term adjustments in daily diet with respect to the particular needs of the individual.
3. The temporary inclusion of medicinal side dishes and other preparations to address any special problems the individual may be experiencing.

1. Daily Diet

Whatever the problem, the standard macrobiotic way of eating is the first step toward recovery. Based on the principles of nature, and reflected in traditional cuisines enjoyed around the world, the macrobiotic approach to diet is a dynamic, broad-based, and flexible means by which individuals and societies can secure their well-being. By this correction alone, many problems begin to disappear as the energy flow within the individual becomes more harmonized, and the organs and systems begin to function in an appropriate and balanced way.

Macrobiotic dietary guidelines, rather than being a set of dos and donts, or a rigid list of foods to eat and to avoid, are actually a flexible set of principles that enable an individual to adapt to his particular circumstances including the broad considerations of: climate, season, and geographical location—coastal region, inland, mountains, city, country—and the more personal considerations of condition, age, occupation, and goals for the future.

The primary step when treating the symptoms of either physical or psychological disorders is to begin eating according to the tenets of traditional and Oriental medicine. The standard macrobiotic diet, as described in a variety of books, represents the application of these principles for the purposes of continual development, prevention, and healing.

2. Specific Adjustments

In addition to changes in general dietary orientation, certain adjustments to the standard macrobiotic way of eating can be made in regard to the individual's condition and particular problem. In order to make appropriate changes, the understanding of yin and yang, or the Unifying Principles, is essential. Determining if the condition is overly yang, overly yin, or a combination of both, and in what particular ways this imbalance is manifesting, we are prepared to offer precise suggestions for bringing the individual back into balance.

For example, if a person is suffering from a yin-type problem—tooth decay, hernia, diabetes, leukemia, asthma, excessive fear, withdrawal, and schizophrenia, are examples—dietary adjustments that will gradually make him more yang are indicated. These are followed only until he reaches a more balanced state. Then, the variety included in the general macrobiotic way of eating will be recommended.

If the individual's problems stem from an overly yang condition—graying hair, scurvy, angina pectoris, prostate and ovarian cancer, duodenal ulcers, short temper, aggressive behavior, or psychosis, for instance—dietary suggestions would be made to gradually make him more yin.

In either case, bringing an individual's condition into balance involves two basic steps, one negative and the other positive: (1) the elimination of extremes of both yin and yang from the diet, and (2) the inclusion of foods from the center of the yin and yang scale. If someone experiencing problems caused by extreme yin simply eliminates the more yin dietary factors, and emphasizes the more yang ones, his condition will soon become imbalanced in the opposite direction, and he will begin showing signs of being too yang. If the problem was a more deep-rooted one, as in degenerative disease, his daily or superficial condition could quickly become too tight, long before the deeper condition changes. This, in turn, will produce strong cravings and the need for yin, and the ultimate effect could be the worsening of the original problem.

Table 12 shows the major food categories in the macrobiotic way of eating. Although centrally balanced, each category can be divided into yin and yang classifications, and appropriate recommendations can be made according to the

Table 12 Foods Categorized by Yin and Yang

EXTREME YANG FOODS

SOME CHEMICALS, DRUGS, AND ROOTS

Refined Salt
Iodized Salt

Crude Gray Sea Salt
Ginseng
Insulin
Thyroxine
Various others

EGGS

Chicken Eggs
Duck Eggs
Caviar
Other Eggs from Poultry or Fish

MEAT

Beef
Lamb
Pork
Ham
Sausage
Bacon
Veal
Wild Game

POULTRY

Chicken
Duck
Goose
Pheasant
Turkey

FISH AND SEAFOOD

Bluefish
Salmon
Swordfish
Tuna
Other Red-meat and Blue-skinned Varieties

MODERATE

FISH AND SEAFOOD

Carp
Clams
Crab
Cod
Flounder
Haddock
Herring
Iriko
Lobster
Octopus
Oysters
Red Snapper
Scallops
Scrod
Shrimp
Smelt
Sole
Trout
Other White-meat Fish and Seafood

CONDIMENTS

Gomashio
Sea Vegetable Powders
Tekka
Umeboshi Plum
Shio Kombu
Shiso Leaves
Green Nori
Yellow Mustard
Green Mustard
Cooked Nori
Roasted Sesame Seeds
Other Traditional Condiments

WHOLE GRAINS AND GRAIN PRODUCTS

Brown Rice
Millet
Barley
Whole Wheat
Oats
Rye
Buckwheat
Corn
Sorghum
Wild Rice
Amaranth
Quinoa
Other Cereal Grains
Sweet Rice
Mochi
Bread
Chapatis
Tortillas
Soba
Udon
Somen
Noodles and Pasta
Couscous
Bulgur
Fu
Seitan
Oatmeal
Corn Grits
Cornmeal
Arepas
Popcorn
Other Grain Products

SEEDS AND NUTS

Almonds
Chestnuts
Filberts
Peanuts
Pecans
Pine nuts
Pistachios
Poppy Seeds
Pumpkin Seeds
Sesame Seeds
Squash Seeds
Sunflower Seeds
Walnuts
Other Temperate-Climate Varieties

BEANS AND BEAN PRODUCTS

Azuki Beans
Black-eyed Peas
Black Soybeans
Black Turtle Beans
Broad Beans
Chick-peas
Great Northern Beans
Kidney Beans
Lentils
Lima Beans
Mung Beans
Navy Beans
Pinto Beans
Soybeans
Split Peas
Whole Dried Peas
Other Beans
Miso
Natto
Okara
Tamari Soy Sauce
Tempeh
Tofu
Other Bean Products

PICKLES

Bran
Brine
Miso
Pressed
Rice Flour
Salt
Salt and Water
Sauerkraut
Takuan
Tamari Soy Sauce
Umeboshi
Other Traditional Types

SEA VEGETABLES

Agar-Agar
Alaria
Arame
Dulse
Hijiki
Irish Moss
Kelp
Kombn
Mekabu
Nekabu
Nori
Wakame
Others

SEASONINGS

Unrefined Sea Salt
Tamari Soy Sauce
Real Tamari
Miso
Rice Vinegar
Brown Rice Vinegar
Umeboshi Vinegar
Sauerkraut Brine
Mirin
Amazaké
Barley Malt
Rice Malt
Grated Ginger Root
Grated *Daikou*
Grated Radish
Horseradish
Umeboshi Plum
Umeboshi Paste
Lemon Juice
Tangerine Juice
Orange Juice
Fresh Black Pepper
Red Pepper
Green Mustard
Yellow Mustard
Sesame Oil
Corn Oil
Safflower Oil
Mustard Seed Oil
Olive Oil
Saké
Saké Lees
Other Natural Seasonings

FOODS				EXTREME YIN FOODS
VEGETABLES	*FRUITS*	*BEVERAGES*	*TROPICAL FOODS*	*STIMULANTS*
Root:	*Fresh and Dried:*	*Regular Use:*	Asparagus	Black Tea
Beets	Apples	*Bancha* Twig Tea	Avocado	Green Tea
Burdock	Apricots	Bancha Stem Tea	Bananas	Mint Tea
Carrots	Blackberries	Roasted Rice Tea	Brazil Nuts	Other Stimulating,
Daikon	Blueberries	Roasted Barley Tea	Cashews	Aromatic Teas
Dandelion Roots	Cantaloupe	Roasted Grain Tea	Coconut	Coffee
Jinenjo	Grapes	Kombu Tea	Coconut Oil	Decaffeinated Coffee
Jerusalem	Honeydew Melon	Spring Water	Dates	Cola
Artichoke	Lemon	Well Water	Eggplant	Soft Drinks
Lotus Root	Mulberries		Figs	Chocolate
Parsnip	Nectarines	*Occasional Use:*	Grapefruit	Cinnamon
Radish	Olives	100% Grain Coffee	Green Peppers	Curry
Rutabaga	Oranges	Amazaké	Kiwi Fruit	Nutmeg
Taro	Peaches	Dandelion Tea	Mango	Other Spices
Turnip	Pears	Lotus Root Tea	Palm Oil	
Others	Plums	Burdock Root Tea	Papaya	*PROCESSED*
	Raisins	Other Traditional,	Plantain	*FOODS*
Round Ground:	Raspberries	Nonstimulant,	Potato	
Acorn Squash	Strawberries	Nonaromatic	Red Peppers	White Rice
Broccoli	Tangerines	Natural Herb	Spinach	White Flour
Brussels Sprouts	Watermelon	Teas	Sweet Potato	Refined Grains
Buttercup Squash	Wild Berries		Tomato	Instant Foods
Butternut Squash	Other Temperate-	*Infrequent Use:*	Yams	Canned Foods
Cabbage	Climate Varieties	Fruit Juice		Frozen Foods
Cauliflower		Cider	*DAIRY FOODS*[1]	Sprayed Foods
Cucumber	*GARNISHES*	Soy Milk		Dyed Foods
Green Beans		Vegetable Juice	Butter	Irradiated Foods
Green Peas	Grated Daikon	Barley Green Juice	Cheese	Foods Produced
Hubbard Squash	Grated Radish	Saké	Cream	with Chemicals,
Hokkaido Pumpkin	Grated Horseradish	Beer, Natural	Ice Cream	Additives, Artifi-
Mushrooms	Chopped Scallions	Fermented	Kefir	cial Coloring,
Onions	Grated Ginger	Wine, Natural	Milk	Flavoring,
Patty Pan Squash	Red Pepper	Fermented	Sour Cream	Emulsifiers,
Pumpkin	Other Traditional	Other Grain- and	Whipped Cream	Preservatives,
Red Cabbage	Garnishes	Fruit-based Mild	Yogurt	Stabilizers
Shiitake Mushrooms		Alcoholic Bever-		Vitamin Pills
Snap Beans		ages of Natural	*SWEETENERS*[2]	Mineral Supple-
Summer Squash		Quality		ments
Swiss Chard			Aspartame	Other Food Cap-
Wax Beans		*SWEETENERS*	Blond Sugar	sules, Tablets,
Zucchini			Brown Sugar	and Similar
Others		Amazaké	Cane Sugar	Products
		Barley Malt	Carob	
White/Green Leafy:		Rice Syrup	Corn Syrup	*SOME CHEMI-*
Bok Choy		Maple Syrup	Chocolate	*CALS AND*
Carrot Tops		Fruit Juice	Dextrose	*DRUGS*
Celery		Cooked Fruit	Fructose	
Chinese Cabbage		Dried Fruit	Glucose	Amphetamines

[1] Brie, Roquefort, and several other salted cheeses that have aged for a long time are classified as yang rather than yin.

[2] Soft drinks, candy, pastries, desserts, and other items containing these sweeteners should also be avoided.

FOODS				EXTREME YIN FOODS
VEGETABLES	*FRUITS*	*BEVERAGES*	*TROPICAL FOODS*	*STIMULANTS*
Chives			Honey	Antibiotics
Daikon Greens			Molasses	Aspirin
Dandelion Greens			Nutra-Sweet	Cortisone
Endive			Raw Sugar	Cocaine
Escarole			Saccharin	LSD
Kale			Sorbitol	Marijuana
Leeks			Turbinado Sugar	Others
Lettuce			White Sugar	
Mustard Greens			Xylitol	*SEASONINGS*
Scallions				
Sprouts				Margarine
Turnip Greens				Soy Margarine
Watercress				Lard
Wild Grasses				Shortening
Others				Animal Fats
				Refined Vegetable Oils
				Herbs
				Spices
				Wine Vinegar
				Mayonnaise
				Hot Pepper

yin or yang nature of the problem. For a more yang-caused problem, we would thus place a temporary and gentle emphasis on those foods in the more balanced to yin range of each category. For more yin-caused problems, the accent would be on foods from the balanced to the more yang section. Of course we still need both the expansive and contractive dietary factors. It is the degree of emphasis that changes according to individual needs.

3. Home-care Preparations

A further refinement of the dietary approach to healing involves the inclusion of special medicinal side dishes, condiments, drinks, and special preparations. These home-care products are usually used for a very short time, depending on the nature of the individual's symptoms and condition. They are employed to alleviate specific, acute or troubling discomfort the individual may be experiencing. Examples of such special needs include: headaches, earaches, stomachaches and the like, fever, swellings, fatigue, skin discharges, digestive difficulties, problems with elimination, fat accumulations, and, for women, menstrual irregularities. Each of these problems is actually a symptom rather than a particular sickness. While the underlying cause is gradually eliminated with a balanced dietary practice and way of life, these and other discomforts can be helped with medicinal food preparations.

A host of first-aid type preparations can also be made from ingredients and equipment commonly found in the home. For details, readers are referred to *Macrobiotic Home Remedies*, by Michio Kushi, edited by Marc Van Cauwenberghe, M.D., Japan Publications, Inc., 1985.

Energetics of Food

We have already seen that body organs exist in a complementary energy relationship. Organs with a more yang, physically compact structure are formed and nourished with proportionally more yin energy, and organs with a more yin, physically expanded structure, are nourished with a more yang energy. There is an extension to this principle. Within the body, the expanding and upward-moving Earth's force activates the right side of the body, and the contracting, downward-moving Heaven's force activates the left side.

In general, organs located on the right side of the body are thus nourished by Earth's force, and organs on the left side are nourished by Heaven's force. This is, of course, a generalization. Do not forget that, reflecting the macrobiotic principle that nothing is completely yang or completely yin, both sides of the body, and all organs, receive both energies. As a rule of thumb, the organs and glands that come in pairs, including the lungs, kidneys, and testicles or ovaries, are activated by the energy related to the particular side of the body they are on. Thus, the left lung, kidney, testicle and ovary are governed by Heaven's force, and vice versa.

The heart and small intestine, situated toward the center, are affected in a similar manner. The right side of the small intestine, and the right chambers of the heart are activated more by Earth's force, and the respective left sides by Heaven's force. The same holds true for the large intestine. The ascending colon and part of the transverse colon receive more Earth's force, and the left section of the transverse colon, the descending colon and the rectum receive proportionally more Heaven's force.

The exceptions are the spleen/pancreas and the gallbladder. Due to their physical structure and close physical and energetic association with their paired organs, these organs do not follow the above pattern. The polarity between these organs and their energetic partners (the stomach and liver respectively) is much less than the other organ pairs. Thus, the spleen/pancreas, although located on the left side, is nourished by slightly more Earth's force, and the gallbladder, located on the right side, receives more Heaven's force.

In a corresponding way, foods can be broadly classified as having either one of these two general affects on the body. Consuming too much of those foods that have the expanding or yin energy and that activate the right side of the body, will weaken the function of the left side. This happens because the left side needs the more contractive force for its activities, but it is not being sufficiently supplied. If we eat too much of those foods that have the contractive or yang effect and that activate the left side of the body, the right side will weaken. In this case the more yin force of earth is deficient, causing troubles in the functions on the right side of the body.

Diabetes mellitus, for instance, is related to the pancreas, which is located on the left side of the body. If an individual consumes extremely yin foods, or even good-quality yin foods in excess and over an extended period, the resulting excess of yin energy will produce a deficiency of the yang force and the left side of the body will begin to weaken. The activity of the pancreas will gradually be disrupted by the overabundance of yin and, depending on the individual's constitution, problems with high blood sugar may develop.

If extremely yang foods are consumed, or too much good-quality yang foods, there will be a deficiency of the yin force, and the right side will suffer. In this situation, the functions of the liver will gradually be disrupted, and related problems, such as jaundice may begin to appear.

Of course, in their extreme, each of these energies will negatively affect their related side of the body. Continuing the above example, a habitual intake of excessive yin items may eventually disrupt the functions of the liver, as illustrated in the case of cirrhosis caused by alcohol abuse. The immoderate consumption of more yang items can create hardness and tightness of the pancreas, leading to hypoglycemia, or low blood sugar.

Atmospheric Energetics

The opposite portions of a twenty-four hour day—the daytime and the nighttime—also reflect this two-sided energetic tendency. Sometimes symptoms arise in the morning, when the atmospheric energy is expanding and rising. Other times, symptoms appear in the evening when the energy is contracting and descending. And of course, some symptoms appear throughout the day.

When problems arise in the morning, the cause is most often an individual's extreme yang condition. Although the atmospheric energy is rising and expanding, the individual's energy orientation is more downward and contracted. His condition is resisting the natural forces, and pain and other symptoms are the result.

In the opposite cause, if the atmospheric energy is rising, the individual's energy could be rising also, but much more rapidly and beyond the range of the atmosphere's motion. The cause in this instance is extreme yin. This situation is less common than the first case, but it too produces imbalances and their consequent complaints.

In the afternoon the atmospheric energy begins to move downward and inward. If symptoms arise in the late afternoon or evening the individual's condition is most likely following the opposite orientation, moving up and outward. In a smaller percentage of cases, the problem may be caused because the individual's condition is contracting faster and beyond the atmospheric motion. This would be caused by excessively yang factors.

If our condition resists the larger atmospheric motion, or if it goes beyond it, physical and mental problems arise as a warning of our imbalance. To relieve such problems, the individual's condition must be brought into harmony with the larger motions of life. To accomplish this, food can be used very specifically according to its energetic nature.

Until recently this understanding was utilized at mealtimes. For instance, cultures around the world ate a porridge-type dish for breakfast. The energy of the soft, moist grain reflected the rising atmospheric motion in the early morning. Nowadays, many people start the day with eggs sprinkled with refined salt, toasted bread, and salt-cured ham or bacon, all of which have an extremely contracting effect on the body. As a result, they seek balance in orange juice, coffee, white sugar, pepper, ketchup, jams, and milk, all of which have an extremely expansive effect.

At dinner time, when the atmospheric energy is moving inward and downward, meals tend to be heavier and more elaborate. This again is a reflection of our instinctive recognition of the movement of the natural world.

Using the Five Transformations of Energy

By employing the principles of the five stages of energy transformation, we can use food to deal specifically with certain organs, systems, and physical complaints, as well as with emotional, mental, and spiritual disorders. We have seen how everything in creation develops through the interaction of both expanding (yin) and contracting (yang) energy, which can be further divided into five sub-stages. This division conveys more detailed information and allows more subtle adjustments.

Suppose, for instance, that the stomach is troubled. The stomach and its paired organ the spleen/pancreas represent the downward soil-type of energy. Associated with this phase are certain items from each food category (see section on the Five Transformations in chapter 3).

The grain that supplies a comparable energy is millet, the related type of vegetables are the round ones like onions and cabbage. The taste is the naturally sweet taste of winter squash and other vegetables and grains. In cases where the stomach's energy and function are inactive, or Kyo, we supply these types of food as side dishes, keeping within the standard macrobiotic way of eating. Using the support (mother-child) cycle, we could slightly emphasize items from the active, fire-like category, or mother, thus indirectly nourishing the soil-like energy, or child.

If, however, the problem is caused by an overactive energy or Jitsu condition, supplying more soil-like energy will aggravate the condition. Using the regulating cycle, we have seen that the upward, tree-like energy (grandparent) moderates the soil-type nature (grandchild). Thus, we can supply small amounts of tree-type energy through such foods as wheat and barley, fermented foods, upward-growing vegetables like leeks and scallions, and items with a sour taste like grain vinegar or sauerkraut, to balance the condition.

Using the mother-child relationship, we could also lessen foods in the gathering, metal-like energy stage, the child, thus drawing off excess energy from the spleen and stomach, the mother.

Suppose the individual's problem is more psychological. Perhaps he suffers from depression, which is seriously affecting his character, job performance, or his social interactions. From the five-transformation chart (Table 4) we know that depression is caused by an imbalance in the metal-type of energy, and more particularly of energy stagnation producing a Kyo or hypo condition.

Starting with the basic step of food, we would suggest the inclusion of side dishes that would supply metal-type energy, including rice, vegetables with a more contracting tendency like watercress and carrot tops, and the occasional use of the pungent taste, in the form of gingerroot, leek or scallion greens, and daikon.

Using the mother-child relationship, we could also supply soil-like energy in the form of foods that nourish the spleen, or mother. Energy will thus flow to the child, the lungs and large intestine, which are nourished more by metal-type energy.

At the same time, by using the regulating cycle, we see that the fire-type energy regulates the metal-type of energy. Thus, if the fire-type energy is excessive, and thus inhibiting the lung's metal-like energy, we could make dietary suggestions that would temporarily reduce this influence.

On the psychological level, we could encourage the characteristics of metal-type energy that reflect a balanced condition, including a more optimistic outlook, the confidence that one can make positive changes in his condition, and a more practical approach to life. Through the support cycle, we could also encourage the characteristics associated with the soil-like energy, including a sense of resourcefulness, and the understanding of others, thus promoting compassion for himself as well as for others.

It is important to remember that the use of the various cycles and the manipulation of energy to or from one organ to another must be based on an understanding of the individual's overall condition. Otherwise we may inadvertently stimulate an already excessive (Jitsu) condition, or sedate an already deficient (Kyo) one. The possibility also exists that new imbalances could be created. In addition, there is the danger of becoming too complicated in our thinking and approach. This will almost certainly generate additional problems.

Body and Food Correspondences

The vegetable and animal kingdom exist in a large complementary relationship. For instance, the leaves of a plant are more expanded. They absorb carbon dioxide and release oxygen. Performing the task of respiration in humans, the alveoli directly correspond to a plant's leaves. They are very contracted, and take in oxygen while giving out carbon dioxide. The blood of animals is red, and is based on hemoglobin. The color of plants is green and is based on chlorophyll.

Plants (and other food items) and bodily organs that resemble one another in structure are created by a similar quality of energy. Such foods can thus be used to strengthen the function of the organs they correlate with. Traditional peoples recognized this relationship, and numerous examples of its uses can be found in the folklore and healing practices of particular regions.

In the extreme, this idea has been extended to eating the organs of certain animals to fortify the same organ in the human body. Eating chicken liver to nourish the human liver is an example. Because mammals and birds are so close to humans on the evolutionary ladder, this practice is not advisable. Although it may help a particular organ, it is likely to harm other organs, as the energetic effect of mammals and birds is very strong. Fish and seafood, being further away on the evolutionary scale, may be used in this way however.

Clams and more particularly cherrystone clams, resemble the structure of the human liver. Their energetic nature is thus comparable, and they can be used to aid the liver's function. Taking three or four cherrystone clams in a bowl of miso soup has traditionally been used in Japan for this purpose. Dried shiitake mushrooms are another example of a structural and energetic correspondence with the liver. They too will enhance the function of the liver.

Beans share a corresponding form and energetic nature to the kidneys. They nourish the kidneys, and in cases of kidney problems can be used medicinally to strengthen the function of these bean-shaped organs. The structure of lotus root resembles that of the lungs. In Oriental countries, lotus root has been a specific remedy in cases of lung problems. Ginseng is another example. Because the mature root often takes the shape of the human body, the ancient Orientals maintained that it could be used for overall rejuvenation.

There are, of course, an abundance of other examples. Each geographical area produces distinct food items that reflect the structure of the human body, and individual cultures developed a variety of recommendations for their use. This collective wisdom presents an interesting challenge for us in the twentieth century. It would be a mistake to suppose that such remedies will work across the board, in all cases of headaches, for instance, or in a more serious example, for every type of cancer. As we now know, all general categories can be divided into the complemental aspects of yin and yang, depending on their nature. This is as true for medicinal applications as it is for classes of illnesses. Treatments of particular problems will consequently differ according to their cause. More will be said on this important point in the chapter on herbal medicine.

Treating Symptoms with Food

Using the principles that: (1) large yang attracts small yang and large yin attracts small yin, and (2) likes repel one another to maintain balance, there is an additional way of dealing temporarily with symptoms of imbalance. In the case of a yang sickness, besides each of the methods discussed above, we can give either small yang to make the condition less extreme, or we can give large yang to neutralize it.

As an example of the latter alternative, if a high fever develops as the result of eating extreme yin, such as sugar or honey, we could give a good-quality yin preparation to stimulate the very active elimination of yin. Then, instead of fever, which is a vigorous discharge of excess heat and energy, the discharge takes the form of liquid and is more quickly released through urination and perspiration.

This principle is used unconsciously by modern doctors when they recommend aspirin for a fever. Aspirin is an extremely yin substance, as shown by its effects on the body—dilation of blood vessels and a reduction in the ability of the blood to clot are just two examples. Such intensely yin effects enable the body to quickly discharge the excess energy of a fever. However, the extreme by-products of this process can have profound effects on the body. A much better preparation would be bancha tea simmered several minutes with raw, grated daikon, with a small amount of tamari soy sauce added at the end. Taken two to three times a day, this drink will accelerate discharge through perspiration, thus reducing the fever.

We have now discussed six ways to use food in healing:

1. Bringing daily diet into a broad balance by means of the standard macrobiotic way of eating.

2. Making specific and temporary adjustments in the standard dietary approach in conjunction with the individual's condition.
3. Suggesting medicinal home-care dishes and preparations for short-term use.
4. Using the Five Transformations of Energy cycle to make precise adjustments, via such energies as taste and the inclusion of items from each general food category.
5. Using foods with a similar structure and thus energy quality as the organ we wish to strengthen.
6. In cases of active symptoms, using either large or small yin or yang to neutralize them.

A further approach also exists. As an offshoot of dietary adjustment, plants and other substances found in one's immediate locale have been used for many thousands of years for healing purposes. In the following chapter we will outline the principles that make herbal medicine a practical and effective treatment for symptomatic relief.

2. Herbal Medicine

The use of substances readily available in one's environment for medicinal purposes seems to be a universal practice. Peoples around the world and throughout history have accumulated a huge body of information detailing the healing properties of locally found plants, animals, and minerals. Oriental and Occidental reference books listing the medicinal uses of naturally occurring items, contain thousands of entries. Acquiring an understanding of the nature of these substances, their uses, combinations, possible side effects, and preparation methods, takes years of study and experience.

This chapter will serve as an introduction to the principles and basic methods of application, rather than cataloging names of plants and what they are commonly used for. Knowing why a preparation works, students and practitioners can learn to judge the yin and yang nature of particular remedies, and their effects on the body, instead of relying on standardized prescriptions. With this background, readers will be in a position to make preparations at home to relieve many discomforts. It should be remembered, however, that herbal medicine is a symptomatic treatment, and, although capable of providing temporary relief, it cannot change the underlying cause of an illness. For this, basic dietary and lifestyle adjustments, along with self-reflection are required.

Modern and Traditional Uses of Herbs

The recent resurgence of interest in the medicinal use of wild plants and herbs is a welcome shift in the way we approach medications. It reflects a growing acceptance of personal responsibility for one's state of health, and the search for therapeutic treatments that enhance the body's own healing abilities. Clearly, this course is in part a reaction against what is perceived as the dangerous products of the modern pharmaceutical industry. This trend is certainly a positive one, and credit should be given to those scholars and practitioners who have kept the art of herbal medicine alive, often in the face of criticism, ridicule, neglect, and in some cases, legal persecution. And yet, along with this popularization comes the risk of using herbal medicine with the same blind faith that we now invest in conventional medications. This highlights the dangers of application or practice without a broad-based understanding rooted in a comprehensive theory.

There is an expanding industry growing up around the use of herbs. This benefits us all by bringing the value of herbal medicine into wide public awareness, disseminating useful information, and making products readily available. However, companies and health-care specialists who are recommending such preparations for medicinal purposes often do so without an understanding of the traditional principles upon which their use was based. There are now full-page advertisements enumerating the benefits of individual items, products transported to areas vastly removed, in terms of climate and geography, from where they were grown, and questionable growing and processing practices. Most distressing of all, recommendations for use too often take the form of rote prescriptions, with no consideration for individual condition or circumstances. At its very best, this practice can lead to frustration and needless expense. At its worst, it can be dangerous.

In the past, a body of general recommendations developed within specific regions, and for the most part, such suggestions proved effective. This was before modern transportation, refrigeration, and food-preservation systems made it possible to violate the environmental principle of eating foods grown in the geographical area in which one lived. Now, tropical products, including fruits, sugar, chocolate, spices, coffee, tea, numerous vegetables, and a host of other food items, are consumed in four-season climates on a daily basis, even in the colder times of year. In the opposite case, people living in warmer climates daily consume grilled steaks, hamburgers, smoked ham, fried eggs, and other items that generate heat and energy in amounts that are far excessive for their particular environment.

When the choice of foods was limited to what grew in one's locale, specific folk remedies were largely effective for the problems that developed in that area. This was because illnesses generally reflected an imbalanced adaptation to the local environment. For example, in the colder New England area, an apple-cider-vinegar-and-honey beverage was highly regarded for its healing properties, especially in the spring season. This is a very yin preparation. It helped to balance an extremely yang condition caused by a dietary pattern characterized by the consumption of excess salt, animal food, and hard, salty cheeses. Such a yin drink could help to temporarily balance an overly yang condition and relieve its symptoms. Yet it would not be appropriate for a warmer region where problems were generally caused by an excessive consumption of yin. This example illustrates the futility of transporting specific remedies from different climatic regions without adapting them to local conditions.

We have seen that illness can be caused by either extreme yin or extreme yang, or by a combination of both. A substance that may help with a problem caused by extreme yin will be useless in the opposite or more yang-caused case. And in fact, it may aggravate it. There is one additional consideration in this scenario. In the previous chapter we explained how the use of aspirin is a reflection of the principle that at its extreme, yin will produce or turn into its opposite. A yin herbal preparation may work in the temporary and symptomatic relief of problems caused by extreme yin. Used with understanding and care, this can be a practical, short-term solution to an acute condition. The dangers of this strategy must be realized, however, lest the cause be ignored and the problem compounded.

Value of Herbal Medicines

In traditional societies, herbal medicine was used with caution and respect, much as prescription medications were treated in the industrial nations just a generation or two ago. Even in cases of serious illness, the use of herbal preparations was often deemed not to be the wisest approach. More often, change of dietary and lifestyle habits were enough. Today, when many of our problems are produced by degenerative disorders that develop over many years, it should come as no surprise that herbal remedies can offer only limited relief, or may not be effective at all.

Herbal medicine was generally used for the temporary relief of acute symptoms or when the processes of digestion and/or elimination were in some way not working well. Such preparations were consequently perceived as having temporary value in extraordinary cases. Today, many people, mistakenly thinking that anything "natural" is by definition good, routinely and repeatedly take herbal medications. This can be just as dangerous as habitually using any other form of medicine because:

1. It masks the symptoms, thus giving the false impression that the condition has improved.
2. It ignores the side effects these special preparations may produce when they are taken over an extended period of time.
3. It reflects the attitude of short-term relief while ignoring the more basic long-term adjustments that are required to eliminate the underlying cause. Such an attitude is simply an extension of our quick-fix mentality, and often amounts to little more than a herbal variation of "pill popping."

Standards of Application

The general standards employed in the use of herbal medicine in traditional and Oriental societies can be summed up as follows:

1. The medication should work efficiently and have no unwanted or unexpected side effects. This type of medication is called *Jo Yaku* (上薬), or high-grade medicine in Japanese. *Jo* means high, and *Yaku* means medicine. Medicines that occasionally cause side effects—depending on the individual, the amount prescribed, and the duration of use—are called *Chu Yaku* (中薬), or middle-grade medicine. When a medicine is effective yet generally produces side effects, it is known as *Ge Yaku* (下薬), or low-grade medicine. Physicians confined themselves to the first and second grades unless the patient's condition or circumstances required otherwise.

2. Products used as medications should be taken from the immediate environment. In addition, they should be easily obtainable, economical, and assessable to all. Exotic or rare ingredients were little valued, an attitude strikingly different from that commonly seen today.

3. Depending on the circumstances and one's level of understanding, practically anything can be used as a medicine. The range of ingredients used in herbal medicine thus includes trees and shrubs, minerals, and animals, as well as plants. The application of this precept requires a deep understanding of the principles discussed in earlier chapters, beginning with the dynamics of yin and yang. Actually, this particular tenet is used all the time, although unconsciously, in daily life.

Someone suffering from low blood sugar, for instance, drinks a cup of coffee, probably with the addition of cream and one or more teaspoons of sugar. This brings the sugar level in the blood up, and the individual receives a burst of energy enabling him to continue his daily routine. In this case, coffee (caffeine), white sugar (sucrose), and milk sugar (lactose) are the medications that temporarily relieve the symptoms of low blood sugar. Unfortunately, this behavior violates the other four principles of medication.

4. Only the minimum amount of medicine found to be effective should be taken, and even then, medications should be used for the shortest possible time. This concept applies even to the highest grade of medicine, which does not produce undesirable side effects. This eliminates the possibility of a patient becoming addicted to short-term help at the expense of long-term healing. It has the additional benefit of cutting the cost of treatment.

5. The medicinal properties of preparations should be understood from the perspective of Ki. That is to say, the basis for considering the effectiveness of a particular remedy is the evaluation of its energetic nature. This is a major point, and more needs to be said about it.

When trying to judge the potency or effectiveness of a plant, the scientific method is to break down and chemically analyze it in the effort to isolate and extract the volatile or operative factor. This so-called wonder ingredient is then either produced synthetically or removed from the plant, combined with fillers, and marketed in tablet, liquid, or other form. Although effective to some small degree, this is a clumsy and wasteful practice which pales in comparison to the sophisticated application of our ancestors. It more often than not creates side effects as harmful as those intended to be helped.

As readers are by now aware, the traditional orientation is inseparably grounded on the understanding of Ki. In this regard, the practice of herbal medicine is based on: (1) the ability to determine the overall quality of energy of a particular plant, and each of its parts, and (2) the prescribing of specific remedies according to their energetic effect on the body.

The fundamental concept of Oriental medicine is harmony between the body and mind, and between the individual and the environment near and far. This is the foundation and common denominator linking acupuncture, massage, prayer, and all other forms of traditional medical treatment. Each is concerned with the balancing of Ki, either activating or sedating it. Consequently, when determining the effectiveness of a substance, its overall energetic effect should be the primary concern.

Traditional and Modern Approaches Compared

The complementary relation of traditional and modern approaches to medications can easily be distinguished when modern medicine is assessed with the above principles.

- *Traditional View:* No unwanted side effects.

Current Approach: Both layman and medical professionals are becoming aware of the dangerous side effects of over-the-counter and prescription medications. There are actually cases in which a medication can cause the same side effects as the condition it is intended to relieve.

We should be aware that anything we take into our body can produce side effects—broadly defined as any effect other than the intended one. In the case of medications, the question for physicians is, are these effects an acceptable price to pay for the relief of a particular symptom. In far too many cases they are not.

Inexpensive paperback guides are now available that list the precautions, side effects, and adverse effects of various prescription and over-the-counter drugs. Readers are encouraged to consult such a book before taking any drug, or simply to gain an appreciation of the price we pay for symptomatic relief.

- *Traditional View:* Use common substances from one's immediate environment.
  Current Approach: Our medications are produced in laboratories and factories, and can be ruinously expensive. This is as true for so-called natural preparations as it is for medicines falling into the more conventional category. Too often, we use herbs grown in vastly different climatic and geographical areas from where we live. And, we seek out rare and unusual ingredients in favor of the commonplace.

- *Traditional View:* Recommendations are based on the principles of nature.
  Current Approach: Lacking the understanding of the dynamics of yin and yang, we not only limit the range of medicines available for use, we inhibit the function of those we do take, and, in many cases, complicate the condition with inappropriate treatments.

- *Traditional View:* Minimum amount used for shortest possible duration.
  Current Approach: Hundreds of thousands of individuals take daily doses of medications for extended periods of time. And often, as time goes on, instead of lowering the amount and the strength, these two factors must be increased to cope with a deteriorating condition. Often, additional medications are prescribed to offset the possible ill effects of the primary medication.

- *Traditional View:* Know the energetic nature of the item used.
  Current Approach: The effectiveness of medications is thought to be due to certain nutritional or chemical compounds. Synthetic substitutes are regarded as being identical to naturally occurring substances. The concept of Ki is not considered.

Principles of Use

Traditional healers recognized that physical or psychological symptoms are reflections of imbalances of the body's energy system. Diagnosis was thus geared toward uncovering this imbalance, and treatments were designed to correct it. The primary categorization of energy is the polarities of yin and yang. Illnesses were classified according to these energies, and remedies were chosen in a similar fashion.

Table 13 Yin and Yang in the Plant Kingdom

	Yin (▽) Centrifugal	Yang (△) Centripetal
Environment:	Warmer, more tropical	Colder, more polar
Season:	Grows more in spring and summer	Grows more in autumn and winter
Soil:	More watery and sedimentary	More dry and volcanic
Growing direction:	Vertically growing upward; expanding horizontally underground	Vertically growing downward; expanding horizontally above the ground
Growing speed:	Growing faster	Growing slower
Size:	Larger, more expanded	Smaller, more compacted
Height:	Taller	Shorter
Texture:	Softer	Harder
Water content:	More juicy and watery	More dry
Color:	Purple—blue—green—yellow—brown—orange—red	
Odor:	Stronger smell	Less smell
Taste:	Spicy——sour——sweet——salty——bitter	
Chemical components:	More K and other yin elements Less Na and other yang elements	Less K and other yin elements More Na and other yang elements

All preparations that fall within the grouping of herbal medicine can likewise be classified according to their yin or yang properties. The classification of the energetic nature of specific herbs and plants was based on multiple factors rather than being limited to a single consideration such as size or color. Table 13 includes some of the criteria used in determining whether a particular plant, or individual parts of that plant, were more yin or yang.

Each section of a single plant can likewise be judged to be relatively more yin or yang. In descending order, from most yang to most yin, the individual parts of a plant are: seed, root, main stem or trunk, branches, twigs, leaves, flower, fruit.

Atmospheric factors also influence the quality of a plant as a whole and of each of its parts. The result is that at different times of the day, month, and year, the same plant will vary in the degree to which it is yin or yang: sometimes being more so, other times being less so. For instance, on a sunny day, the yang influence of heat and light will draw moisture upward, making the part of the plant above ground and toward the periphery more yin, and leaving the roots drier, and thus more yang. At night these qualities will be reversed. Moisture moves inward and downward, making the upper part more yang than it is during the daylight hours, and the roots more yin. And, after a rain, a plant will be more lush and thus more yin, while during a dry spell it will be harder and drier and thus more yang.

The same dynamics work throughout the full- and new-moon portions of the lunar cycle. During the full moon, moisture will be drawn upward, and during the new moon, the moisture will settle in the lower sections. In a similar way, the same plant picked in the spring, summer, and fall will have different energetic, nutritional, and chemical effects.

By understanding these influences, we have at our disposal an immense range of energetic qualities for medicinal use. In addition, preparation methods provide further flexibility. Table 14 lists examples of how the quality of a substance can be altered to make it more yin or more yang.

Table 14 Ways to Adjust Yin and Yang Qualities

	Yin Influence	Yang Influence
Selection	Pick in the morning to mid-afternoon	Pick from late afternoon to late night
	Pick as the moon nears full	Pick near the new moon
	Pick in spring/summer	Pick in autumn/winter
	Use stems/leaves	Use roots/branches
Preparation	Soak the plant	Dry the plant
	Use raw	Cook the plant
	Use fresh	Store before use
Cooking	Shorter-time	Longer-time
	Low temperature	High temperature
	Add sweetener	Add salt
	Quick boil, steam	Dry roast, grill, bake, boil long time

Five Transformations of Energy

Besides classifying herbal medications into general yin and yang categories, a more detailed division can be produced with the five transformations of energy. The five general effects on the body of various preparations were classified in a number of ways. In terms of body temperature, five general influences were seen to be produced by different qualities of Ki. Remember that a more active energy flow generally produces warmer temperatures, while a less active flow generates cooler temperatures. The distinctive qualities of temperature a substance could generate within the body were classified as: cold, cool, plain, warm, and hot.

Another type of influence is the direction in which a medication affects the body's energy flow. Possibilities include: a downward effect, an inward effect, a balancing effect, an outward effect, and an upward effect. This means that Ki can be adjusted in various specific ways according to individual needs.

Variations in taste, color, texture, shape, and other qualities can similarly be grouped into the five stages of energy. The five transformations cycle generates a huge number of specific effects to choose from. As long as the principles are understood, a practitioner can flexibly prepare medications to suit the needs of the patient both at his initial visit, and as his condition changes over the course of the illness.

With this range of options, energetic effects can be appropriately matched to the related symptoms or set of symptoms. For example, problems can be classed into one of two general categories: (1) Kyo or yin conditions manifesting in a more inactive and chronic type of symptom—such as hardening, stagnation, cysts and stones, weakness, a pale complexion, and the sensation of being cold; (2) Jitsu or more yang conditions appearing as more active and acute symptoms—such as fever, swelling, coughing, heat, and redness.

It is also possible to distinguish five general categories for any particular symptom. This includes temperature, body area affected, and energy level. In the case of pain, the five stages are: (1) sharp, (2) strong, (3) moderate, (4) dull, and (5) mild.

With this kind of orientation, the immediate nature and cause of the presenting symptoms can be identified and treated in very specific ways, and steps can be taken to alter the underlying cause.

Preparations

Depending on the nature of the problem, and the judgment of the practitioner, herbal medicines can consist of a single ingredient, a combination of several ingredients, or a more complex mixture. When using multiple ingredients, physicians recognized the need to create a relative balance in the preparation to facilitate its intended affect. In application, this is a throwback to the principle that everything contains both yin and yang, and that nothing can consist solely of one of these qualities.

In Oriental medicine, this understanding was summed up in the concept known as *Kun-Shin-Sa-Shi*, (君臣佐使) or Lord, Minister, Assistant, and Servant. This states that the efficacy of a particular preparation depends on the interaction of complementary properties. The implication is that for effective operation, a blend of both yin and yang qualities are necessary. In a two ingredient, overall yin preparation, the primary yin ingredient would be complemented by the addition of a lesser amount of yang. This helps to activate and accentuate the general yin effect, much as a small amount of salt is used in cooking to bring out the sweetness of grains and vegetables.

In a more complicated mixture, this concept would be extended to include a smaller volume of yin and an even smaller volume of yang. For a yang preparation, these qualities would be reversed. This relationship is depicted in Figure 52.

Fig. 52 Combination of Yin and Yang in Herbal Preparations

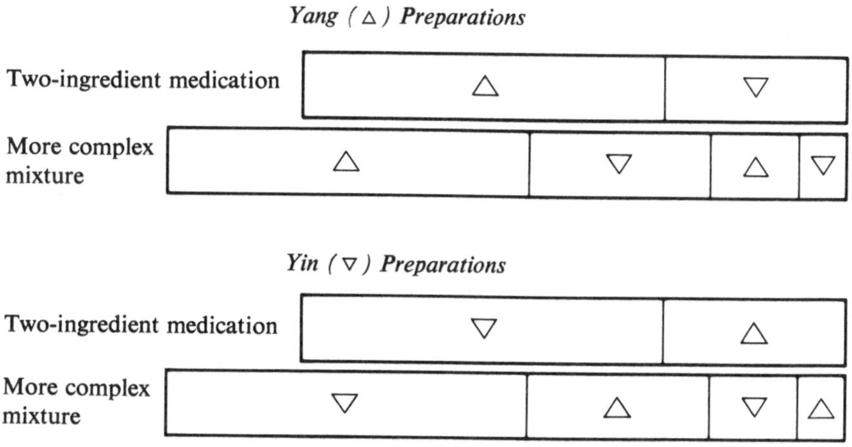

Yang (△) Preparations

Two-ingredient medication	△	▽		
More complex mixture	△	▽	△	▽

Yin (▽) Preparations

Two-ingredient medication	▽	△		
More complex mixture	▽	△	▽	△

The above proportions vary according to a physician's judgment and the patient's need.

Conclusion

As members of the animal kingdom, human beings exist in a polar relationship with the vegetable world. Without the nourishment of plants we could not exist. Although we use vegetable products in many areas of our lives—from clothing to building material for our homes, from our daily newspaper to fragrances for our perfumes—we seldom consider the implications of this dependence.

Traditional societies, living much closer to nature than we do today, appreciated and recognized this bond. They intuitively grasped the principles of life. With the experience gleaned from thousands of years of applying these tenets, they learned to utilize the products of their environment to adapt to and flourish within their particular setting. A culture's unique cuisines, medicinal cooking, and specific herbal medications reflect this accommodation honed to a fine art.

Today, we have lost this understanding. We divorce ourselves from our environment to whatever extent, and in whatever ways we can afford. We have no appreciation for the partner that makes our lives possible, and no recognition of the principles that regulate our existence.

But this can change. All that is needed is the desire to be healthy, and the wish to make this world a better place for each of its inhabitants, in whatever form they exists. The tools we use in this personal and global transformation are the unifying principles of life and their application to all aspects of daily life, starting with daily diet. If it would not be so simple, it could not work.

3. Prayer

In this and the following chapter we will learn to make adjustments in the quality and intensity of the body's Ki by employing the vibrations of sound, the power of the mind, and the energy streaming from the hands. Through these (and related) techniques, problems of both a physical and mental nature can be dealt with practically and precisely. Not limited to healing, however, we will also review ways to utilize Ki to enhance our own overall condition, thus supporting personal growth, or the development of consciousness.

Based on the dynamics of yin and yang, these practices are uncomplicated yet effective. And, as we shall see, they nourish the giver as well as the receiver. They have the additional benefit of focusing our attention on the reality of Ki, thus widening our perception of, and participation in, the huge process that is life.

The concept of prayer encompasses two broad complementary categories: (1) the more yang vocalization of sounds, words, and chants, and (2) the more yin use of the mind, via thoughts, meditations, and visualizations. Each of these components, and the variations they encompass, employs modifications in the quality of Ki to achieve specific effects on the body and psyche. In this chapter we will discuss the vocal form of prayer. The principles of using the mind to manipulate energy, which can be called silent prayer, will then be addressed.

How We Use Sound

To some degree, we all vary the qualities of our voice in response to the demands of the diverse situations we pass through during the day. Humans routinely and instinctively use such alterations to produce specific effects on themselves, others, and in their immediate surroundings. Picture if you can an adult addressing an infant in the tone of voice he uses when speaking to a friend. Or reverse the situation. Try visualizing an adult speaking to a co-worker in the same way he would to a three-year-old child. These are comical images, impossible to take seriously. In these simple examples, we see the energy of sound being altered to match, respectively, the vibrations of the young child and the adult. In a similar way, we become quiet, reverent, or boisterous according to the setting we are in, such as a doctor's office, a church or synagogue, or an athletic event.

The fact is, everyone modifies the energy of the sounds they produce—and numerous other behavioral aspects—to harmonize with the circumstances they find themselves in. This is a sign of flexibility and adaptability, which is another way of describing health. Life is, after all, a process in which we constantly adjust to the ceaseless patterns of change we pass through, over the course of a day, a season, a year, a lifetime.

Since ancient times, prayer, in the form of chants and song, has been used in healing practices. This is equally true for the chanting medicine man, the suffering individual, petitioning God for relief, and the concerned parent singing a lullaby to soothe an ailing child. In addition, humanity has routinely employed sound to express, exult, or ease the human condition. One need only consult the hymn- or praybook of his particular faith to see the range of human needs expressed vocally. There are songs and prayers for weddings and funerals, baptisms and coming of age, of confession and penance, thankfulness and celebration, and for each major stage in an individual's, family's, or community's life. Until fairly recent times, almost all peoples chanted or sung their holy scriptures. And, in earlier times, oral transmission was the only means by which specific teachings, traditions, and legends were preserved and passed from one generation to the next.

Sound as Energy

Sound is of course a vibration, as is the physical body, the other dimensions of the Self, and all objects and processes. The various tones and pitches humans are capable of producing generate different frequencies of energy which can be used to harmonize, activate, or sedate these states. This is the basis of our ability to make mental and physical adjustments with the voice. Particular sound vibrations influence and correlate to specific chakras, meridians, systems, and organs. They consequently affect individual physical and psychological attributes.

The qualities and effects of sound fall into two complementary categories: yin and yang, with a wide range in-between. Higher-pitched, more yang sounds, are produced with a closed mouth. They generate vibrations at a faster speed, and produce a more alert and active state. Corresponding to the compact head region, the more yang sounds activate the brain and its functions, as well as the throat, midbrain and crown chakras.

Lower, more yin sounds, are produced with an open mouth. They produce a slower rate of vibration and generate a more relaxed state. This quality of Ki is related to the trunk of the body in general. Specifically, the more yin sounds activate the organs, glands and functions in the lower trunk, and the genital and abdominal energy centers.

Sounds falling into the mid-range activate body parts and functions located in the middle of the trunk, along with the solar plexus and heart chakras. Such sounds are produced with a half-opened mouth.

As a general rule of thumb, yin sounds are used to help relax and soothe a more tight condition, as when one is experiencing undue stress. In the opposite case, yang sounds can be used to alleviate an overly loose and expanded condition, as evidenced when one is having difficulty concentrating. The more balanced sounds help to produce a centered state. Specific uses of yin and yang sounds will be discussed shortly.

Physiologically, the mechanism of human sound involves the resonating cavities in the head, the larynx, lungs and diaphragm, and the vibrations produced by the vocal cords, throat muscles and uvula. However, the energies which create sound vibrations originate in the forces of Heaven and Earth. Thus, when our personal condition is in harmony with these large forces, our sounds and words represent the power of life itself. Under such circumstances, our verbal expression conveys an accurate vision of nature, and can have a powerful influence on ourselves, others, and our surroundings.

True sound is the precise energetic representation of an object or process. Such intonations have a certain meaning, power, and influence on the physical and spiritual world. There exists in the folklore of both the East and West the belief that if one knows the true "name" or sound of a thing, one can understand its nature, and make use of its attributes. In the Bible there are numerous references to the power of the spoken word, including this excerpt from Proverbs, 25: 11 "A word fitly spoken is like apples of gold in pictures of silver."

It is in the opening verses of *The Gospel According to John*, however, that we find perhaps the most succinct expression of the influence and significance of sound in our lives: "In the beginning was the Word, and the Word was with God, and the Word was God. . . . And the Word was made flesh, and dwelt among us (and we beheld his glory, the glory as of the only begotten of the Father), full of grace and truth."

In the scheme of the macrocosm and microcosm, all objects and phenomenon exist simultaneously on each level of life. Because everything is a reflection of Ki existing at different rates of vibration—from the most condensed vibratory rate to the most refined—all things can be expressed in manifold ways and in various dimensions. In the world of art, for example, portraits express, with light waves, the character of the individual represented, and landscape paintings distill the essence of the depicted scene. In the concert hall, the classic works of music accomplish the same effect with the vibrations of sound. These examples are no different than what each of us does on a day-to-day level. That is to say, we express our individual qualities of body and mind via the words we choose and the manner in which we vocalize them. Our vocal expression thus reflects the energetic quality of our physical, emotional, intellectual, and spiritual consciousness.

Readers are reminded of the discovery by Dr. Rutherford mentioned in Part 1 of this book. When the frequency of a thing is altered, its structure immediately changes in response. Thus, if we can adjust, by whatever means, the quality of our own or another's energy, we can make profound changes in the physical and spiritual qualities that are expressions of that energy.

It was on this basis that traditional societies developed a refined understanding detailing the influence that sound has on our lives. Our ancestors recognized that sound could be used to manipulate the body's Ki in very precise ways. They used the voice, and other sources of sound, to enhance particular qualities. Medicinally, this concept was extended to the treatment of a wide range of physical and psychological disorders.

We have seen that physical illness is a reflection of imbalanced energy. By using various sounds and chants, this disharmony can be adjusted, not just generally, but in specific ways to suit the individual condition. The theoretical foundation of this practice is no different than that used in herbal medicine, massage, acupuncture, or any other therapeutic technique that makes adjustments in the flow of Ki. It is simply the application, or the means employed to alter energy, that differs.

Many people believe that certain words or chants have an inherent, and mysterious power, and in a sense this is true. Certain sounds or combinations of sounds do have power, especially when repeated often and regularly. But there is nothing mysterious or magical about these effects if we understand the concept of Ki, the principles of yin and yang, and the energetics of the body.

The Basic Sounds

Although the spoken language now differs from culture to culture, all languages share a common origin. This may sound like an unnecessarily broad assertion, but if we remember that we all have a common heritage—the seven-orbited spiral of physical development—and share a similar energetic and physical structure based on the planet's own energetic body, the fact of an intuitive and collective pattern of expression will not seem so surprising. The Biblical account of the Tower of Babel is a metaphorical description of the fragmentation in language that took place many thousands of years ago.

This movement toward diversification in language is in turn a reflection of one-half of the vast historical cycle alternating between unity and uniqueness, as already discussed. Accordingly, with the coming of the complementary era—which is rapidly approaching—we can anticipate the development of a unified language. As societies the world over begin centering their diet and lifestyle on the Unifying Principles, the common source of vocal, and indeed all forms of expression, will come to the fore.

Cultural and regional (as well as individual) variations will of course continue to exist, due to unique environmental and personal conditions. Yet a unified thread will exist within this variety, mirroring humanity's shared heritage.

The basis of sound created by human beings is the flow of the forces of Heaven and Earth within the body. The throat chakra, the area where sound is produced, governs expression and creativity. When our condition is clean and strong, the charge in this and the body's other energy centers is well-balanced, and thus the sound of our words is capable of representing the basic energies of life, and all of the manifestations they create. Under these circumstances, sound becomes a positive and powerful medium for healing and growth.

In the Orient, the art of perceiving and using the power of sound is known as *Koto Dama* (言霊), or "the spirit of words." This translation can be expanded to read "the study and application of the potency of sounds and words." Within the range of the human voice, there are fifty basic sounds, grouped into ten categories according to their energetic nature. Words are produced by the combination of these sounds, and their origin and influence can be discerned by knowing the significance of the particular sounds. The vowels represent the foundation or source of all the other sounds, and thus their relevance has particular meaning.

The consonants are divided into complementary groups—the yang sounds of materialization, K, S, T, and N, and the more yin sounds of spiritualization, R, Y,

Table 15 Vowels and Their Meaning

Letter	Sound	Association
A	ah	Infinity
I	ee	Life, energy, Ki
U	uu	Harmony
E	eh	Creativity, art, expression
O	oh	Matter, materialized state

Table 16 The Fifty Basic Sounds

Microcosm Earth	R	Y	M	H	N	T	S	K	Heaven	Macrocosm
WA	ra	ya	ma	ha	na	ta	sa	ka	A	Infinity
WI	ri	yi	mi	hi	ni	ti	si	ki	I	Life
WU	ru	yu	mu	fu	nu	tu	su	ku	U	Harmony
WE	re	ye	me	he	ne	te	se	ke	E	Creativity
WO	ro	yo	mo	ho	no	to	so	ko	O	Materialization
Sounds of Spiritualization					Sounds of Materialization					

M, and H. Table 16 shows the relationship between these basic sounds. The vowels represent the beginning, essence, or the macrocosm of infinity, and the sounds of "W"—Wa, Wi, Wu, We, and Wo—represent the end result, or the microcosm of infinity. In between, are the various manifestations that develop between these two poles.

The columns running horizontally in Table 16 represent different stages of existence. The vertical lines depict variations in these categories. The information in the chart can be used in the following way. According to the diagram, "K" is the beginning sound, representing movement of straightforward, pure energy. "A" is the sound of infinity. The combination of these two in the sound "Ka" thus produces "infinite, pure energy." Each of the fifty basic sounds can be understood in this way. For example, the meanings of the sounds of "K" are:

- *Ka*—infinite, pure energy
- *Ki*—energy's appearance in life
- *Ku*—very harmonious energy
- *Ke*—pure energy manifesting as art or beautiful expression
- *Ko*—matter, an object manifested of energy

By extending this concept, the inherent meaning or energetic quality of any word can be understood. Examples from the Japanese language include:

- *Ka-Ra-Da* or "body." *Ka* means "infinite, pure energy," *Ra* means "spiralic motion," and *Da*, a variant of *Ta*, means "individualized." Thus, in Japanese, the word "body" means "infinity manifested in individual form (Da) by pure energy (Ka) in a spiralic motion (Ra)."
- *Ya-Sa-I* or "vegetable." *Ya* means "energy extended in all directions." *Sa* means "mild, harmonious energy," and *I* means "life." Thus, the word "vegetable" means "very gently expanding energy, representing life."
- *Su-Ru*, a verb meaning "to do." *Su* means "mild harmony," and *Ru* means "spiralic motion." The verb "to do" hence carries the implication of "acting in a harmonious, spiralic fashion."
- *Ko-Me* or "rice." *Ko* means "pure energy manifested as a small object."

Me means "creatively going in space." Therefore the word for rice means "pure energy being released into the environment."

- *I-Ne* or "rice plant." *I* means "life," and *Ne* means "art." Ancient Japanese apparently regarded the cultivation of rice as the "art of life."

The languages of each civilization can be understood in this manner. For instance, when slightly modified, all English words can be pronounced by using these fifty ancient sounds. The English word "rice," becomes *Ra-I-Su. Ra* means "infinite force, spiralically moving." *I* means "creating life." *Su* means "very harmonious, mild energy." The spirit or connotation of the word "rice" in the English language is "harmonious, spiralically moving energy, that creates life."

When searching for the energetic implication of particular words, remember that it is the spoken form of a language, the pronunciation, and not the written pattern that is of concern.

Healing with Sound

These fifty sounds, and their combinations in the form of words, chants, prayer, and song, can be utilized to adjust an imbalanced state of Ki in any bodily part or function. They can be used to generate or sedate, harmonize, and make peaceful. In a similar manner, sound can help break up stagnation, and disperse any dark, heavy vibrations we may be generating, or that has accumulated in our rooms and home.

The basic areas of application include:

- Overall toning of the primary channel
- Producing general yin or yang effects
- Working with the major organ systems
- Influencing the chakras and their related physiological and psychological effects
- Manipulating the energy of the meridians and organs

Toning of the Primary Channel

As we have seen, the primary channel is our basic connection with the forces of life. The foundation of our health and consciousness depends on the quality of this elemental energy flow in the body. If, along this current, there is hardness or accumulations of fat and mucus, the charge will not run smoothly and strongly, and various physiological and psychological imbalances will begin to manifest. To help reverse this condition, as a general method of tonification, and to promote the growth of personal consciousness, the sound of *Su* (pronounced as the name Sue) can be chanted.

Simply sit in a comfortable position, with the body relaxed and the spine straight—which facilitates the flow of the forces of Heaven and Earth. Breathe out and in several times, and then, on the exhalation, chant *Su* until the breath is expended. Repeat from five to ten times, or more if desired. The hands can be held in prayer position, at the level of the heart. As a comfortable alternative, they can be placed, face up, on the lap, with the left hand resting on the right, and the pads of the thumbs lightly touching.

Performing this simple practice daily will have a deep and harmonizing effect on the flow of Heaven's and Earth's forces within our body.

Balancing the Yin and Yang Functions

We have discussed the body's two primary poles earlier. The abdominal chakra represents the energetically yang (structurally yin) partner in this pair, and the midbrain chakra is the energetically yin (structurally yang) associate.

To stimulate the functions of these respective centers, thereby creating harmony within ourselves, we use the complemental sounds of "Ah" and "Mm." "Ah," pronounced with an open mouth, represents the macrocosm of the infinite universe. It generates a more yin quality of vibration, and thus activates the energetically yang abdominal center. "Mm," voiced with the mouth closed, represents the microcosm, or the infinitesimal manifestation of life. It produces a more yang vibration which nourishes the energetically yin midbrain chakra.

To harmonize these two energetic centers, take a comfortable position, with the spine straight and the body relaxed. After sitting quietly for a minute or so, begin to focus the inhalation downward toward the abdomen. If comfortable, the exhalation should be longer than the inhalation. After five or so such breaths, add the sound of "Ah" on the exhalation. Attention can be directed toward the Hara, or the mind can remain still and empty. Chant five to ten times, or longer if desired, and then sit quietly for a moment before continuing.

Now begin to direct the inhalation upward toward the midbrain. The emphasis should be on the inhalation so that the upper body actually rises slightly as we inhale. Inhalation should be longer than the exhalation. After about five of these breaths, begin to chant the sound of "Mm" with the mouth closed, the lips lightly pressing together. We can either visualize energy moving outward from the center of the brain, or the mind can be kept empty and still. Repeat the sound of "Mm" as many times as the sound of "Ah" was chanted. Then sit quietly for several minutes.

Another method to establish harmony within ourselves, and polarity between ourself, or the microcosm, and Infinity, or the macrocosm, is to chant the sounds of *Fu Hi. Hi* means "spirit" or "fire" in Japanese. It is also the word for the number one. *Fu* means "wind," and "differentiation." In addition, it is the word for the number two.

Together, these sounds reflect the fundamental mechanism of the universe: all phenomena, although appearing to consist of two sides—the front and back discussed earlier—actually are produced by and reflect the oneness of life.

With the spine straight and the body relaxed, sit for a minute or so with an empty mind. Then begin to breathe in through the mouth, making the sound of "Hi" (hee). Imagine that you are taking in energy from the most distant region of the universe. Direct the breath toward the head. On the exhalation, make the sound of "Fu," imagining that you are returning energy to the infinite. Visualize the exhalation originating from the abdominal area and spiraling outward toward distant space. Repeat the entire breath five to ten times, or more, and then sit quietly for several minutes.

This exercise enables us to melt the boundaries between the large and the small Self, thereby generating feelings of oneness and profound peace.

Activating the Organ Systems

The digestive system is structurally more yin, the nervous system is structurally more yang, and the circulatory system exists as a balance between these two. To create a harmony among these functions, the sound of "AUM" can be chanted. As described above, "Ah" stimulates the abdominal chakra, and the digestive system as a whole, along with the lungs and respiratory system. "Uu" is a more balanced sound, and activates the heart region and the circulatory system, together with the related excretory system. "Mm" energizes the midbrain in particular and the nervous system in general.

Sitting in a comfortable position, breathe slowly and deeply three or four times. The mouth can be slightly open. The exhalation should be emphasized, lasting up to three times longer than the inhalation.

Then, on the exhalation, begin to vocalize the sound of "Ah" with a widely opened mouth, with attention focused on the Hara area. Part way through the exhalation, begin to chant the sound of "U," with a more rounded mouth. Attention can center on the heart and upper-body area. Finally, pronounce the sound of "Mm" with a closed mouth. At this time, attention shifts to the midbrain and head. Repeat this chant from five to ten times, and then sit quietly for a minute or two.

The sound of "AUM" harmonizes the functions of the body's systems, and has the additional benefit of stimulating the primary channel.

Activating the Body's Five Basic Energy Centers

From the chart of the fifty basic sounds, we know that the vowels are the primary representations of energy. In sequence, each sound can be classified along a range from yin to yang. Following is a list of the vowels, along with their yin or yang energetic qualities and the chakra that each vowel influences.

Vowel	*Sound*	*Energy*	*Chakra*
A	(as in "ah")	Most yin	Abdominal center
I	(as in tree)	Minor yang	Throat center
U	(as in true)	Balanced	Heart center
E	(as in way)	Minor yin	Stomach center
O	(as in rose)	Most yang	Midbrain center

In order to establish the balanced functioning of the chakras, this series of sounds can be repeated in sequence, either once over a single exhalation for a relaxing effect, or for a more active stimulation, repeated two or more times during a single exhalation. Individual sounds can be repeated in the same way to influence particular chakras and their functions.

Manipulating the Energy of the Meridians and Organs

Individual sounds can be correlated to specific organs and their related meridians. This is so because each sound generates a similar vibration as the meridian it is paired with. Table 17 lists the individual organs and their related sounds.

Table 17 Sound Energies and Their Related Organs

Sound Vibration	Related Organ
Ha	Lungs
Ho	Large Intestine
Shi (she)	Heart
So	Small Intestine
Ji (gee)	Kidneys
Bo	Bladder
To or Ka	Liver
To (toe) or Da	Gallbladder
Hi (he)	Spleen/Pancreas
Ii (ee) or Yi (ye)	Stomach

To sedate an overactive or Jitsu condition, extend the sound in a gentle way, over a single, long exhalation. To activate an underactive or Kyo condition, repeat the sound several or more times, in a more animated fashion, over a single exhalation. As a general tonification, a halfway approach can be taken.

To address individual meridians and organs, simply repeat the associated sound for several minutes or more as described above. Remember, too, that psychological traits correlate with particular meridians. To deal with specific emotional problems, or to enhance certain characteristics, the sound energy of the related meridian can be used with benefit.

Combinations of Sounds

Prayers and more complex chants, which are the combinations of sounds, are an essential component of spiritual practices. The effects of particular prayers or chants rest on the unique blend of yin and yang energies used. Some chants activate one or more of the lower energy centers, and produce more physical energy and vitality. Others generate a more spiritual type of energy, and stimulate one or more of the chakras situated in the upper part of the body. A third category promotes a balance between these poles by stimulating both areas of the body.

Sound can thus be used in an effective way not only for healing but to enhance various functions and qualities. With practice and sensitivity, we can begin to create our own prayers and chants. And, we can understand how and in what way the prayers of various cultures work.

The prayers of one's particular faith can, of course, be used in a similar manner. Recited regularly, either aloud or silently, and with an appreciation for their meaning, they create powerful images for personal growth. Such prayers are, after all, reflections of the insights and inspirations of our ancestors. They have been proven effective over many generations of use.

Meditation

If there is a common denominator among the principles of self-development taught throughout the ages, it is the assertion that the quality or breadth of personal consciousness determines the character of an individual's life. To make lasting changes in one's external circumstances, students are admonished to turn inward, to examine and alter the thoughts and perceptions that are creating their limiting or troubling outward conditions. Circumstances are recognized as being the effects of our basic assumptions and beliefs concerning reality. Hence, the futility of working toward outward improvements without simultaneously recognizing the origin and cause of our difficulties.

We have probably all heard stories of individuals who have reversed a severe illness or overcome a grave personal problem via prayer, positive affirmation, or visualization. In a similar vein, numerous contemporary programs and books instruct us on how to use the mind to develop a positive self-image and to gain more fulfillment. Although each of us has the potential to achieve comparable feats, practically speaking, few of us possess the will or the vitality to make such a profound change in our physical condition and our psychological makeup through mental processes alone. This issue was addressed in Part 2, in which we discussed the two-way influence of body and mind. The most practical way to accomplish a change of mind, and the only way to ensure lasting growth, is to engage all aspects of the Self—body, mind and spirit—starting with daily diet and lifestyle practices.

Rather than reiterating this discussion, we will limit ourselves here to specific methods to engage the mind in the pursuit of health and personal growth. However, as the positive effects of these practices begin to manifest, we will do well to review the universal principles on which they are based. Then, by extending these precepts to other dimensions of life, we will be pursuing the holistic approach to well-being.

In this section, we will outline the principles of constructively using the mind in the pursuit of personal growth, and will present several practical examples. For a detailed examination of this and other types of self-development practices, readers are referred to *The Book of Dō-In: Exercises for Physical and Spiritual Development*, Michio Kushi, Japan Publications, Inc., 1979.

Yin and Yang Meditation Practices

The mind can be used in the same way we employ the energies of sound to activate or sedate physical and mental functions and qualities. That is to say, by focusing our attention on certain chakras, meridians, organs or body parts, we can exert a profound influence on the quality of Ki within them. Psychologically, by regularly holding certain images in our mind, we can begin to realize those qualities in our lives.

As subtle and apparently mysterious as it appears to be, the mind is no different than anything else in creation: it operates according to the principles of complementary opposites, or yin and yang. The two poles employed when purposely engaging the powers of the mind can be summed up as: (1) empty-mind meditation, a more yin practice in which we temporarily suspend our individual desire and will, and seek to merge with infinite consciousness, and (2) the more active use of images and the intentional directing of Ki for particular purposes. Entailing as it does the application of personal will and intention, and the focusing on particular attributes, this is a more yang practice.

Together, these two systems of mentally altering our vibrational quality form the basis for the multiplicity of meditation practices found throughout the world. Examined closely, any self-development application will be found to emphasize either the deliberate and intense affirmation of certain traits, or the dissolution of ego and obsessive patterns of thought. In the meditation methods of Yoga, for instance, both options are available, although the more yang method—in which a particular quality is emphasized—is often recommended initially, in order to focus and then calm the mind. At later stages, this orientation gives way to the more yin technique, in which individual awareness merges with universal consciousness.

This, then, is the goal of empty-mind meditation: to develop a peaceful, undisturbed mental state so that the energies of life, represented by the forces of Heaven and Earth, smoothly charge the Self. Through our daily, and indeed our moment-to-moment thoughts and emotions, the Ki flowing through the body takes on certain qualities or energetic patterns, which, if reinforced long enough, we go on to realize in the material world. By temporarily ceasing or at least slowing this process of personal creation we begin to dissolve the constraints of our limited and perhaps distorted consciousness and to open ourselves up to the unity of existence. This is what happens in moments of inspiration or profound insight. Our habitual, and finite vision of reality suddenly gives way to the panoramic recognition of the oneness of life.

Remembering that the body and mind are simply the reverse sides of the same coin, as perception widens through the regular practice of this exercise, physical consciousness, represented by the body, responds as well. As energy begins to flow in a harmonious way, physical stagnation and hardness dissolve, overly loose and swollen conditions begin to firm, and in general, the body begins to mirror the natural harmony of life. To perform the empty-mind exercise:

> Take a comfortable sitting position, with the spine straight and the body relaxed. An aligned spine facilitates the flow of Ki along the primary channel. To promote this condition, gently swing both arms forward and up over the head. Then raise the head so that the face is pointed toward the ceiling. Hold this stretch for a moment, then lower the head and bring the arms down in the front. Repeat two or three times.
>
> Tension in the body impedes the circulation of energy. As an additional means to dispel physical stress, raise and tighten the shoulders, while pulling

the neck and head down, like a turtle retreating into her shell. At the same time, press the hands down on the thighs, about half-way between the knee and the hip. Hold for several seconds, release, and then repeat.

Often, this exercise will cause the head, neck, shoulders and upper arms to shake, which is a sign of blocked energy being released. There will probably be less shaking the second time.

To perform the empty-mind meditation, place the hands, palms up, on the lap, with the left hand resting on the right. The thumbs can be lightly touching. This hand position allows the body's energy to circulate in a peaceful and balanced way.

The sound of "Su" can be chanted five to ten times as a preliminary step to further harmonize ourselves. Then, we simply sit quietly, without thought, for several minutes or more. The eyes can be lightly closed, and the breathing natural.

The mind should remain still and empty. However, do not resist any images that may arise. This will immediately set up subtle tension in the body and will frustrate our purpose. Rather, simply let go of the thoughts as soon as you become aware of them.

Performed regularly, perhaps morning and evening, this uncomplicated practice will have a deep effect on our consciousness. Intuition, or the direct perception of reality, will be enhanced, thus producing insights that foster personal growth. On a physical level, the body's systems and functions benefit from the smooth flow of Ki: overactive states are sedated and underactive ones are gently toned. The empty-mind exercise thus provides a comprehensive influence on both physical and spiritual states.

Visualization, or the active use of the mind to produce specific physical and psychological effects, is a more yang type of exercise. As already mentioned, teachers throughout the ages have emphasized the critical impact that thoughts have on our lives, especially ideas and images that are a habitual part of our character. In a very real sense, nothing exists except the mind. That is to say, everything that we perceive and experience is the product of our state of consciousness. Individuals interpret the same event differently, as does the same individual at different times, depending on the extent of his judgment and the state of his health. Once we make our assessment of an experience, that judgment will have reality for us, and we will act accordingly.

Thus, for instance, if the prospect of an upcoming event causes us stress and perhaps fear, our actions (and even our metabolic functions) will be appropriate responses to a threatening encounter, no matter what the reality of the situation turns out to be. This may involve a public speaking event, undergoing a job interview, or taking an examination at school. In these and similar cases, we ourselves form a menacing mental picture and then react to that image rather than to the reality of the experience.

The key to the successful application of visualization techniques lies in changing the energetic vision that we have created, thereby altering our perceptions, expectations and reactions. Quite literally, we are what we think, or, as the well-known adage puts it, "As a man thinks, so he becomes."

On a daily basis, we can make gradual efforts to "change" our mind through simple practices that will enhance the qualities we aspire to. In a general way, we do this by modifying the quality of the subtle "food" we consume. The books we read, the music we listen to, the movies we watch, the people we regularly associate with, the qualities and goals we aspire to, these and other factors have a direct influence on our state of mind. Anyone wanting to change their consciousness will do well to select these and other influences according to their personal aspirations.

As a simple illustration, several years ago, a woman in her mid-thirties was suffering from an enlarged heart and an irregular heartbeat. On the psychological side, she would experience panic attacks during the night, in which she would waken with a wildly beating heart and feelings of fear, sometimes bordering on terror. These experiences gradually subsided as she made dietary and other lifestyle changes. Early one morning, however, she phoned to report that the night before she had had a recurrence of the attacks, and was now afraid that they had only temporarily subsided. Upon questioning, she recalled how upset she had become while watching a particularly violent video shortly before bed the previous evening. As she then realized, "this type of 'food' has just as powerful an impact on my psyche as my meals and snacks."

On a more specific level, distinct psychological and spiritual qualities can be reinforced or developed by vividly and regularly holding their image in the mind. In this way we are mimicking natural processes, in which physical form materializes around the previously fashioned energetic pattern. Esoteric Buddhism employs this concept frequently, sometimes emphasizing particular qualities, other times using archetypes.

As a preliminary to this practice, the empty-mind exercise can be done in order to calm the mind. Once the body and mind are relaxed, the chosen quality is envisioned in as much detail as possible. This might be a better sense of humor, more confidence, patience, or kindness, for instance. Or, it might be the image of more wisdom and spiritual understanding. The point is to generate the desired image as clearly as possible and to hold it without the use of force. With practice this happens effortlessly.

Misgivings and skepticism, although understandable at this stage, inhibit the flow of Ki, and thus interfere with the reality of the energy image we are fashioning. Set these and other negative emotions aside, if only for the few moments required to do this meditation. As changes begin to take root, such feelings will fade in the face of the reality of personal growth. Remember, too, that although theoretically possible, instantaneous change is not the goal. For most of us, change and growth will come gradually and gently in response to our persistent efforts. It is by our basic, day-to-day physical and mental habits that we shape our character and our future, a concept nicely summed up in the following folk rhyme:

> Sow a thought, reap an act;
> Sow an act, reap a habit;
> Sow a habit, reap a character;
> Sow a character, reap a destiny.

Healing

For healing purposes, we take a similar approach. After first relaxing the body and calming the mind, we vividly visualize the particular state we wish to realize. This can be very specific, such as the dissolving of a cyst or tumor, or the strengthening of the immune system, or more general, such as the picturing of vibrant health and vitality. Done regularly, and in conjunction with other lifestyle changes, such practices are a realistic way to consciously engage Ki in a purposeful manner for healing.

As a variation, we can focus on a particular chakra, visualizing it actively pulsating with energy, and vitalizing the physical and psychological qualities it entails. Or, we can work with all of the chakras, working our way up from the lowest to the highest, spending a minute or so picturing the robust functioning of each. The same can be done with each of the organ pairs in turn, with a single organ pair, or with an organ and its meridian.

Focusing on the Hara or Midbrain

A further pair of meditations can be used therapeutically according to personal need by making use of the body's yin and yang energy centers—the midbrain and the abdominal chakras, respectively. When we are nervous, worried or emotionally upset, the exercise accentuating the energetically yang abdominal center can be employed. This practice helps to focus Ki in the Hara region, our physical center of gravity, thus generating a sense of stability and a rooted sense of well-being. The metabolism is activated, and power and endurance—the physical equivalents to courage and confidence—are fostered.

> Sit in a comfortable position, with the spine straight and the body relaxed. The hands are placed on the lap, palms up, with the thumbs lightly touching. The eyes are closed and pointed downward, as if focusing on the Hara.
>
> At this point, an optional breathing practice can be employed to accentuate the benefits of the exercise. Inhale deeply, imagining energy streaming down to the abdomen, energizing this center. At the end of the inhalation, hold the breath for several seconds (if comfortable), and visualize the Hara chakra (about two inches below the navel) being actively charged. Then exhale slowly, flattening the abdomen as you do so. The exhalation should be longer than the inhalation if comfortable.
>
> Repeat this sequence for several minutes, then gradually return to normal breathing. At this point, attention can remain fixed on the abdominal chakra, and the visualization of energy pulsating from it can be maintained for several minutes or longer.

In the opposite case, when we are tense or tight, or are feeling overwhelmed with stress, the yin type of meditation, emphasizing the midbrain chakra, can be used for its relaxing and calming effects. This practice will slow the metabolism and produce a cooler body temperature. It widens perception, so that worries and fears are seen in perspective, and enables us to recognize both their causes and solutions.

- Take the same relaxed and straight sitting position as described above. The

> mouth can be held slightly open or kept loosely closed. The eyes can be either kept half-open or closed, with the focus upward toward the midbrain chakra—between and about an inch above the eyebrows. The head can be held with a slight upward tilt.
>
> As a means of accentuating the effects of this practice, a breathing exercise can be employed before the visualization. Inhale in a long, slow manner, focusing the breath upward toward the midbrain. When correctly done, it will feel as if the air and Ki are lifting the upper body. During the inhalation, visualize energy flowing to and charging the midbrain chakra. The inhalation should be gentle and slightly longer than the exhalation.
>
> Repeat this sequence for several minutes before returning to normal breathing. Then focus on the midbrain chakra, using, for instance, the image of energy or light pulsating from it. Continue for several minutes or longer.

These two exercises are but general illustrations of how the body and mind can be influenced by focusing on certain energy centers. The addition of corresponding breathing techniques and, if desired, related sounds, can reinforce the desired effect.

With practice, these, and other methods that you can develop for yourself, become almost second nature, and we begin to look forward to our daily sessions of personal alchemy. Over time, we recognize that the energy of life is ours to use, or misuse, and gradually we learn to extend this concept to other areas of our life.

From this brief study it is clear that prayer is indeed a powerful and practical tool available to each of us. However, as described in this chapter, prayer is quite different from the passive repetition of meaningless words, or the insincere petitioning for relief from problems that we ourselves have created, that commonly comes to mind when the word is mentioned. In modern society, too few people have the real faith necessary to prayer with humility and yet with the positive expectation of results. On the other hand, far too many of us ridicule the idea of prayer as the product of either superstition or wishful thinking.

Like so many other concepts that have come down to us from the epoch when civilization was based on a metaphysical orientation, the notion of prayer as an energetic tool has been distorted, at times mysticized, and finally removed from the practical aspects of daily life. Nevertheless, for those who understand the principles of yin and yang, and the spiral of life—which articulates our relation with Infinity—prayer can be as pragmatic as physical exercise in our efforts to achieve well-being.

4. Palm Healing

The art of palm healing has been instinctively used throughout history and by all societies and individuals. This is as true in the twentieth century as it was in ancient times. If we bump a knee or have a headache, the reflexive action is to place our hand over the painful area. When a child has a stomachache or scrapes an elbow, it is mother or father who touches or holds the spot to make it better.

In the Bible, there are many accounts of Jesus healing by the laying on of the hands. It is an often overlooked fact that the disciples themselves actively practiced this art, and in fact, the credibility of their teachings was in many cases supported by their ability to heal in this subtle and apparently mysterious way. In Acts, Chapter 5, Verse 12, we are told, "And by the hands of the apostles were many signs and wonders wrought among the people." Chapter 19, Verse 6, reports, "And when Paul had laid his hands upon them, The Holy Ghost came on them; and they spake with tongues, and prophesied."

In ancient times, palm healing was a widely used symptomatic treatment in the Far East. We use the term "symptomatic" because even on this refined level, only the symptoms of a problem are dealt with. The cause, as we have seen, lies in the individual's way of life, and ultimately in his view of life. Until these considerations are addressed, true healing can never take place.

The practice of palm healing was developed into a sophisticated art in the Orient, and was known in Japan as *Tanasue-no-Michi* (手末之道), or the "Tao of hand application." The Japanese word *Te Ate* (手当) means "applying the hands," or "hand application." Although in recent times this term has been expanded to include treatment in general, its meaning indicates that the origin of healing is based on humanity's ability to make direct adjustments in the body's Ki or energy. When combined with dietary corrections, these two practices form the essence of all the healing arts.

As a outgrowth of dietary adjustment, herbal medicine represents the specific use of food as medicine. Palm healing is the basis upon which the subsequent therapies of massage, moxibustion, and acupuncture emerged. These latter applications serve as more specialized modes of altering the body's Ki, and require progressively more training and equipment, and often treatment is given by a professional practitioner.

Breathing practices, chanting, and certain meditation practices fall into the category of more personal methods of Ki regulation. Employed alone, or in conjunction with palm healing, they have a profound influence on the body's energy, and consequently on each aspect of the Self. Such practices are often used in combination with palm healing to enhance its effectiveness.

Palm healing involves the application of the hands to a troubled area of the body for relief. The term can be a source of confusion, however, for, as we shall see, it is not the palms themselves—or even the individual who is giving the application—that does the healing. The name can lead to other misunderstandings as well. One student, reading an announcement for a palm-healing class, phoned to inquire about the connection between macrobiotics and caring for palm trees!

A clearer description of this form of therapy is the use of the hands to direct the universal motions of centrifugality (expansion) and centripetality (contraction) to particular areas of the body for the purpose of correcting energetic imbalances. When we use palm healing we are utilizing the forces of yin and yang, or Heaven's and Earth's forces, rather than expending personality vitality. This is an important point and more will be said about it shortly.

The Energy Circuit

We have seen how the polar energies of Heaven and Earth course vertically through the center of the body, forming the primary channel. The interaction of these two forces creates and charges the body's seven major energy centers. The meridians branch out from these chakras and flow to all areas of the body, nourishing every cell. In addition, energy is generated internally from the food and air we consume, and circulated outward, via the blood, throughout the body, and out into the environment.

Another important point to remember is that the physical body developed along the pattern first laid down by the energy spiraling into the ovum from the mother's meridians. The material body is thus a reflection of and a more condensed form of this more refined energy structure. For this reason, treatments such as palm healing, which directly influence the flow of Ki, can be remarkably effective.

In addition to the chakras aligned along the primary channel, there are numerous other energy centers within the body. These include the center of the palms, and the tip of each finger. The right hand is charged by Earth's more yin, centrifugal force, and the left hand by Heaven's more yang, centripetal force. The energy of the right hand soothes and disperses excessive or overactive energy. This type of influence is called for when the problem being treated is judged to be Jitsu or overactive. The left hand supplies and activates energy. Its influence is used when the problem is Kyo or underactive. Many symptoms are caused by stagnation within the body, and in this case we use the right hand to dissolve and draw out the excessive or stagnated energy.

Because of their complementary energetic relationship, when we join the hands, as in prayer, the positive and negative energy centers merge into a single, balanced stream. The resulting peaceful and harmonious feelings reflect the deep wisdom of our ancestors who first taught us to join our hands in prayer. In the Orient, there are numerous other hand positions, called *mudras*, that accentuate precise physical and spiritual characteristics. They do this by regulating the flow of Ki to particular organs, systems, meridians, and chakras in order to augment their related physical and psychological aspects.

The overall influence of the right and left hands can be adjusted to vary the intensity of their particular effect. This is done by using different sections of the palm to direct energy.

The three general areas of the hand are:

1. The middle area or the center of the palm. This is the region of the strongest energy charge.
2. The intermediate area, or the top of the palm, where the fingers join the hand. A more midway degree of energy intensity is generated here.
3. The peripheral area, or the tips of the fingers. This sector channels the lightest charge of energy.

The fingers also vary in the intensity of their respective charge. In descending order of strength, these are: the thumb, the middle finger, the index finger, and, of about equal strength, the last two fingers, the ring and little finger.

Fig. 53 Energy Spirals on the Palms and Fingers

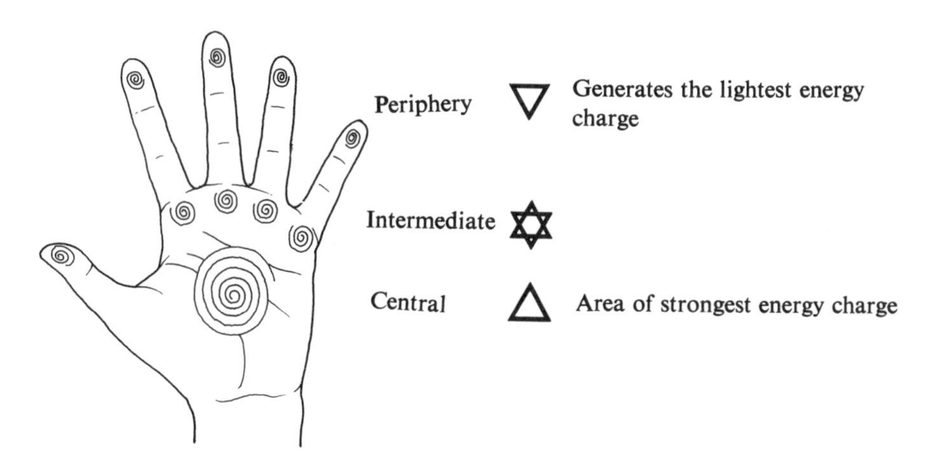

Source of Healing Abilities

Before examining specific techniques, it is important to recognize that the source of these rejuvenating abilities is the motion or force of infinity itself. The individual giving the application is simply the medium through which life, in the form of yin and yang energies, flows. It is not by our personal power that we provide relief. If this were so, we would soon grow tired and depleted as we gave a treatment. When properly performed, palm healing actually has the opposite effect. Because the forces of Heaven and Earth are flowing actively through the giver during treatment, he feels stronger and more energetic afterward.

Some people think that only extraordinary individuals are capable of treating with the palms. As long as we are alive, energy streams within us. The difference in healing ability among individuals is an indication of how smoothly and strongly this process goes on. Personal power is a reflection of one's energy quality. Thus, to be an proficient healer, one needs only be an effective conductor of the energies of creation.

Generating Healing Abilities

There are two considerations involved in enhancing one's ability in palm healing. First is our day-to-day condition, which must be: (1) robust in order to generate an active flow of Ki within the body, and (2) flexible and clean in order to heighten the reception of external Ki and the generation of internal Ki, and to enhance the smooth flow of both within the body. Taken together, these two qualities are simply another way of saying that we must be in good health.

The basic point in realizing and maintaining a vital condition is daily diet, as discussed earlier. In addition, activity is necessary to support the dynamic interchange of external and internal Ki. Within this category, there is again an complementary relation to be considered. Physical activity, representing one pole of this partnership, is of course essential. Movement generates Ki and allows for its orderly discharge. It also prevents or breaks up stagnation, and keeps the body firm and flexible.

The other partner in this relationship is mental and spiritual activity. An open and curious mind complements a vital physical condition. And, a cheerful and optimistic outlook enhances the flow of Ki. This of course works from the other direction as well. If the body's energy flow is strong, our attitude will be positive and confident, and our mentality alert.

The second factor to augment the practice of palm healing involves special preparation on the part of the practitioner immediately prior treatment. These steps are meant to facilitate the smooth flow of Ki within the body.

Preparation for Applying the Hands

- Ideally, the giver will be in a better or at least a similar state of health as the receiver. Although no harm can result if this is not the case, the treatment will be more effective under these conditions.
- In general, if the giver is right-handed, the right hand is used to direct Ki, while the left hand is used in one of the complementary ways discussed below. If the giver is left-handed, this pattern is reversed.

  For more detailed applications, the hands can be used according to the quality of energy the giver wishes to apply. This depends on the Kyo or Jitsu condition of the symptoms, as discussed earlier.
- Before beginning, check the condition of the hands. Palms that are wet, sticky or oily, swollen, or too warm or cold, indicate an imbalanced condition. In the short-term, wash and dry the hands before treatment. Lifestyle changes must be made to effectively improve the underlying condition that produces these symptoms.
- Wait about three hours after eating before giving treatment. We have already discussed the complementary relationship between physical and nonphysical food. The more of the former we take in, the less of the later we receive.

To Generate Ki

1. Take a comfortable sitting or standing position, with the back and shoulders relaxed and straight. To facilitate this position, raise your arms until

they point toward the sky, and then continue slightly back over the head. Lift the head up and back to the extent that the eyes are looking toward the sky. This will accentuate the stretch of the spine. Then slowly lower the head and drop the arms to the sides. Repeat this stretch several times.

2. Next, bring the hands together in the position commonly used for prayer. By using the thumbs to touch the chakras along the primary channel (particularly the midbrain, throat, or heart center), we activate the hand's charge.

   For example, lightly touch the thumbs on either side of the throat, and either maintain an empty mind or visualize energy flowing to the hands. To accelerate this charge, we can chant the sound of *Su* (as in the name Sue) from five to ten times.

   Another method is to bend the arms at the elbows, and raise the forearms so that the hands are shoulder height, with the palms pointing upward. Sit quietly, with calm breathing and an empty mind.

   As a variation of this practice, keep the right hand raised, and the left hand down at the side, with the palm facing the floor. In this position we receive the forces of both Heaven and Earth.

3. A minute or two of sitting quietly or of simple meditation can help prepare the giver for palm-healing application.
4. Just before giving treatment, the palms can be rubbed together briskly yet lightly, to facilitate the flow of Ki.

Considerations during Application

- Either maintain an empty mind, or visualize the active movement of energy through the primary channel, out along the arms, and streaming from the hands, soothing or vitalizing the area being treated.

  Maintaining an empty mind insures that the flow of Ki along the primary channel is not disrupted by the energy of thoughts and emotions. Visualization, or the use of the mind to direct Ki flow, enhances whatever effect we are trying to produce. This involves holding the image of energy, warmth, or light flowing from the hand, and suffusing the part of the body being administered to.
- Breathing should be synchronized between giver and receiver, so that both partners inhale and exhale together. After explaining this to the receiver, the giver can easily follow the respiration of the receiver by either watching, feeling, or listening to his breath.

  Also, to generate a smooth flow of energy, the breathing of both partners should be deep and peaceful, as opposed to being shallow and irregular.
- In the Northern Hemisphere, sit facing south, so that the head spiral and the Yu points on the back receive the optimum amount of Heaven's force as it comes from the north pole. In the Southern Hemisphere, this position is reversed.
- Only the palms of the giver should touch the person receiving the treatment. If we touch with other parts of the body, Ki flows from two or more spots, and we dilute the effect.
- Apply the palms lightly to the area being treated, or hold them one to two

inches above the area. Do not press or use muscular effort, as this defeats our purpose of inducing a smooth flow of energy between giver and receiver. Remember that tension or hardness blocks the flow of Ki.

- The receiver should be made comfortable. Either a sitting or reclining position is fine, depending on the type of application being given.
- If the giver starts to feel numbness or coldness in the hands or arms, he can stop the application and rinse the hands in cold water. The application can then be continued after a brief rest.

Breathing Techniques

The breath can be used to assist whatever effect we wish to produce with palm healing. A pair of complementary breathing practices can be used for specific results. For a more harmonized influence, a middle-type of breathing can be employed.

Fig. 54 Emphasis in Yin and Yang Breathing Techniques

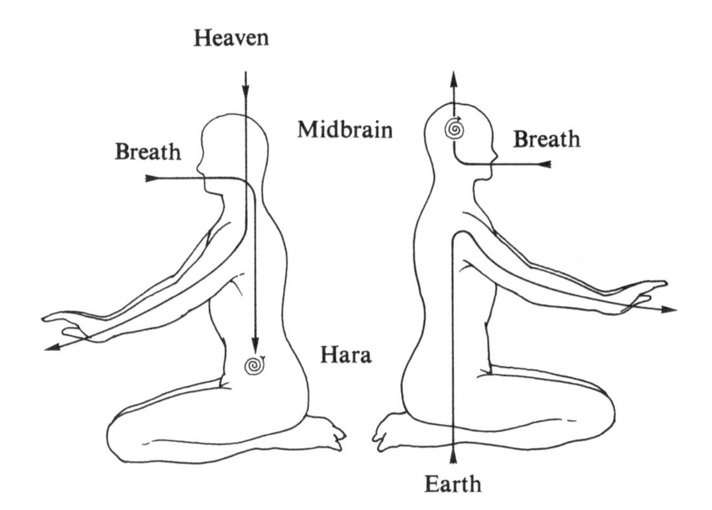

Yang-style breathing to accentuate Heaven's force

Yin-style breathing to accentuate Earth's force

- *Yin Breathing:* Increases the flow of Earth's force. Inhale upward, visualizing the breath moving to the midbrain chakra and on to the hair spiral at the top of the head toward the back. The emphasis is on the inhalation. Yin breathing imparts a light feeling, slows the metabolism, and generates a cooler temperature.

- *Yang Breathing:* Increases the flow of Heaven's force. Inhale downward, concentrating on the lower abdomen and the Hara chakra. Exhalation should be longer than inhalation. Yang breathing produces a rooted feeling. It accelerates the metabolism, and produces a warmer temperature.

- *Balanced Breathing:* Generates a more harmonious flow of Heaven's and Earth's forces. Inhale toward the central part of the body, the heart chakra. Exhalation and inhalation should be equal. This style of breathing normalizes metabolism and body temperature.

Detecting Ki

If we are using palm healing as a form of therapy rather than a tonic or preventive measure, or to enhance certain physical or psychological qualities, we can begin with diagnosis. Of course, we can use this form of examination at any time—on ourselves or others—to better understand one's state of health. There are numerous methods for detecting and interpreting the body's Ki flow, several of which are listed below. With practice and experience, one can begin to develop useful variations and entirely new approaches.

It is important to remember that although we are dealing with energy, this aspect of the individual is just as much a part of his person as is the physical body. Thus, we should approach energy diagnosis and treatment with the same care we would use when physically touching someone.

Diagnostic Methods

- The receiver sits in a comfortable position. The giver sits behind him. Starting on either side of the head, the giver positions his hands several inches from the physical body, and slowly moves the hands down over the shoulders and along the sides. Repeat, moving from the head down the front of the body, and do the same down the back.
- To assess the condition of chakras, have the receiver either lie on his back or sit in a comfortable position. Start at the lowest center, placing the hand several inches above or away from the body. Slowly moving the hand back and forth will bring the palm across the chakra, making it easier to distinguish the area of active Ki flow. Once the center is located, hold the hand still for several moments, or gently move it closer and farther away to distinguish the energetic quality of the center.

  After a minute or so, gradually move the palm up along the primary channel to the second, or Hara chakra. Repeat the above sequence and then continue, one by one, to the other chakras.

During the first several attempts at diagnosing Ki quality, attention should be directed to simply feeling the partner's energy body. With experience, we can begin to detect differences in the quality of energy at various locations. At some spots it may be very active, or Jitsu, and at others, inactive, or Kyo. There will also be various characteristics in between these two poles.

In the case of Jitsu, the hands will be moving along and come to an area of active energy discharge: the temperature may be noticeably warmer, and one may feel what can be described as an incline or hill rising from the general level of the energy body. In the case of Kyo, the hands may find a hole or depression, or the temperature may be discernably cooler. With such sensitivity, we can begin to perceive the condition of the chakras and meridians, and the organs and systems, and intuitively understand the appropriate adjustments to make.

Treatments

The practice of palm healing is based on the basic principles of complementary opposites that are echoed throughout nature. In the human body, reflections of this order appear in a myriad of antagonistic partners. For example, the relation between: the upper and lower, front and back, left and right, horizontal and vertical, center and periphery, expanded and contracted, hollow and solid, and active and sedate parts of the body. We can make use of these patterns to devise effective and varied methods of treatment.

The Digestive and Nervous Systems

The body's basic polarity exists between the digestive and nervous system and their respective centers, the Hara and the midbrain. Being structurally more yang, the midbrain attracts and processes the more refined, or yin, external Ki. The structurally more yin Hara area is the point from which internal Ki—taken from food and transformed into blood—begins its outward course from the center of the body out of the environment.

There is a simple application to harmonize these two systems, and the physical, mental, and spiritual functions they govern:

1. Beginning at the tailbone, the giver slowly moves his hand up the receiver's spine, over the head, and down the face to the nose. Use the synchronized, yin breathing, and move the hand only on the inhalation. Cover about four inches per breath. Hold the hand over the nose for a minute or so, and then slowly detach. Because we are using Earth's force, use the right hand for treatment. The left hand can lightly touch the ground, or at least be pointing downward.
2. Beginning at the mouth, the giver slowly moves his hand down the center of the body along the spiritual channel, ending at the Hara. Use the synchronized yang breathing, and move the hand only on the exhalation. Keep the hand at the Hara area for several breathes. Because we are using Heaven's force, the left hand can be used for application. The right hand can be bent at the elbow, with the palm facing toward the sky. If this is not comfortable, let it hang loosely at the side.
3. Next, treat the beginning and end of the nervous system by placing one hand on the tailbone and the other on the forehead. Use the synchronized yin breathing, and both partners can chant the sound of "Mmm" or "Nnn," which are more yang sounds, to stimulate the brain and nervous system. Continue this for several minutes.
4. To treat the beginning and end points of the digestive system, place one hand lightly over the mouth and the other on the Hara area. Use the

synchronized yang breathing, and both partners can chant the sound of "Ah" or "Su." These are more yin sounds and serve to activate the physically yin digestive system. Continue for two or three minutes.

5. To coordinate the two systems, place one hand at the tailbone and the other over the mouth—the systems' beginning points. Use the synchronized, balanced breathing, and continue for several minutes. Then slowly detach.

Treating the Chakras

The body's five basic energy centers, or chakras, can be treated to stimulate their respective functions. In this way, we nourish their related physical and mental qualities. We can use the front and back relationship in this case. Before beginning, diagnose each of the chakras as explained earlier in this chapter. Pay particular attention to any Kyo or Jitsu condition of each center. Check again after finishing the application, noting any changes in energy quality that may have taken place.

The receiver sits in a comfortable position. Beginning at the lowest of the five centers, the giver places one hand on the Hara region and the other hand in the area directly opposite on the back. Use synchronized breathing, and to accelerate the charge, chant the sound of "Su"

Continue for about five breaths, then slowly move the hands up to the stomach energy center, front and back. Repeat the treatment as described above. Follow these steps at each of the remaining basic chakras—the heart, throat, and midbrain.

Upon completing the midbrain center, slowly detach the hands in an upward and outward direction. After finishing, ask the receiver how he now feels, and if he noticed any sensations during the application. This is a helpful way for both partners to learn about the dynamics of Ki.

Treating Chronic and Acute Problems

Symptoms or general conditions can be treated according to their Kyo (deficient) or Jitsu (excessive) nature.

- If the problem indicates Kyo, or hypo, symptoms, the giver provides energy and stimulation. If the receiver is pale and weak, or the Ki is perceived to be underactive in some other way—often the case in chronic health problems—energy must be supplied.

  Use the left hand, or Heaven's force, for application, and both partners can do the synchronized yang breathing. The sounds of either "Ah" or "Su" can be chanted to accelerate the treatment.

- In cases where Jitsu, or hyper, symptoms are manifesting, the giver drains and calms the receiver's energy. If the symptoms are actively discharging, as in a high fever, frequent coughing, or fiery inflammation, energy must be drawn off.

  The right hand, or Earth's force, is used for application in this case, and both partners can do the synchronized yin breathing. The sounds of "Mmm" or "Nnn" can be chanted to supplement the treatment.

In Cases of Acute Pain

- Use the front and back relationship to soothe the area.
- Treat the area with the right hand, and position the left hand facing downward.
- Treat the area and with the other hand lightly hold the finger or toe that the related meridian runs to.
- Treat the painful area and its complemental area. Refer to Part 1, chapter 5, for these relationships.

Treating the Organs

The organs can be administered to in numerous ways, using the various complementary relationships within the body. Which hand, breathing technique, and sound to use depends on the purpose of the application. Use the more yang varieties to supply energy, the more yin types to drain energy, and the more balanced techniques for general toning. Suggestions for treating the organs include:

- *Front and Back:* In this method, simply place one hand on the front of the body over the organ to be treated, and the other in the opposite position on the back. For example, when treating the liver, apply one hand on the front, lower-right side of the rib cage, and the other in the same position on the back.

- *Periphery and Center:* Using this relationship, the giver places one hand over the affected organ, and the other hand lightly grips the end of the finger or toe through which the related meridian runs. The tsubo or points along the related meridian may also be used in this treatment, according to the desired result. Refer to chapter 4 of Part 1 for details on the special uses of the tsubo.

  Also, because the meridians of the lower- and upper-body organs generally run to the fingers, and the middle organs flow to the toes, a coordinated treatment can be given. For an upper- or lower-body organ, lightly grasp all the fingers, and for a middle-body organ, grasp all the toes. The other hand can be used to administer to the affected organ.

- *Upper and Lower, Expanded and Contracted, Internal and External:* Using these relationships, the organs and their related facial area can be used in treatment. The giver places one hand over the organ, and the other on or over the related facial feature. (See Part 1, chapter 5, for these correlations.)

- *Antagonistic and Complementary Partner:* Using this relationship, we treat one organ by making use of the polarity it shares with its partner. For instance, when treating the heart, the other hand is placed on the small intestine.

- *For a Comprehensive Treatment:* Begin by treating the organ itself, front and back, then the organ and its meridian, then the organ and its partner, and finally the organ and its facial correlation.

Emotions

Problems with the emotions can be treated in a similar manner. According to the five transformations of energy, each emotion is energetically connected with a particular organ pair. Problems along the meridian or within the organ will be reflected in the corresponding emotion. And, because imbalanced emotional expression influences the related meridian and organ pair, this style of treatment will produce a very clear physical and emotional effect. Variations in the techniques used depend on whether the emotion is being repressed or exaggerated, and whether the related organ and meridian are Kyo or Jitsu.

Self-treatment

Palm healing can easily be used as a self-treatment not only for dealing with particular problems but as a general tonic given daily or regularly in much the same way that we take exercise to stay fit. It can also be used to enhance the functions of organs and systems when no problem exists.

If we wish to develop a particular emotional expression, intellectual capacity, or spiritual quality, we can activate the related organ, system, and chakra. For example, the heart chakra is related to the qualities of love, peace, and harmony. By tonifying the heart center, these qualities can be amplified. Remember also that the heart's corresponding time of day is noon, and the related season is summer. At either of these times, a general application to this energy center will help reinforce these attributes and enhance the organ's functions. This does not mean that applications at other times will not be effective however.

Obviously, some techniques are difficult to do on oneself, but there are many ways to comfortably help. Examples include making use of the relationship between: the organ and its partner, the organ and its facial correlation, and the use of one hand on the organ, and the other facing either upward or downward, depending on the effect desired. Or, in this case, we can simply let the other hand hang at the side or rest on the floor if we are lying down.

Know Thy Self

One of the most commonly expressed axioms in both religious and philosophical teachings is the counsel to "know yourself." Each of us has particular strengths and weaknesses, good points and bad points. Becoming aware of these qualities, and learning how to enhance the former and compensate for the latter, is a form of personal alchemy.

In *The Gospel According to Thomas*, Jesus, replying to the question of how to enter the Kingdom of Heaven, replied, "When you make the two one, and when you make the inside like the outside, and the outside like the inside, and the above like the below, and when you make the male and the female one and the same, so that the male not be male nor the female female; . . . then will you enter the Kingdom." This idea is identical to the macrobiotic teaching that when we can flexibly use the principles of yin and yang to change sickness to health and sadness into happiness, we will have reached the point of being free human beings.

Palm healing offers us a valuable tool for personal development. It is an effective means of both understanding our condition and, when necessary, of changing it. With experience, our vision of life grows broader as we come to recognize and use the basic principles of the universe. Readers are encouraged to practice regularly, to develop new techniques, and to share this art with family members and friends.

5. Exercise and Massage

This chapter marks the transition in our discussion from preventative and health-care practices that individuals can do for themselves, with little training or special equipment, to those that require the services of a professional. Certainly both exercise and massage can be done in or around the home. Some basic instruction is needed for the practice of massage, although no supplementary equipment is generally called for. Massage can be performed as a self-application, or given by a layperson or a specialist.

Curiously, formal training and supervision, and an array of high-priced paraphernalia have become almost obligatory with popular forms of exercise. This trend raises both the expense and time commitment involved. The obvious drawback is that, under such circumstances, relatively few people are able or willing to pursue a regular workout routine. The troubling decline in public health (among all age groups) and the soaring increase in medically related expenses are, in part, a result of this growing complexity and consequent lack of physical activity.

Exercise and massage are important aspects of a holistic health-care strategy. Performed, and in the case of massage, either given and/or received regularly, they produce vibrant health, elicit a solid sense of physical and mental well-being, and enhance personal growth. Both have been used since ancient times not only for prevention, but as a therapy to enhance recovery from illness or injury. Often overlooked is the value each has in treating emotional and mental ailments. This is true in the general sense that physical activity and massage help promote relaxation by reducing stress and accumulated tensions, and in a specific way, in which certain exercises or massage applications are employed to treat particular meridians and energy centers, and their corresponding psychological characteristics.

Numerous spiritual-development traditions have long emphasized the importance of exercise, self-massage and therapeutic massage for the growth of consciousness. In modern society, many of us find it difficult to grasp the correlation between physical, psychological and spiritual well-being. Now that we have examined the relationship between the human energy system and mental and spiritual characteristics, we can readily appreciate the value of such practices.

Continuing with the progression from the simplest to the more complicated therapies and personal-development approaches followed in Part 2, exercise will be the first topic of discussion. Massage, as both an application we apply to another and as self-massage, will follow.

Who Needs It

Most of us are aware of the need for physical activity. If our physicians have not encouraged us to pursue some form of exercise, there is little chance that we have escaped related news articles and special reports in the media. Findings issued regularly by governmental agencies and medical associations routinely reinforce the benefits of and the necessity for physical activity. Earlier, we applied the macro or holistic outlook to identify several central advantages of physical activity. These include: producing flexibility of body and mind by dissolving stagnation and hardness; fostering the activities of all systems and functions by regulating the flow of Ki within the body and throughout all dimensions that collectively make up the Self; and generating vitality, alertness and the growth of consciousness by normalizing the two-way exchange of Ki between the individual and the environment.

And yet, despite these benefits, relatively few of us pursue a consistent program of physical culture. Admittedly, we may exercise sporadically, wearing ourselves out in one session only to allow days or even weeks to pass before we schedule another. Or, we may be so tired at the end of the day that the last question we want to ask ourselves is "did I do my exercises today." Both sentiments miss the point.

Human consciousness is grounded on, although certainly not limited to, physical existence. To put it another way, the quality of our lives depends upon the state of our physical health. "Physiology precedes psychology," is a basic tenet in macrobiotic thought. The implication is that the integrity of our biological condition determines our emotional, mental and spiritual well-being. The validity of this premise is so obvious that we often fail to note it. Most of us have probably experienced the fact that poor physical health strongly colors our psychological state. The mechanism of this bond is rooted in the subtle energy of Ki, through which consciousness develops within the interrelated dimensions of being.

As a consequence, when we dismiss our lack of physical activity with the excuse that there are more pressing demands on our time, we are undermining the very basis of our health and vitality, and our ability to remain active and alert in our everyday lives. This attitude mirrors our collective short-term view of life, which can be summed up in the "buy/enjoy now, pay later" attitude that characterizes modern society. Then, months, years or even decades later, when endurance and spirit begin to flag, we may choose to self-medicate ourselves with stimulants, begin a program of nutritional supplements in a misguided attempt to circumvent the need to keep active, or seek the type of professional assistance that too often ignores the root of the condition.

The plain fact is that everyone needs to be physically active—children as well as adults. Common sense, modern science and traditional teachings share a recognition of this truth. If this fact were followed up in the form of governmental, educational and business policies, and incorporated into the lifestyles of individuals and families, much needless suffering would be avoided. Billions of dollars could then be diverted from public and private health-care costs to investments far more productive to social welfare.

Physical Activity or Systematic Exercise

Until just a few generations ago, physical activity was an intimate, inescapable part of daily existence. At the turn of this century approximately 90 percent of American families lived on farms. This was before widespread mechanization, which means that most chores were done by hand. Even in cities, physical activity was an unavoidable part of life. We walked to work, climbed stairs, cleaned our yards, performed home repairs and maintenance, and did numerous household chores.

Today, labor-saving devices that were once undreamed of have evolved into necessities. So common have they become, that few of us ever stop to consider their existence and influence. In fact, the terms "automatic" or "electric," that once distinguished these conveniences from their manual counterparts, are today most often dropped. When was the last time you heard someone refer to an "automatic" clothes washer, or an "electric" dryer, for instance.

We are certainly not suggesting that such items are inherently harmful. Rather, by recognizing the consequent transformation in lifestyle they have produced, we become conscious of their impact, and of the need to set priorities and to compensate in our daily routine. Additionally, we may want to reflect upon:

- The degree of reliance we place on our home appliances;
- The amount of time we work to pay for such items versus the benefits received;
- The loss of vital skills and abilities that were once routinely taught and carried out by family members—such as maintaining one's home and yard, building furniture, sewing clothes, growing vegetables and flowers, providing entertainment within the family setting, and even a basic competence in cooking meals (and the consequent dependence on specialists for all such services); and
- The environmental impact that the production, use and disposal of such appliances invoke.

No other historical period has provided so many individuals with the opportunity, desire and very real need to devote their time, money and energy in the pursuit of fitness. For some, this is a positive sign, a reflection of the sophistication of our modern way of life. After all, our days are no longer spent doing meaningless and demeaning physical labor. And yet, in many cultures, work was at one time regarded as a rewarding experience, and as a means of self-expression. The once common terms "vocation" and "calling" suggested that one's occupation was both a lifetime commitment to mastering the requisite skills, and a means of fostering character development. People used their bodies and minds to create beauty and utility, and found fulfillment in doing so.

Today, the situation is reversed. We spurn manual labor, and grudge our hours on the job, then turn around and sell our time for the money to pay for labor-saving and entertainment devices. As individuals, families and a nation, we have mortgaged our future for the luxuries that, in excess, destroy physical health, dull the mind, and retard spiritual growth. Then, like our lifeless white bread which must be nutritionally supplemented, our one-sided lifestyles require periodic doses of exercise which our daily activities fail to provide.

The lack of physical activity that characterizes modern life has intensified the need for allotting time on a regular basis for exercise of some sort. For many, the question of how to select an effective fitness program within personal time and financial constraints is a primary consideration. Fortunately, we already have at our disposal a set of workable standards to guide us, as we will examine in the next section. Before we do, however, remember that regular exercise does not absolve us from using common sense as we go about our daily routine. Opting for physical exertion over the use of mechanical devices whenever possible is a simple and often ignored means of maintaining health. Walking, gardening, bicycling, climbing stairs, doing household chores and numerous other activities save money while promoting well-being.

Five Guidelines to Follow

Part 1 of this book introduced the attributes that characterize traditional and Oriental societies, and illustrated how they are applied to the theory and practice of healing. Although now divorced from modern medicine, physical culture was at one time an intimate part of a holistic health-care system. These five principles, based on a comprehensive view of life, thus provide a serviceable compass for choosing a practical program of physical activity. They clarify the purpose of exercise and provide direction for fashioning a strategy based on individual needs. Following the order given earlier, these guidelines indicate that our exercise practices (and approach to massage as well) should be:

1. *Holistically oriented.* Exercise need not be limited to narrow goals such as building muscle, enhancing cardiovascular functions, or weight loss. However valuable each of these considerations may be, they lack a comprehensive approach to well-being. The danger with such an orientation is that by concentrating on a single quality, mechanism or body part, we ignore the comprehensive functioning of both the physical body and of the entire Self, and thus risk overall balance. Developing one attribute is often done at the expense of another—a choice must be made between bulk and flexibility, strength and endurance, explosiveness and speed. This paradox reflects the front-and-back character of life. Because it can not be circumvented, care must be taken to avoid extremes—extremes, as we have seen, inevitably turn to their opposite.

To be truly effective, exercise must foster the integrated health of all organs, systems and functions, and recognize the wider association of physical body, emotions and mind, and spirit. This, of course, is the holistic approach that is stressed throughout this book.

2. *Oriented toward an energetic vision of life.* We have examined the constitution of the human energy system, and the dynamics of mankind's interaction with the larger forces of nature. Our approach to physical activity will be partial if we fail to recognize the ramification of those influences: namely, that Ki, or energy, is the foundation of physical health. The primary focus of exercise should consequently be directed toward the enhancement of this energy flow. This, in turn, demands the holistic approach enumerated in guideline one.

Vitality and health are produced by the harmonious flow of Ki within the body, and the smooth interchange between the energy we take in and the energy we return to the environment. Weak muscles, lack of endurance, poor digestion and elimination, or impaired immune function, are foremost a reflection of "poor circulation" of energy. Building muscles does not automatically eliminate such problems, although improving energy flow does, of necessity, enhance the functioning of all organs and systems. Thus effective efforts to eliminate such conditions are built on an understanding of Ki.

3. *Geared toward the source of health and well-being.* Instead of focusing on symptoms, such as poor muscle tone, lack of stamina, or rigidity of joints, ligaments and muscles, the cause of these problems must be addressed. It is ironic that people visit a health club several times a week for a vigorous workout, while their diets are loaded with empty calories and fat, and their lifestyles are otherwise sedentary. Many of us fail to realize that no fitness program can work in isolation, divorced from the general orientation of our life. To be successful, our efforts must be reinforced by a lifestyle that fosters and complements our exercise sessions. The role of exercise is supplemental to these more basic considerations.

4. *Intuitive rather than conceptual.* Today, exercise patterns go in and out of style almost as quickly as New York fashions. Such programs are based on an analytical approach to life. Supported by prevailing scientific and medical findings, various programs, techniques and equipment are designed to zero in on a specific attribute or problem. Unfortunately, the scope of such advise is severely restricted. While capable of generating the target results, the benefits are most often realized at the expense of other functions and body parts. This is because such strategies recognize only a partial vision of human existence.

This outlook is no different than the dietary fads that regularly sweep the country. In both cases, the latest craze is likely to be expensive, and may be dangerous. Conceptually based, it will inevitably be partial, leading to imbalances which in turn will generate their own set of problems. In contrast to this fragmented approach, traditional patterns of exercise articulate a holistic strategy based on a metaphysical comprehension of humanity's origin and destiny. The starting point is physical health, but the purpose is to develop the whole person.

5. *Practical rather than theoretical.* The significance of this guideline is that, ideally, our exercises and physical activity will be an integral part of daily life. Additional expense, time, and special facilities and equipment will be unnecessary or at least held to a minimum. To the extent that such factors are involved, the number of individuals and segments of society able to participate decreases—a fact that clearly violates the principle of practicality. No matter how good, theoretically, a fitness program may appear, if it is not generally applicable to all segments of society, and adaptable to a variety of circumstances and personal conditions, it must be considered impractical.

In summation, our approach to physical activity must be just as "ecological" as our approach to environmental concerns and agriculture. The application of these traditional guidelines to the more conventional aspects of medicine proved to be effective, cost-efficient, safe and accessible to all. Their employment to physical culture—an additional dimension of health care—will prove equally productive.

Two Poles of Exercise

The variety of exercise systems available to the average person is astonishing. From Tai-chi to jogging, from the martial arts to some celebrity's program for sex appeal, we have a supermarket selection to choose among. The sheer range of this assortment can be bewildering and frustrating. How can one know where the benefits and drawbacks lie, and equally important, what criteria can be used to determine which system is "right" for me.

An overall orientation is provided by the above guidelines. Specific tools for distinguishing the poles that exercise naturally falls into, and for classifying individual patterns along the continuum from one pole to the other, are furnished by the principles of yin and yang. With this information it becomes easier to judge the nature of particular routines, and to select the one that suits our needs and goals.

By way of comparison, the focus of one partner in this pair of exercise categories represents a more dynamic, focused approach. It is used, consciously or unconsciously, as a means to discharge excess energy by elevating the pace of metabolic processes. Oriented more toward the physical dimensions of life, it is the product and reflection of modern and Western civilization.

The complementary orientation is directed toward the spiritual, or nonphysical. It is used to regulate the flow of energy within the body, and between the individual and the larger environment, by stimulating the chakras, meridians and tsubo. Reflecting a more integrated, holistic approach, it typifies the worldview of traditional and Eastern cultures.

Classified by the nature of its movements, modern exercise is generally more yang—comparatively fast, abrupt, strenuous motion, resulting in elevated rates of respiration and heartbeat, and the discharge of large amounts of caloric energy and body fluid. Interestingly, the short-term result of this more yang exercise is to produce a more yin state. The blood becomes acidic as a by-product of increased metabolic activity. Lowered blood sugar levels result in less energy and mental alertness. Our movements slow and we fell pleasantly tired and relaxed, or in the extreme, we may feel exhausted.

The opposite, more yin type of exercise includes slower, smoother, steady movements, the active use of the mind as well as the breath to enhance the routine, and relatively milder increases in heart and respiratory functions. In fact, the greater the proficiency in this approach, the more our movements reflect the effortless motion that is characteristic of the natural world.

The short-term effect of this more yin style of exercise is to sustain a more yang condition. The blood remains alkaline, blood sugar levels are steady, and thus physical energy remains stable. Circulation of blood and Ki is enhanced, the mind is alert, and muscles and body systems are toned but not taxed.

Following is a summary of the distinctions between the two approaches.

Modern/Western		*Traditional/Eastern*	
Physically oriented		Energetically oriented	
Discharges excess energy		Regulates energy flow	
More yang movements		More yin movements	
More yin short-term effects		More yang short-term effects	
Based on an animal-food diet		Based on a grain/vegetable diet	
Time and space intensive		Less use of time and space	
Requires special equipment		Little or no equipment needed	
Body	Emotions	Mind	Spirit

As is the case in any other pair of opposites, neither of these categories is superior. Both systems have their value, and certainly it is impossible to label either as good or bad. The desirability of one approach over the other is related to individual physical condition and temperament, and to the environment in which one lives. The fast-paced, stress-filled life in large cities, for instance, often produces bodily and emotional tensions that can be therapeutically addressed by a vigorous game of tennis or a brisk swim. The strengthening of cardiovascular and respiratory functions and enhanced metabolic processes are additional advantages.

Beyond these considerations, however, lies the question of why we must work so hard to ensure supple muscles and arteries, efficient circulation and respiration, digestion and elimination, and the proper functioning of organs and glands; and what is the most effective means of achieving this end. Supporting and underlying each of these states is the smooth flow of Ki. When choosing our exercise, both physiological and energetic factors need to be kept in mind.

Cultural Adaptation

Exercise patterns, like other customs and habits, represent a culture's specialized adaptation to its unique physical, temporal, and social environment. The various interpretations of hatha yoga (the practice of yoga's physical postures) in different countries is a fitting example of culture adaptation.

Now practiced around the world, this splendid system for physical and spiritual development has been modified by various societies to suit their special circumstances. In India, the extreme heat and consequently more yin diet produces a slower, gentler approach, with the emphasis on spiritual consciousness. In the United States and Europe, the colder climate and resultingly more yang diet produce a more physical approach, with the accent on weight loss, stress reduction, and in general "keeping fit." Social and environmental factors in Japan create a very physical, somewhat strenuous brand of yoga.

Each interpretation is the natural product of the environment where it flourishes. To the question of where the genuine yoga is being practiced, the answer can only be, wherever it is performed with a dynamic consideration for one's environment and personal circumstances.

Even within a particular culture, personal objectives and conditions vary. Some individuals will need to focus on developing physical vitality (becoming more yang), while relaxation (a more yin quality) may be the concern of others. In both cases, the unifying principles of yin and yang facilitate a penetrating appraisal of our personal circumstances to determine an exercise program most suitable for well-being and continued growth.

East and West

The modern approach to physical exercise has slowly evolved in response to our changing biological conditions, and social and physical environments. Mirroring our need to discharge accumulated energy, exercise patterns have become progressively more active and rough. This pent-up vitality is in large part the result of excessive animal-food consumption, which releases enormous quantitites of energy. Animals are the accumulation and condensation of the vegetable, mineral and preatomic realms. They incorporate a powerful concentration of calories and of more subtle energy. Consuming animal foods produces a strong burden of energetic and metabolic by-product elimination on the body and psyche.

Historically, Western diets contained comparatively large amounts (although small by today's standards) of animal foods and fats. This was partially due to colder temperatures, shorter growing seasons and poorer soil conditions. Such a diet supported hard physical labor and survival in colder, sometimes harsh climates.

Since the Industrial Revolution, and especially since the beginning of this century, proportionally more yang foods—eggs, hard, salty cheeses, meat—have been consumed, while daily life itself has become progressively less physically demanding. This combination of factors has produced vast amounts of excess energy in the body that must somehow be discharged.

Athletics are one outlet commonly used for this purpose. Not only is a growing percentage of the population participating, the character of our popular sports and recreations has also been altering to meet the needs of our own changing physical and psychological conditions. (This is also true of our other types of pastimes, and is obvious in the content of the television programs and movies we watch, and the music we listen to.)

Looking back over the last four or five decades, an obvious trend emerges toward more active, strenuous, competitive sports, which at their extreme, are violent. This development parallels the growing imbalance between the body's incoming and outgoing energy—we are taking in far more than we can return to the environment through ordinary channels.

The so-called gentlemanly sport of baseball is a product of the nineteenth century, while American football—perhaps the most explosive of team sports—is truly a metaphor for twentieth-century America. It is no coincidence that, along with Western dietary patterns, the popularity of American football is now spreading to Europe and Asia.

In a sense, Western athletics are therapeutic—although at times extreme, they are appropriate to current social and personal conditions, and in fact they could not be otherwise. They do help release energy, relieve tension, alleviate anxiety, and in general make us feel better. Physiologically, they offset, to a certain degree, the complications generated by our dietary excesses. However, such activities cannot address the underlaying cause of this intense energetic and nutritional buildup; they cannot prevent or eliminate it.

In the East, traditional systems of exercise reflect a nonphysical or spiritual orientation. This approach emerges from a diet centered around whole grains, beans and vegetables, and relatively little animal food. The milder climate, longer growing season, and fertile soil support this dietary approach.

The goal of Eastern exercise is the same as all other traditional therapeutic practices: to regulate Ki flow, and thus to develop and refine the energetic or spiritual body. Yoga, Tai-chi, Dō-In, Aikido, Qigong and others are all designed to normalize the circulation of energy for physical health and vitality, while leading to the larger goal of personal growth, culminating in enlightenment or self-realization.

Ki-related exercises serve the dual purposes of preventative medicine and, when the need arises, of treatment. They are a form of "self-massage" and can be used to balance an underactive or overactive energy flow in the body. With experience, Ki exercises can be employed quite effectively in treating specific problems or general complaints. Reflecting a holistic approach, they are equally effective and exact when dealing with the emotions and mind. Traditional practitioners recognized this ability, and prescribed such movements or exercises regularly.

Modern life, of course, differs considerably from traditional patterns. Even with a balanced diet (in terms of yin and yang in relation to personal and environmental conditions), moderate types of Western-style exercise can be pleasurable as well as beneficial. While discharging built-up energy, they also break down and release dietary excesses from the past. Equally important is their genuine, if less precise, ability to generate Ki. This is why physical activity in daily life is a major aspect of the macrobiotic approach to well-being.

Ki Exercises

Now that we have examined the two poles of physical activity, an example of the less-familiar Ki-related exercises will be helpful. The following *Meridian Exercises* are taken from Michio Kushi's *The Book of Dō-In: Exercises for Physical and Spiritual Development.*

Especially designed to influence the meridians, and their related physical and spiritual characteristics, the effectiveness of these exercises is based on their ability to harmonize the circulation of energy. When performing the exercises, hold the posture at its extreme point for one or two breaths. This will accelerate the energy flow of the meridians, resulting in the release of any stagnation and a normalization of Ki circulation. The related organs and systems, and the body parts through which the meridian runs, will be positively affected.

With these, or in fact any Ki-related exercise, do not be discouraged if stiffness or weakness prevents you from duplicating the movements exactly as described. Approximate each exercise to the best of your ability, while using your mind to visualize the ideal form. Remember that physical reality is created by energy patterns. Through our thoughts and images we influence our physical body.

Another important point is to be consistent. It is preferable to do a shorter routine on a daily basis, rather than a longer one irregularly. Executed daily, and in conjunction with a balanced diet, the body will respond in a relatively short time. After just a few weeks, you may be surprised to notice your increasing suppleness and endurance.

Meridian Exercises

1. Exercise for the Lung and Large Intestine Meridians

We stand with our feet apart, slightly more than shoulder width. The hands are behind the back, palms turned outward, with the thumbs hooked together.

In that posture, we raise the arms and simultaneously raise the head, looking up toward the ceiling (Fig. 55). Then, we bend forward as far as possible, keeping the thumbs hooked together (Fig. 56). At that time, we notice that the lung and large intestine meridians running on the arms and hands are well extended, and that the muscles covering the lungs and connected with the large intestine are also pulled. At the extreme point, we hold the posture for a while, breathing slowly two times in a relaxed condition, which results in the active flow of energy along the lung and large intestine meridians as well as the active circulation of blood along the related muscles.

If we change the hand position so the other thumb is on top and we perform the same postures again, we notice which side of the meridians—the right or the left—is in a more disorderly condition, by greater feelings of pain or strong tension in one side.

Fig. 55

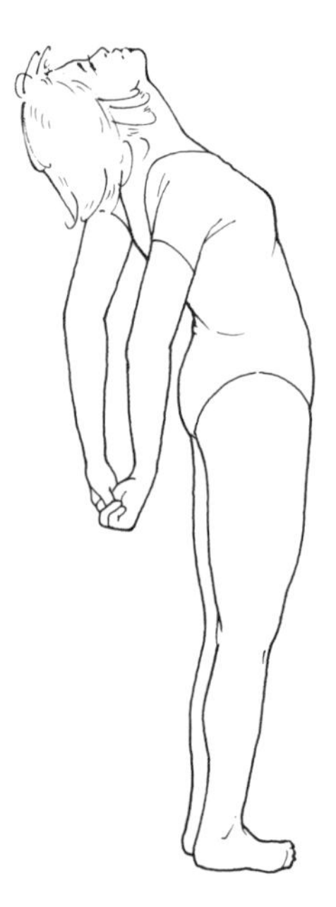

Fig. 56

2. Exercise for the Spleen-Pancreas and Stomach Meridians

We sit with natural right posture and clasp our hands together. Raise the hands up and slowly bring them back over the head, as illustrated (Fig. 57). Gradually lower the body backward to the floor, to the extent the shoulders touch the floor. If we extend our body and both arms enough to attach to the floor, the spleen-pancreas and stomach meridians running vertically in the front part of the body are strongly extended and we also feel stimulation to the region of the spleen, pancreas and stomach.

Keeping the posture, we breathe deeply two times, which accelerates the smooth running of energy and blood along the meridians and muscles.

If we change our hands so that the other thumb is on top, we notice that one side has more abnormalities than the other.

Fig. 57

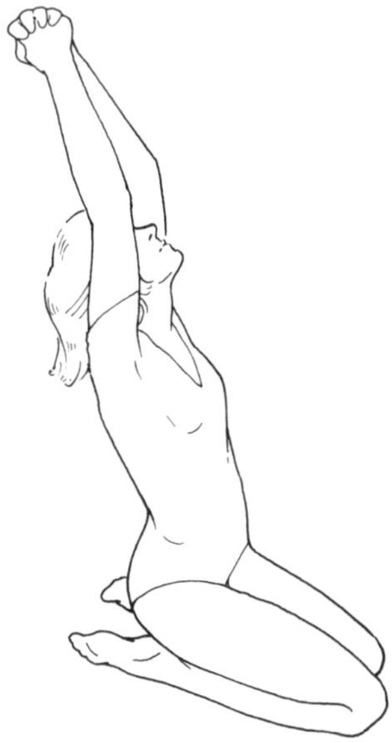

3. Exercise for the Heart and Small Intestine Meridians

We sit with the legs open wide, the knees bent toward the floor and the soles of the feet together. Hold the hands around the toes and bring the feet in toward the body as much as possible. Then, slowly bend forward, trying to touch the forehead to the thumbs (Fig. 58). In this posture, with all joints relaxed, we repeat slow breathing two times. During this breathing, we notice energy and blood streaming actively toward the heart and small intestine.

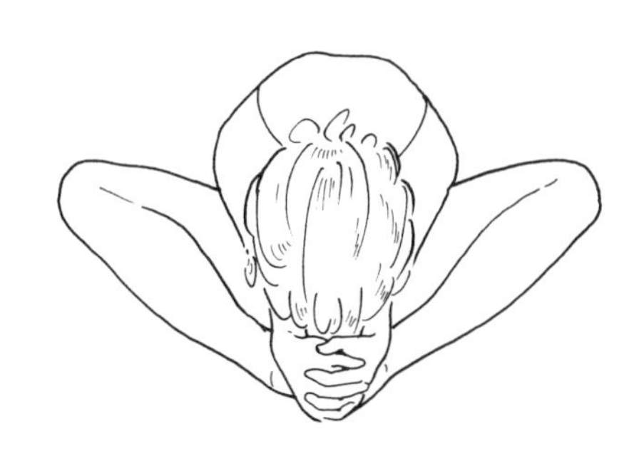

Fig. 58

If either knee is higher than the other, we feel more tension in that side and disorderly symptoms appear more in that side.

4. Exercise for the Kidney and Bladder Meridians

We sit on the floor, extending the legs, the backs of the legs touching the floor, and the feet held straight up vertically. Then, extend the arms and grasp the toes with the fingers.

Slowly bend the upper portion of the body toward the front, making the head touch the knees (Fig. 59).

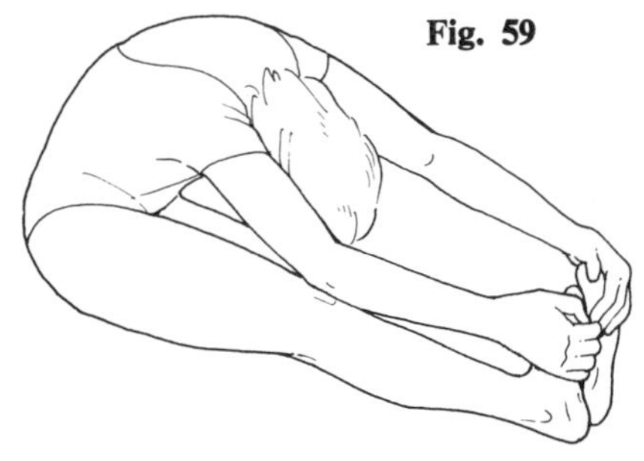

Fig. 59

Keeping that bending posture, we breathe deeply and slowly two times. At that time, through the kidney and bladder meridians, energy starts to flow more actively. If one of the knees tends to rise, or if more tension is felt along the back muscles of one leg, that side of the kidney function is more disordered than the other.

5. Exercise for the Heart Governor and Triple Heater Meridians

We sit in the lotus flower posture. Then, we cross the arms and hold each knee with the opposite hand, pressing down on the knees (Fig. 60).

We slowly bend forward as far as we can (Fig. 61).

Keeping this posture, breathe two times slowly, keeping all muscles relaxed. At that time, energy passes actively through the heart governor and triple heater meridians, stimulating vertically the central region of the body and the back spinal region. If we change arms so that the other arm is crossed on top and compare this posture, we may feel much more tension in one side of the body than in the other, which indicates that that side has more stagnation.

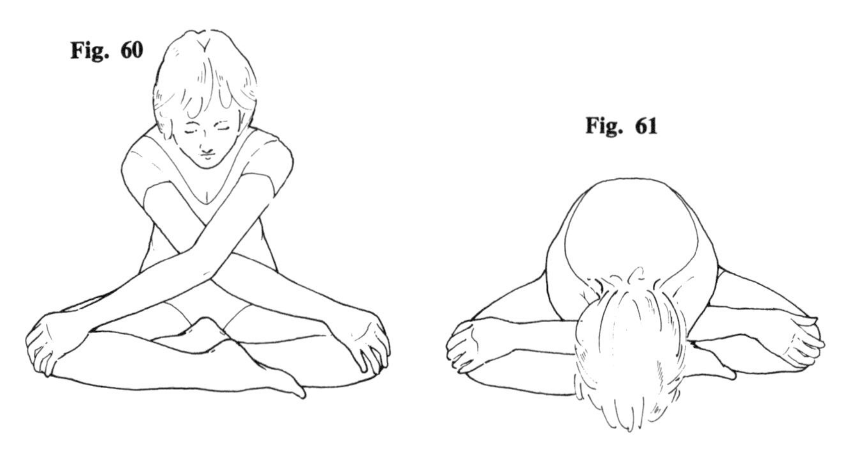

Fig. 60

Fig. 61

6. Exercise for the Liver and Gallbladder Meridians

We sit with both legs extended to the front, opened as widely as we can. Do not

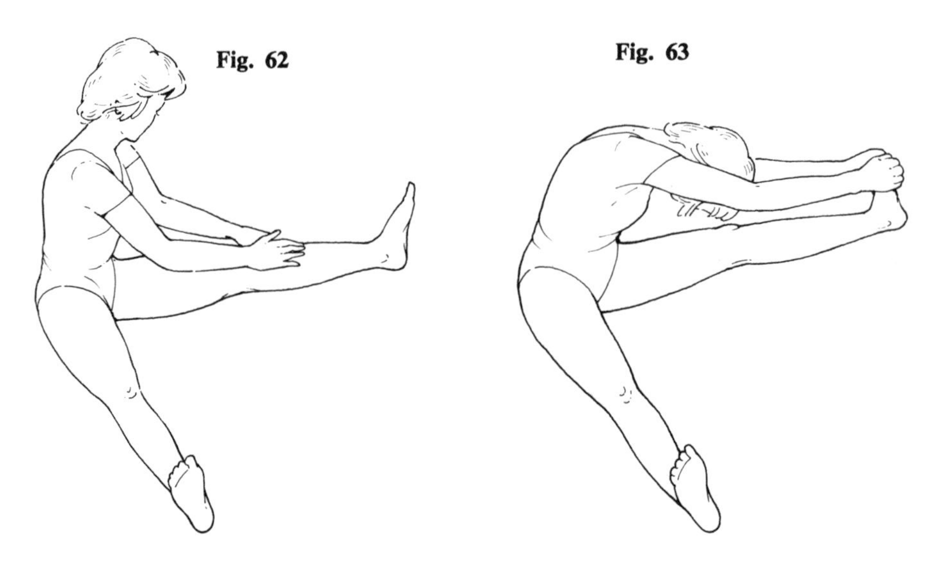

Fig. 62

Fig. 63

raise the knees, but keep them attached to the floor (Fig. 62). With the fingers extending forward, reach both arms toward one foot, bending forward as far as possible (Fig. 63). We slowly breathe two times in this posture, during which we can feel that the liver and gallbladder regions are being stimulated. Then, we raise our body and reach toward the other foot.

When we alternate left and right, we notice that it is more difficult to reach the foot on one side. There are more disorders and stagnation in that side.

In Summary

Physical activity is an essential part of life, which we ignore at the peril of both bodily health, and emotional and mental well-being. The question of whether or not one needs systematic exercise is a personal one. Be aware however, that life in the last decades of the twentieth century too often fails to provide opportunities for a comprehensive and balanced use of the body.

The additional consideration of using exercise not for prevention but as a therapy for physical or psychological aliments should not be overlooked. Instead of reaching for the medicine bottle the next time you experience constipation or stiffness, stress or depression, try some form of physical activity. (Better yet, why not eliminate the cause of such conditions entirely by dietary and lifestyle changes.)

Finally, when considering if regular exercise is necessary, the element of continued personal growth, or the development of consciousness should be considered. Indeed, this is the genuine purpose of exercise, as of life in general.

When deciding which type of exercise best suits our needs, we should remember that our lifestyle influences what we enjoy, what we are capable of, and what we need. Intellectually, we may choose a particular exercise program for its supposed benefits. However, if our condition and way of life does not support that particular activity, we will find it very difficult to follow through. And yet, if we do continue, we will most likely find our daily life altering in response to the changes that the exercises have produced. To use an extreme example, it would be difficult to be a vegetarian (no cheese or eggs) boxer. One would either have to start eating animal foods or give up the sport.

By using the principles of yin and yang, we can select and adjust exercises to support our present condition, and to help us develop those qualities that will foster our plans and dreams. As our condition and circumstances change during our lifetime, so too will the activities we are attracted to, and that provide the most benefit to us. This is the beauty of life—it is full of variety and new experiences appropriate to our level of development.

Massage

Webster's Ninth New Collegiate Dictionary defines massage as "manipulation of tissues (as by rubbing, stroking, kneading, or tapping) with the hand or an instrument for remedial or hygienic purposes." The origin of the word "massage" is traced to the French *masser* "to massage," and the Arabic *massa* "to stroke." This dual derivation is no coincidence, since it was the French who initiated a renewed Western interest in massage in the sixteenth century, and it is likely that the ancient Greeks acquired and modified a system of massage from the middle East.

The above definition is of course utilitarian, a barebones depiction of a sophisticated health-care practice. The fact is, massage, like all forms of medical practice, is both a science and an art. As a science, practitioners need to be familiar with anatomy and physiology. They must be conversant with various pathological states, if only to avoid compounding any already existing problem, and they should be proficient in evaluating the psychological states and needs of their clients. If they are employing the energetic forms of massage, therapists will also have studied the human energy system, the principles of Oriental medicine, and the application of various traditional diagnostic techniques.

As an art, therapists will work to develop a distinctive "touch" and a sense of confidence and ease when handling the human body. They will learn to discern when a client's physical and mental condition require a slow, gentle approach; when a stronger application is called for; when certain areas of the body need more time and attention; and when others should perhaps be avoided. Practitioners of traditional massage will strive to enhance their perception of, and ability to interpret, the various states of Ki. All of these abilities come from proper training, wide experience, continual study and reflection, and ultimately, the gradual unfolding of consciousness.

A Generation Gap

In the United States, at least, there is a generation gap that to a large extent determines one's attitude toward massage. (In Europe, appreciation is likely to depend on one's access to health spas.) Individuals whose attitudes and values were shaped before the social transformations that began to unfold several decades ago may frown on, and perhaps feel uncomfortable with, body work, even in a clinical milieu. Many of those who came after are less likely to be uneasy with physical contact and bodily manipulation.

Over the last several decades, starting with the cultural transformation that swept much of the Western world in the 1960s, there has been a rebirth of interest in massage A multiplicity of methods have emerged as practitioners assimilate techniques from various massage styles and add their own insights to what they have studied. Today, massage is once again taking a respected place within the health-care repertory. Dozens of informative books discuss the theory and describe the practice of diverse styles; excellent practitioners can be found in many cities; well-qualified instructors teach at schools that offer certification; and legal restraints—along with the unfortunate stigma of illicitness long associated with massage (the infamous "massage parlors")—are slowly being removed.

This revival springs from the same impulses that gave birth to the entire field of holistic medicine: a desire for a nonviolent, noninvasive medical practice, one that sees illness as an issue involving the entire person, and that in turn sees an individual in a multidimensional context. Massage, as a safe, simple, and whole-person therapy, clearly satisfies these objectives.

Macrobiotic education has long been a pioneer in the teaching and promotion of massage—both as a therapeutic technique and as a tool for personal development. Following the tenets of traditional and Oriental medicine, an energetic style of massage, called *shiatsu* (which we will discuss at length), was introduced in the United States by macrobiotic teachers three decades ago. Since that time, tens of thousands of individuals have learned how to employ this simple health-care application on themselves, their families and their friends.

Like all aspects of traditional medicine, the macrobiotic emphasis is not confined to the use of massage for the reversal or even the prevention of illness. Rather, massage represents another tool for the development of our physical, mental and spiritual Selves.

The Origins of Massage

Kneading or stroking a stiff or sore, hard, cold or numb body part is an instinctual act, one we can witness a dozen times a day if we are observant. The face and head are commonplace areas of this usually unconscious habit. Individuals routinely rub their temples or eyes; worry the bridge and tip of the nose, the forehead, and the ears; stroke the chin or hair; and knead the back of the head and neck, all for very good reasons.

As we have seen, the head and trunk reflect a complementary relationship. What exists internally and in expanded form within the body cavity, is represented on the head externally and in compact form. Thus, to influence the glands, internal organs and systems, stimulation can be applied on the surface of the head and face. But the significance of this behavior does not end here. The energetic relationship between organs and psychological states has already been detailed. When we stimulate areas of the face and head, we are also nourishing various emotional and mental qualities as well.

By understanding the system of correspondences between the head and trunk, and between specific physical and mental states of consciousness, as discussed in Part 1, we can recognize which qualities are being addressed. This is a key point. With such insight, we can proceed to accentuate the particular attribute, or take steps to address the relevant condition, in a comprehensive fashion, via diet, outlook, and other lifestyle factors.

Many thousands of years ago, our ancestors developed this intuitive method of self-massage into a coordinated and systematic pattern of therapy. Traditional societies around the world at one time practiced, and in many cases still use, massage for a host of objectives. For instance, applications were devised to promote well-being during pregnancy, to relieve complications during delivery, and to enhance milk production in lactating mothers; to foster growth in infants and young children; to heal the sick and injured; to maintain vitality in the elderly; and to address emotional problems for individuals of all ages.

The Decline of Massage

Two powerful historical forces are responsible for the decline of massage, first in the West and then in the modern world. The association of the body and the physical senses with moral weakness was a major factor in destroying the credibility of massage in Western societies. The divorce of the body from the soul, and the denigration of the one and the celebration of the other, is a classic example of front-and-back thinking. This attitude reflects the either/or approach discussed earlier, in which we value and pursue one partner of a complementary pair and ignore the other. The inescapable result of this fragmented value system is the creation of extremes—in thinking and behavior—which in time lead to unlooked for and equally excessive consequences.

Gradually, the body and its needs came to be regarded as a primary source of evil, an attitude that profoundly influenced the development of Western civilization for many centuries. This outlook was forcefully, if clumsily, confronted by the sexual revolution of the 1970s. With hindsight, this upheaval in values and behavior brings to mind the image of a huge watch spring, wound too tight, that suddenly lets loose in an explosion of pent-up and uncontrollable energy.

Closer to our own time, the advent of the Scientific Revolution severed the connection between body and mind with the force and apparent finality of a sledgehammer blow. The subsequent ascendancy of modern medicine, with its preoccupation on bacteria and viruses, technology and pharmaceuticals, seemed to perform the coup de grâce to any official endorsement of massage as a therapeutic and preventative technique.

In the Far East, it was the introduction of Western medicine that greatly diminished the reputation and popularity of massage. With its clinical approach to physiology and anatomy, its awesome precision and rational theories, Western medicine drove massage to the fringes of respectability. In Japan, the centuries-old practice of traditional massage as an essential component of established medicine, lost its legal status. Later, when it was re-franchised, the therapy was scorned by Western-trained physicians and consequently shunned by a large portion of the population.

The situation today is more promising. Mirroring the natural principle that extremes invariably turn into their opposites, the disregard for the human body, and for the utility of body manipulation, is predictably being replaced by a growing interest in massage and in the wider field of related therapies loosely categorized as "bodywork."

Benefits of Massage

Reflecting its holistic nature, massage is capable of addressing each dimension of consciousness that collectively comprise the Self. The range of its effectiveness is limited only by the training, skill and vision of the individual practitioner. This is a broad claim, one we will not pass over without clarification.

The front-and-back relationship of the body and mind has already been established, as has the energetic (Ki) mechanism of this association. Whether intentional or not, whether physically or energetically oriented, all massage applications manipulate the body's subtle energy to some degree. In the hands of a skilled and knowledgeable therapist, Ki can be adjusted in precise ways to influence the various aspects of individual consciousness. As countless individuals are experiencing, massage can be a practical tool in enhancing emotional well-being and spiritual growth, just as surely as it can for nurturing physical health.

A sample of the physical benefits of massage include: basic stress reduction and relaxation; enhanced blood and lymph circulation, and the resulting improved nourishment, oxygenation, and waste removal from the cells; toned glands, organs and muscles; and revitalized functioning of the organ systems. Massage fulfills one of the primary purposes of traditional medicine: the prevention of illness by eliminating incipient problems long before they develop into serious conditions.

The list of specific categories to which massage can be successfully applied is as comprehensive as human nature itself:

- *As a health-maintenance practice*, regular massage can be employed much like daily exercise to keep body and mind fit.
- *As a first aid measure*, massage can be used as a noninvasive remedy for a host of complaints including but not limited to cramps, nosebleed, toothache, earache, headache, asthma attacks, hemorrhoids, constipation and diarrhea. Following an injury, massage can minimize tissue damage and accelerate recovery time.
- *As an effective therapy for chronic conditions.* The list of chronic conditions that can be assisted with massage is extensive. As a medical therapy, massage can be profitable used with practically any problem that falls within the category of chronic disorders. This includes such apparently intractable conditions as diabetes mellitus, arthritis, prostate problems and male impotency, herniated spinal discs, gallstones, and a wide range of others.

  This does not mean that massage therapists will recommend against consulting one's doctor, or suggest that conventional medical therapy be discontinued. Nor is it meant to imply that massage alone can eliminate such complaints. Rather, in conjunction with other lifestyle factors discussed in this book, massage can vitalize the body's own recuperative abilities. As this occurs, the stage is set for genuine healing as opposed to symptomatic relief.
- *For emotional and psychological complaints.* Traditional physicians/philosophers made no practical distinction between physical and mental well-being. The two were considered to be mirror images of each other—the condition of one is reflected in and affected by the quality of the other.

The specific relationship between emotional/mental states and the body organs has already been detailed. In this respect, massage works by vitalizing both partners in the body/mind association. This is accomplished by restoring a healthy energy flow to the chakras, meridians and tsubo. Once energetic harmony is established, the psychological symptoms of the former imbalance will begin to fade.

- *As a means of enhancing the growth of consciousness.* Understanding our strengths and weaknesses, and articulating our aspirations, enables us to use massage to support the direction and pace of our development. We may choose to concentrate on definite characteristics, for instance, more patience or a brighter outlook, or we may resolve to proceed in a more general way, perhaps concentrating on developing insight or the spiritual side of our selves. In either case, with an grasp of the human energy system, massage can be a practical agent in our pursuit of growth.

Admittedly, not all styles of massage or all practitioners feel competent to address such a wide range of human needs. As an energetic application, however, massage has the potential to be used as a truly holistic medicine. (The word "medicine" is used here in its traditional sense, namely, as a way of maintaining well-being and fostering personal evolution.)

The obvious questions arise as to why we have been so slow to take advantage of massage, and why its practice is still not a generally recognized and utilized tool within the medical profession. Aside from the two points mentioned earlier, we might add that the low-tech, hands-on approach to health care may lack the glamour and prestige of modern medicine. Massage may simply seem too modest a therapy in a field routinely judged by the complexity of its procedures and the degree of specialty of its practitioners.

It is our hope that this book will inspire a sense of competence and responsibility in the areas of personal well-being. Massage, and the other commonsense alternatives discussed, represent the agents for a degree of individual freedom rarely seen in contemporary society.

Complementary Approaches

The general field of massage can be divided into two pairs of complementary categories. One relationship exists between *self-massage*, in which an individual applies stimulation to him- or herself, and massage given to or received by another. This twosome will be discussed in detail in a moment. The second pair describes the distinction between modern and traditional, or Eastern and Western approaches.

The focus of modern and Western massage is physical, or more yang. Its purpose can be summed up with the concept of renewal. Firmly based on anatomy and physiology, and directed more toward the corporeal aspects of health, Western massage is used to restore the vigor, flexibility and health that an individual may have once enjoyed.

Not surprisingly, the mechanisms used in this pursuit are the complementary methods of sedation and stimulation. On the one hand, modern massage techniques can be used to disperse excess energy; break down hardness of tissue, muscle and tendon, and stiffness in joints; sooth frazzled nerves and relieve tension. Conversely, it can also be used in a reverse course to activate the circulation of blood and other body fluids; stimulate the function of organs, glands and systems; and tone the skin and muscles.

Masseurs generate specific results by selecting from an assortment of techniques and by varying the yin and yang influence of each application, for example, by using either gentle or strong pressure, slow or fast movements, superficial or deep penetration, and centripetal or centrifugal motions (toward or away from the heart, upward or downward along the spine, the more yang kneading or the more yin stroking).

The complementary orientation, represented by traditional and Far-Eastern massage, is energetic in focus, and thus more yin. The emphasis here is on maintenance and enhancement of body and mind. Grounded on the principles of Oriental medicine, traditional massage is used to regulate the flow of energy within the body, and between the individual and the larger environment. Personal development is the hallmark of this approach.

Also using techniques of sedation (a yin process) and stimulation (a yang process), traditional massage accomplishes its task by working on the chakras, meridians and tsubo that comprise the human energetic system. Although its starting point differs from its modern counterpart, its physical benefits are similar to those listed above. Going beyond such considerations, however, is the attention paid to the mental health and spiritual development of individuals.

A discussed in the preceding section on exercise, both approaches have their value, and the desirability of one over the other is directly related to individual condition and lifestyle. Reflecting these mutual benefits is the fact that Oriental practitioners long ago incorporated Western medical concepts and techniques from Western massage into their routines. And, in recent years, Western practitioners have begun to assimilate the philosophy of energetics and specific applications from Oriental massage.

In the West

Massage itself has been employed around the world since earliest times. In the West, the classical Greeks, and after them the Romans, made extensive use of massage. It is likely that the practice was assimilated from ancient Egypt, or from civilizations further east. This could have occurred along the celebrated Silk Road, an ancient trade route linking China with the West, and used as an conduit for goods, and indirectly as a passage for the two-way exchange of discoveries, inventions and ideas. (Marco Polo's celebrated journey from Italy to China followed this course.) We know that further back in time, massage was an important part of the venerable Ayurveda medical and health-maintenance system of ancient India.

After the demise of massage in the West, more than a thousand years were to go by before it was again given serious consideration in Europe. In the sixteenth century, on the eve of the Scientific Revolution, French researchers began to investigate the therapeutic possibilities of massage. Several centuries later, their work influenced the development of Swedish massage, which forms the basis for what today can broadly be categorized as Western massage. It is interesting to note that Swedish massage was designed to reproduce the benefits of the sophisticated Swedish system of exercise.

This close association between exercise and massage is not accidental. Massage can be regarded as an extension and more specialized, concentrated, and specific form of exercise. While supplying many of the benefits of exercise, massage requires more training; often, though certainly not necessarily, falls into the realm of professional application; and obviously requires someone to apply it (with the exception of self-massage). In this sense, massage straddles the fence between health-care practices that center on the home and the family and those falling into the category of specialized care.

Numerous variations of Swedish massage and entirely different techniques have been developed over the years, particularly during the last several decades. Applications now range from gentle manipulation and subtle applications such as "therapeutic touch," an offshoot of palm healing, to deep-tissue manipulation. Often stretching the limits of massage as it is conventionally defined, these practices have inspired the more pliant heading of "bodywork" to accommodate them. When comparing Western and Eastern massage, a distinction should thus be made between the basic form of Western massage, represented by Swedish massage, and the newer Western applications, whose techniques may share less resemblance to their forebear than they do to their Eastern counterparts.

Eastern Approach

Massage has been a primary component of Eastern medicine for thousands of years. *The Yellow Emperor's Classic of Internal Medicine* explains that massage was developed in the central region of China to meet the specific needs of individuals living in that particular geography and climate. To quote from *The Yellow Emperor's Classic*:

> The people of the regions of the center eat mixed food and do not (suffer or weary at their) toil. Their diseases are many: they suffer from complete paralysis and chills and fever. These diseases are most fittingly treated with breathing exercises, massage of the skin, and exercises of the hands and feet.

Just as we can distinguish between orthodox and contemporary interpretations of Western masssge, a pair of complementary approaches can be discerned within the broad category of Eastern massage: (1) a physically oriented application—for stiff joints and muscles, and problems caused by stagnation in the circulation of blood and energy, for instance—which is commonly known as *amma*, and (2) an energetically oriented application, called shiatsu, which more specifically addresses the meridians.

Amma (or *anma*) refers to the form of massage whose origins in China are referred to in *The Yellow Emperor's Classic of Internal Medicine*. As we are told, geography and climate, and the lifestyle developed to match these factors, tended to produce complaints arising from what was generally regarded as stagnation. Amma was developed to expressly address such conditions. When it was incorporated into the formal body of Chinese medicine at the time of the Han dynasty, amma was thus classified as a specific remedy for such dysfunctions.

An energetically oriented pattern of massage was also developed in China, by the Taoists. It emerged as part of a comprehensive self-development practice, similar to yoga in India. Perhaps owing to the secrecy surrounding Taoist teachings, this form of application was not widely disseminated, although it is still practiced in China. Interestingly, recent developments in energetic forms of massage mirror, if not in fact incorporate, such practices.

Along with other forms of Oriental medicine, amma reached Japan in the sixth century and soon became a primary therapeutic tool used by physicians. Steeped in the principles of the Far-Eastern worldview, amma practitioners rub (*am*) and press (*ma*) along the meridians and over the tsubo to adjust Ki in various ways. Applications are also employed, however, in the framework of a more physical orientation to more directly stimulate the flow of blood and lymph, improve muscle and skin tone, dissolve hardness in muscles, and improve nerve function. Joint manipulation, used to enhance mobility and flexibility, is a further aspect of amma.

Distinctive applications in amma include rubbing and stroking for purposes of stimulation; kneading to dissolve hardness of muscles; joint manipulation to break up deposits; vibration and tapping to enhance nerves and muscles via stimulation; and pressure to stimulate the tsubo, and for the more direct soothing of conditions like neuralgia and muscle cramps.

It is no coincidence that, in some of its techniques, amma is similar to Western massage. With the introduction of modern medicine, including Western massage, traditional medicine lost its primary position as a medical therapy. In an effort to save their art Japanese amma practitioners studied aspects of Western medicine—including anatomy and physiology—and incorporated Western massage techniques into their routines. These efforts were successful in gaining legal status for amma. However, the practice never succeeded in regaining its former stature and was regulated to the ranks of folk medicine. Today, amma exists as a blend of Western and Eastern healing philosophies and applications. Although health insurance pays for amma treatments, these are limited to conditions involving muscle stiffness, back problems and painful joints.

Shiatsu

In the long history of Oriental medicine, shiatsu is a very recent development. While its origins are founded on the practice of amma, shiatsu, as a distinct massage application, emerged in this century as a comprehensive therapeutic system, going beyond the scope of amma applications.

Shiatsu, literally meaning "finger" (*shi*) "pressure" (*atsu*), is a Japanese innovation. It evolved from the above-mentioned efforts of amma practitioners to accommodate the concepts of Western medicine in order to gain legal recognition.

Troubled by the dilution of their theoretical background, a few practitioners began to delve deeply into their Oriental medicine heritage. The result was simultaneously a retrenchment and a broadening of the range of massage therapy: a revival of traditional concepts, and an expansion of the application of massage to aspects of healing not specifically addressed by amma.

After decades of effort on the part of practitioners, in 1964 the Japanese government legalized shiatsu as "a form of manipulation administered by the thumbs, fingers, and palms, without the use of any instrument, mechanical or otherwise, to apply pressure to the human skin, correct internal malfunctioning, promote and maintain health, and treat specific diseases." As the official definition suggests, shiatsu is a versatile tool, capable of addressing a wide range of issues related to health and well-being.

Practitioners use the fingers and hands, as well as the elbows, feet and knees, to stimulate the tsubos and meridians. Some schools place their emphasis more directly on the physical factors that disrupt the body's energy flow. Examples include the tone and flexibility of muscles; the mobility of joints; and the structural integrity of the skeletal system. Other schools work more directly with Ki in order to rectify energetic imbalances. It should be noted that this difference is more of style than of substance. Both employ the principles of Oriental medicine to promote a vital and harmonious energy flow.

The general purpose and application of shiatsu are akin to those of acupuncture. This similarity accounts for the English word "acupressure" which is often applied to shiatsu and other energetically oriented forms of massage. In both therapies, after diagnosis to determine the specific cause and nature of energetic imbalances, the meridians and tsubo are manipulated in a variety of ways to normalize the flow of energy within the body. In acupuncture the manipulation is done with needles, and in shiatsu, with the hands and fingers.

Treatment in either discipline is geared toward the energetic distortions which cause the symptoms we commonly think of as sickness. A headache in the back of the head, for instance, may be caused by an imbalance of energy in the bladder and its related meridian. The discomfort in the head is simply a reflection and consequence of this imbalance. Rather than working directly or exclusively on the head, a practitioner is likely to focus attention along the entire bladder meridian, perhaps to its partner, the kidney meridian, and possibly to other meridians as well, in accordance with the principles discussed in Part 1.

It should come as no surprise, then, that diagnosis is an essential factor in effective massage. In fact, several forms of diagnosis—abdominal and meridian diagnosis—are viewed as being basic components of actual treatment. Practitioners are trained to interpret the condition of the meridians and tsubo during application, and conversely, to perform abdominal and meridian diagnosis in a way that influences that condition of the meridians. From this simple application alone, minor imbalances tend to be corrected, though more specific methods are generally required.

Although any combination of diagnostic methods listed in Part 1 are utilized, the primary method of evaluation used in shiatsu is abdominal diagnosis. Specific regions of the abdomen are energetically connected with the ten organ meridians and the two functional meridians (the heart governor and the triple heater). By gently pressing these areas, a sensitive practitioner can identify the energetic state —Kyo (empty) or Jitsu (full)— of each meridian. This knowledge is essential for a professional therapist, as it allows him or her to address the cause of the individual's complaint. If shiatsu is practiced at home, for minor problems or as a health-maintenance practice, exact diagnosis is not crucial. However, learning this form of evaluation is an excellent means of cultivating one's perception of Ki.

Applications

As a holistic therapy, shiatsu can adress a wide range of physical and mental conditions. Applications include:

1. *Spinal correction.* The condition of the spinal column is a major influence on, and accurate indicator of, one's state of health. Physiologically, nerves branch out from the spine to all areas of the body, relaying impulses back-and-forth from the brain. Energetically, the Yu (entering) points, located on the back, along the spine, are actually the beginning of individual meridians. Distortions along the spine or at the Yu points can consequently be a major source of energy disruption. For this reason, spinal correction is an important accessory to any treatment. Techniques used in shiatsu are not complicated, but do require training for accurate application.

2. *Manipulation of joints.* The joints are frequent sights of stagnation and hardness, which diminishes the flow of energy (as well as the circulation of body fluids). This blockage may in turn lead to any number of physical and mental complaints. Joint manipulation techniques used in shiatsu are similar to those employed in amma.

3. *The application of pressure* (along the meridians). Perhaps the most common image of shiatsu, pressure application is the primary element of a shiatsu treatment. By applying pressure to the tsubos and along the meridians, a practitioner endeavors to influence the quality and intensity of Ki in general and very specific ways. Nuances of application vary from school to school, although several key principles regarding the application of pressure need to stressed:

    1. Body weight rather than muscular strength is used to apply pressure. There should be no strain or tension in the wrists, hands, fingers or any area of the body. Rather, the therapist positions himself so that the weight of the body supplies the necessary degree of pressure.
    2. Pressure is directed to the center of the receiver's body, for instance the center of the leg, arm, head or whatever body part is being addressed. This reflects the natural movement of centripetal force, which spirals inward toward the center of a thing. When we mimic this natural motion we accentuate the effectiveness of therapy.
    3. Apply steady pressure. Rather than quick, abrupt or jerky motions along a meridian or over a tsubo, the practitioner holds each application of pres-

sure, allowing time for the stimulation to penetrate the tsubo. The amount of time pressure is applied to a particular tsubo or body part varies from three to ten seconds up to a minute or more, depending of the needs of the receiver.

In a related fashion, rather than breaking the connection with the receiver, practitioner learns to keep the fingers or hand in contact with the body when moving from point to point along the meridians.

4. Utilize the hands in a complementary fashion. One hand is used to apply pressure while the other hand remains stationary in order to convey a counterbalancing energy and sense of support. This is of course another way of saying that the hands are utilized in a yin and yang fashion.

During a shiatsu session, a practitioner presses along each meridian, lingering at certain points according to need. The condition of each tsubo is noted to determine overall condition and also to assess any changes that may be taking place in response to treatment. Variations in holding time, pressure (light or heavy), pace of application (slow or fast), as well as the selection of application styles enable a practitioner to make precise adjustments.

Reflecting a holistic and traditional background, shiatsu practitioners do not limit their treatment to body manipulation. On the educational side, the importance of diet, outlook, relaxation and other lifestyle factors in maintaining health is firmly stressed. One immediate suggestion likely to be made is the practice of Ki-based exercise—various postures and movements employed to balance the meridians, with specific exercises for each meridian. Routines are recommended as a specific form of therapy to accentuate treatments and as a general means to promote well-being.

Returning to the example of a headache in the back of the head, executing the exercises specific to the bladder and the kidney meridians (see the Meridian Exercises for an example) may be enough by itself to bring relief. Shizuto Masunaga, creator of Zen Shiatsu—perhaps the most sophisticated style of shiatsu being practiced today—developed an extensive system of Ki exercises, including the meridian exercises discussed earlier in this chapter. Masunaga's *Zen Imagery Exercises* is an excellent source of information and suggestions for physical and mental exercises designed to enhance energy flow.

A Shiatsu Treatment

Following the tenets of traditional medicine, a shiatsu treatment is straightforward. No special equipment is called for, other than a low cushion for the head and perhaps a blanket to make the receiver comfortable. The receiver wears loose clothing and removes any jewelry before a session. During the course of application, the receiver will be asked to assume several positions, including:

- A sitting position, so that the head, shoulders and back can be approached
- A lying position, alternatively on the right and left side, then on the stomach and finally on the back

The giver too changes his position and posture to best apply the standards mentioned above.

A massage session can take anywhere from forty-five to ninety minutes, depending on the needs of the receiver. After the receiver is made comfortable in a supine position, the practitioner will establish contact by quietly sitting beside him or her, with his hands gently resting on the receiver's body. Then, abdominal diagnosis will begin. The receiver next takes a sitting position, and treatment will commence. At the end of the session, diagnosis will probably be repeated to determine the effectiveness and response.

Various forms of application will be used in the course of a shiatsu application. These include: pressing with the palms, fingers, elbows, knees or feet, to regulate the energy system; undulation with the palm, especially over the lower abdomen, to sooth the internal organs and meridians; rubbing and stroking, to stimulate the circulation of blood and lymph; kneading the muscles, to break up hardness; grasping with the fingers and hands to stimulate the meridians and tsubo; joint manipulation, to break up deposits in the joints; and spinal adjustments, for both structural and energetic purposes. Specific applications vary to suit the condition and needs of the receiver.

Certainly, much more could be said about shiatsu (this goes for amma and Western massage as well). Our intention is simply to introduce readers to the value of massage and to illustrate the relative orientation and techniques of various approaches. Also, the emphasis has been more on the use of massage for healing and in a clinical setting. In reality, massage's primary role is the prevention and enhancement of health in the family setting. Interested readers are encouraged to refer to the books listed in the bibliography and to seek out other titles that may have been overlooked.

Self-Shiatsu

In the 1960s, Michio Kushi began to introduce the art of *Dō-In* at his classes and seminars. Dō-In is a comprehensive system of practices and exercises specifically designed to enhance physical, mental and spiritual development. Its origins are as old as humanity itself, and its formal structure has served as the basis for subsequent sciences of human development. In its scope, Dō-In is similar to the practice of yoga in India, and Taoism in China, in that it is a holistic approach to well-being, including diet, exercise, massage, spiritual practices such as chanting, breathing techniques, visualization, meditation, and other lifestyle factors.

One aspect of Dō-In is a system of self-shiatsu, performed as a health-maintenance technique, and as a means to foster personal growth. Because self-shiatsu was the first segment of Dō-In introduced by Kushi, the two terms are sometimes used interchangeably. This is a mistake that Kushi's comprehensive book, *The Book of Dō-In: Exercise for Physical and Spiritual Development* set to rest, although occasionally the terms are still confused.

Self-shiatsu is generally done in the morning. The intent is to activate Ki throughout the body via direct stimulation of the meridians, and, augmenting this goal, to break down any stagnation and hardness. In general, the application proceeds in sequence, moving smoothly from beginning to end. Specific steps of the routine can be selectively used, however, to generate particular physical and mental qualities. An abbreviated example of self-shiatsu follows. Readers interested in a detailed discussion are referred to Kushi's *The Book of Dō-In.*

To start off, a simple meditation and chant are recommended to calm the body and mind. Take a comfortable sitting position, with the spine straight and the shoulders relaxed. With the palms facing upward and resting on the lap, left hand on top of the right, close the eyes and perform the empty-mind meditation, described earlier, by simply releasing all thoughts.

After several minutes in this quiet state, chant the sound of "Su" five to ten times. The hands can be joined in prayer position, either at heart level with the back of the thumbs gently pressing against the heart chakra, or at the throat, with the pads of the thumbs resting lightly against either side of the larynx. This hand position sends additional energy through the hands and fingers: energy that will then be reapplied to the body.

The general sequence of self-shiatsu is:

1. With loose wrists and lightly closed palms, pound the top of the head in a counterclockwise direction. Next, do the back and then the sides of the head.
2. Rub the ears vigorously, upward, outward and downward. Because there are tsubo for the entire body on the ears, this practice has an overall toning effect.
3. Cup the right hand over the right ear and rhythmically tap the back of the hand with the left index and middle finger. Tap in pairs—one, two; one, two—ten times, then repeat on the left ear.
4. Rub the face briskly, starting with the cheeks, then the forehead and finally the nose.
5. Massage the gums, top and bottom, with the tips of the fingers.
6. With the pads of the index and middle fingers resting lightly on the closed eyelids, softly press the eyes and release. Repeat ten times.
7. With the hands cupped over the eyes, look upward as far as possible, and then downward. Repeat ten times.
8. With the hands in the same position, look as far left as possible, and then as far right. Repeat this sequence ten times. Then revolve the eyes in a clockwise circle and then a counterclockwise circle. Repeat ten times in each direction.
9. Gently rotate the neck in a clockwise and then a counterclockwise circle, three times each way. Next, lightly pound the sides and back of the neck with the heel of the palm.
10. Pound the left shoulder with the right hand about ten times, then reverse shoulders.
11. With the hands and fingers, squeeze down along the arms, from the shoulders to the wrist. Start on the outside of the arm, then do the inside.
12. Press the back of the hand on a line from the wrist to the tip of each finger.

Rotate each finger in left- and right-hand circles. Then massage the palm as well, in lines from the wrist to the fingertips. To finish, press the center of each palm with the thumb.

13. Lightly pound down along the chest, front and side, then down along the abdomen, front and side.
14. Bend forward and lightly pound the kidney region, then down the lower back. Stand and repeat on the buttocks.
15. Pound down the legs to the knees, front, inside, outside, and back. Then, with the heel of the palm, rub from the knee to the ankle—front, back and sides.
16. Rotate each ankle several times in both directions. Then press down over the top of the foot, on a line from the ankle to the tip of each toe. Rotate each toe in left- and right-hand circles.
17. Massage the bottom of the feet with the thumbs.
18. Stand and jump lightly about ten times. The shoulders and arms should hang loosely at the sides. Then repeat about ten times using only one foot and then the other.

Regular performance of this routine stimulates the smooth flow of energy, activates the circulation of body fluids, and energizes the glands, organs and systems. It is an ideal way to start the day and a valuable tool in anyone's health-maintenance program.

Clearly, exercise and massage are practical agents in anyone's personal development program. In various forms, both have been practiced around the world, throughout history. Developing the body, mind and spirit has been the goal, and the principles of traditional and Oriental medicine have provided the guidelines.

We are fortunate today to be able to select from numerous approaches to suit our physical and mental inclinations. And, with health statistics unquestionably reflecting the increase of bodily and mental complaints in modern society, the need for these practices has never been greater.

When we fail to take the initiative for our well-being, problems may eventually develop that require the ministrations of a professional. In the next chapter, the most widely known and clinically oriented aspects of Oriental medicine, acupuncture and moxibustion, are discussed.

6. Acupuncture and Moxibustion

The image commonly elicited by the mention of Oriental medicine is that of an acupuncturist inserting needles into a patient. As we now know, this picture reflects a naive perception of the breadth of the holistic healing arts. When determining an appropriate form of treatment, a traditionally oriented physician surveys the entire spectrum of therapeutic categories described in Part 2, rather than routinely resorting to acupuncture. Adhering to the dictates listed earlier, the physician would recommend the simplest treatment deemed effective, and then utilize it for the shortest time possible. Inevitably, he would offer dietary and lifestyle suggestions to support whatever treatments are required, and to ensure that the underlying cause of the problem is addressed.

In a clinical situation, practitioners have three immediate and specific means of influencing Ki—massage, acupuncture and moxibustion. (Herbal medicine is another effective and commonly used tool employed for this purpose. However, because of its depth and sophistication, it is most often practiced by someone specializing in this area, and who probably works out of a herbal-medicine pharmacy.)

Acupuncture, and its therapeutic partner, moxibustion, complete the shift in our study from therapies performed on the personal level and in the home and family setting, to those executed by health-care professionals working in a clinical environment. Minimum requirements for practitioners include several years of formalized training—to master the principles of Oriental medicine, various forms of diagnosis, meridian and point location, and needle and moxa technique—the passing of a government sanctioned licensing examination, and ideally, an apprenticeship with an accomplished professional. Additional years of experience, study and reflection are necessary to refine these skills. Wisdom and intuition, the hallmarks of a genuine healer, are the cumulative result of such persistent effort.

Due to the detailed knowledge and technical precision required to practice acupuncture and moxibustion, this chapter will be the shortest in this part. The basic concepts utilized in acupuncture are identical to those of Oriental medicine in general, as discussed in Part 1. Leaving the mechanics of application to more specialized works, we will limit ourselves to the outlines of what may be, for many readers, unfamiliar forms of healing.

Acupuncture

Acupuncture is defined in one English-language dictionary as "the originally Chinese practice of puncturing the body with needles at specific points to cure disease or relieve pain." These "specific points" are of course the tsubo or energy points along the meridians. And the instruments used for the "puncturing" are the very thin, solid (as opposed to hollow) acupuncture needles.

The purpose of acupuncture is identical to all other traditional medical therapies:

to restore balance within the body's energy system. We have seen that traditional physicians regarded the source of illness—physical or psychological—as an energy imbalance. In diagnosis and treatment, healers looked beyond the overt symptoms to address this underlying cause. Thus all forms of treatment were designed and applied to return the circulation of Ki to a harmonized state. As this was accomplished, symptoms would naturally disappear.

Ministrations were specifically geared either toward sedating, or draining, the excess energy in a *Jitsu*, or full condition, or to supplementing, or toning, deficient energy in a *Kyo*, or empty condition. Tonification is accomplished by supplying a light stimulation, and paradoxically, sedation is produced by the application of stronger stimulation. This practice is a reflection of the principle that, at its extreme point, a condition or circumstance will change to its opposite. Thus, the general result of strong stimulation to an already overactive point or meridian is a reflexive sedation.

Over and above point selection, numerous other factors can be employed to vary the yin (sedating) and yang (toning) effects of an acupuncture treatment. Elements include the material, length, thickness and design of the needles; the method of needle insertion and withdrawal; the amount and type of stimulation (if any) of the inserted needle; and the length of time the needle is kept in place. The following section will consider some of the ways a practitioner has at his disposal to produce either of two opposite effects—sedation and tonification—and numerous states in between.

The Needles

Needles are the primary tools used in acupuncture. With an understanding of the principles of Ki, a practitioner can wield these simple instruments to treat numerous physical and psychological complaints. Variations in the characteristics of needle construction serve to differentiate and fine-tune the desired effect.

Material. The first acupuncture needles were made of sharpened stone or bone. Records indicate that slivers of bamboo were also used. Later, iron needles were utilized, and they are still employed for particular purposes: in cases where a very strong stimulation is required, and in an indirect form of moxibustion, in which the herb is burned on the handle of an inserted needle.

The next development in needle material was the production of needles made of alloys of either gold or silver. Again, both types of materials are still in use today, amid some controversy. One school of thought asserts that the type of material a needle is made from has no influence on its effects. The opposite view states that specific substances possess distinct yin and yang properties and should be used accordingly. In a general way, both opinions are correct.

With our recognition of the duality or complementarity of life, it is clear that different materials will indeed vary in their receptivity and conductivity of Ki, and consequently, in their sedating or toning characteristics. And yet, by choosing among meridians and points, and by using various needling techniques, the same distinction can be accomplished with any needle, regardless of its construction.

Today, most needles are made of stainless steel, which has certain advantages over other materials, including: painless and smooth insertion, due to the ability to manufacture thinner needles; easy sterilization; a longer life (although with the increasing use of disposable needles, the importance of this last factor is negated); and being relatively inexpensive. Naturally, stainless steel lacks the specific advantages of the previously mentioned materials, and there are times when a physician may insist on using something other than stainless steel to produce a particular effect.

Thickness and Length. Chinese needles tend to be thicker than the Japanese variety. The standard range in the diameter of Chinese needles is 0.26 millimeters to 0.46 millimeters. Japanese needles generally range from 0.17 millimeters to 0.33 millimeters. The length of needles depends primarily on the area of the body where insertion takes place, although the treatment's purpose also plays a role. Very short needles, for instance, are utilized when they are to be left in place for several days or longer. The purpose of such treatment is to generate a mild, continuous stimulation. Tape is used to keep these flat-headed needles (approximately 5 millimeters in length) in place.

For the much briefer, in-clinic forms of treatment, relatively short needles are used for the ears, head and limbs, while longer varieties are the choice for insertion on the trunk. The general range in the length of Chinese needles is 12.7 to 127 millimeters. The Japanese variety runs from 10 to 90 millimeters.

Needle Shape. Acupuncture needles come in a variety of forms, determined according to their use. The Chinese classics identify nine distinct styles of needles, designed for specific applications. These fall into three common categories, including: a blunt-point type used not for insertion but for kneading the points and the meridians to release stagnated energy; a razor-edge style for cutting or pricking the skin; and a sharp-pointed variety used for insertion. The thumbtack-type needles used for implantation (mentioned above) are a more recent development.

In terms of effect, thicker and longer needles produce a stronger stimulation, while thinner and shorter varieties provide a lighter influence. Blunt needles, used for stimulation on the skin's surface, yield a milder effect than the needles used for insertion.

Needling Techniques

Needling technique refers to the type and amount of stimulation used on a needle during insertion, after insertion, and during removal. The purpose of these assorted manipulations is to enhance the intended effects of either sedation or tonification. Examples include:

- Moving the needle up and down after insertion;
- Turning a needle clockwise or counterclockwise during insertion and removal, or while the needle is in place;
- Inserting part way, then either slowly or quickly completing the movement;

- Inserting completely and then partially withdrawing; and
- Vibrating the needle while it is inserted.

As a general rule, more stimulation, a higher frequency, and a greater speed of stimulation produce a stronger, more yang effect. This, in turn, is used for sedating an excess condition. Less stimulation, a lower frequency, and a slower speed of stimulation provide a milder, more yin influence. A lighter application is used in tonification.

A summation of the factors employed to control the general effects (sedation or tonification) and the specific degree of influence, is presented below.

To Tonify	*To Sedate*
Light stimulation	Strong stimulation
Thin needles used	Thick needles used
Shorter needles used	Longer needles used
Insertion time shorter—2 to 3 minutes	Insertion time longer—up to 30 minutes or more
Less points treated	More points treated
Buffing the skin surface with blunt needles	Inserting the needle into the tsubo
Little or no needle manipulation	More needle manipulation
Manipulate needles slowly and infrequently	Manipulate needles quickly and frequently

The Treatment

When an individual visits an acupuncturists, the physician's first task is to complete a thorough diagnosis. Once the patient's overall condition is assessed, and the energetic cause of any problem is determined, a course of treatment is chosen. If acupuncture is called for, various tsubo are selected for treatment according to the nature of the problem. The criteria used in choosing which points to treat, and in what way Ki is to be manipulated, are those presented in Part 1, chapters 3 and 4.

Treatments are designed to reestablish a harmonized pattern of Ki flow, which in turn promotes the proper functioning of glands, organs and systems. Once this is accomplished, the consequence of this energetic distortion, the physical and psychological symptoms, will spontaneously disappear. A number of sessions are usually required to ensure a stabilized flow of energy, although relief can appear after just a single treatment.

The period of time required to reestablish the proper circulation of Ki depends on a number of factors, including: the patient's overall condition; the nature of the problem and how long it has been present; and how well the individual is able to follow the physician's lifestyle recommendations, in order to eliminate the source of the problem.

Initially, sessions may be scheduled several times a week. As one's condition begins to respond to treatments, once a week or less may be sufficient. The length of each treatment can range from twenty to thirty minutes to an hour or longer. The number of tsubo administered to varies from one or several, to a dozen or more—although, in general, the total is much less than this.

The general sequence of steps in a treatment is:

- Diagnosis (at each visit)
- Disinfection of the area to be treated
- Location of the point or points
- Needle insertion
- Needle manipulation
- Needle withdrawal
- Disinfection again of the treated area
- Diagnosis to confirm the effectiveness of the treatment

Contrary to expectation, little, if any, sensation is felt during needle insertion. As the needle reaches the tsubo, however, a vague feeling is usually experienced. The Chinese call this "the arrival of Ki," and it is often felt as a localized numbness or tingling at the point. The arrival of Ki is considered an important sign that the tsubo has been correctly located, and if it is not felt, the physician may reinsert the needle. Alternatively, either the needle will be left in place in the expectation that the Ki will "arrive," or one of several manipulation techniques will be tried in the hopes of inducing it. Individuals in a very weak condition may not experience such a sensation, in which case a therapy other than acupuncture may be required.

Once a needle is inserted, a practitioner may manipulate it in various ways (as discussed above) to enhance its influence. Or, the needle may simply be left in place for a period of time. In either case, the physician will carefully observe the patient for signs of reactions or discomfort—such as hot or cold sensations or dizziness—caused by the movement of Ki.

Insertion Methods. Inserting an acupuncture needle properly is a skill that demands both training and experience. There are two basic methods of needle insertion for which numerous modifications exist: (1) If the Japanese-style needles are used, a guide tube, which simplifies insertion and practically eliminates discomfort, is commonly employed. The needle is placed into the shorter guide tube, so that its handle protrudes. The tube is then placed directly over the point, so that the needle tip is flush against the skin. Then the top of the handle is tapped lightly so that the tip penetrates the skin. The tube is then slipped off, and the needle is inserted to the required depth via pressure applied to the handle.

The classic Chinese method of needle insertion does not require the guide tube. The left thumb and index finger anchor the needle against the skin, and the same fingers on the right hand grasp the handle. The left hand is then used to push the needle through the skin, while the right hand applies pressure from the handle.

Safety Considerations. With concern over contagious disease, such as infectious hepatitis and, of course, AIDS, being transmitted via the needles, hygiene is a major issue for individuals considering acupuncture treatments. From their first days in the classroom, students are taught to exercise the same scrupulous care in maintaining cleanliness as their Western-medicine counterparts. Consideration for hygiene extends from the physician's dress and person down to the most inconsequential piece of equipment in the clinic. The most obvious safety concern for the practitioner and patient alike, centers on the reuse of needles.

Rather than being discarded after each use, needles are examined for signs of wear—blunt tips, bent shafts, loose handles—and then are either discarded or sterilized for reuse. The primary method of needle sterilization is the *autoclave*—a pressure-cooker type device that destroys microorganisms with intense heat and pressure. Patients have the additional option of purchasing needles that are then reserved for their personal use, after, of course, being sterilized before each treatment. With the recent introduction of pre-sterilized, vacuum-packed, disposable needles, anxiety over the safety of needles has been eliminated.

Contraindications. Concerning itself with the underlying energetic cause of an illness rather than symptoms, acupuncture can be helpful in a wide assortment of situations. There are, however, conditions for which acupuncture is considered to be inappropriate, including infectious disease and malignancies. Additional precautions include a variety of body parts which are off limits to needles. The eyes, the genitals, and the internal organs are examples. There are also a number of "forbidden points" which practitioners are taught to avoid needling due to the strong reaction that acupuncture elicits.

Acupuncture, then, is a very effective means for manipulating the body's circulation of Ki. As befits a form of therapy based on the principles of nature, its effects are subtle and at times slow acting. Before physical changes begin to manifest, the circulation of the body's subtle energy must be reestablished in a harmonized way.

Refined over several thousand years, acupuncture is a medical science that today offers a practical complement to our more conventional forms of health care. As interest in holistic medicine continues to grow, we can expect to see a parallel expansion in the use of acupuncture for physical and psychological complaints.

Moxibustion

Even within the realm of strictly clinical treatments, acupuncture is often not the preferred treatment in Oriental medicine. A patient's condition often calls for an alternative means, called *moxibustion*, for harmonizing the flow of Ki within the body. Moxibustion refers to the burning of a special herb (called *moxa*) for the purposes of sending heat stimulation, and a strong charge of Ki, to the tsubo, meridians and, at times, directly to specific parts of the body.

The herb's common name is mugwort and its botanical name is *Artemisia vulgaris*. The English word, "moxa," comes from the Japanese, *mogusa*, meaning "fragrant herb." The plant grows wild in China and Japan, in parts of Europe and probably in North America as well. Explaining the origins of moxibustion, *The Yellow Emperor's Classic of Internal Medicine* tells us that the people of northern

China developed a medical therapy by selecting a product readily available in their environment (the mugwort plant), and a form of treatment (heat) to complement the climatic conditions (cold and dampness) in which they lived. Eventually, moxibustion was incorporated into the collective body of Oriental medicine and applied whenever an individual's condition warranted its specific energetic effect.

Production and Use

The young leaves of the mugwort plant are picked in late spring. They are then dried and the stems are removed. For higher grades of moxa, the thin stem running along the center of the leaf is also extracted. Finally, the leaves are ground several times in a stone mortar to produce fibrous material which is then allowed to mellow for a period. Variations in the production process result in a number of quality grades, each having a slightly different effect. The higher grades tend to be finer, more pliable, burn evenly to the end, produce minimal smoke and ash, burn with a low temperature and yet produce a deeply penetrating heat. The lower grades are coarser, harder, burn unevenly with a tendency to go out, produce more smoke and ash, and burn with a higher temperature which produces more heat but less penetration.

One of the unique benefits of this particular herb is its oil, which, when burned, produces a penetrating heat and an aromatic, non-irritating fragrance. However, the moxa plant is not the only substance that can be used in moxibustion. Dried miso and dried grains of cooked rice have traditionally been used in Japan, and even paper can be utilized. Although generations of use have proven the effectiveness of the mugwort plant, any substance can be used as long as it burns slowly, without a flame, and does not damage the skin.

Moxa is used in two general forms: (1) Practitioners most often employ the loose type, from which they roll cones of various dimensions—from the size of a grain of rice to the proportions of an adult's thumb nail and larger—and (2) a pre-rolled stick, which resembles a cigar in length and thickness, which both practitioners and laypersons may use.

In Japan, moxibustion is still commonly used for self-application by the older generation to promote health, and as a remedy for various ailments. Matsuo Basho, the highly regarded seventeenth century *haiku* poet (poetry of 17 syllables), is famous for his walking tours throughout the country. Before one such journey he wrote in his dairy, "Tomorrow I set out for the north. Today, in preparation, I applied moxa on stomach point number 36" (*Ashi-no-San-Ri*, on the outside of the leg, along the shin bone, several inches below the knee). This tsubo is well-known for its ability to induce vitality and promote longevity. People from all walks of life, including teachers, monks, and samurai, routinely stimulated it with moxa.

Treatments

The intensity of stimulation of a moxibustion treatment can be varied by factors such as:

- The size of the cone (small cones produce mild stimulation, larger cones produce a stronger stimulus);
- The tightness of the cones (loosely rolled cones produce a lighter stimulation than tightly packed ones);
- The number of cones burned in succession—can range from 2 or 3 to as many as 10 to 20. The strength of stimulation increases along with the number of cones used; and
- Whether the treatment is applied directly to the skin (strongest stimulation), on top of another substance (a milder stimulation), such as a bed of salt or a razor-thin slice of ginger, garlic, or scallion (each has its own stimulating properties), or by passing a moxa stick over a tsubo (a much gentler stimulation).

In general, the purpose of a moxibustion treatment is stimulation—a charge of energy is transmitted to the tsubo and along the meridian. The application is most often called for when symptoms are Kyo, or empty. However, by varying the application, the opposite, or sedating, effect can also be produced by stimulation. This is a recapitulation of the principle used with acupuncture needles whereby light stimulation is applied to tone, and a strong stimulation is implemented to sedate.

Thus to tone a Kyo (empty) condition, a mild stimulation is given with relatively smaller, loosely rolled cones. Only several cones are used, and the practitioner may pause between each application. For purposes of sedation of a Jitsu (full) condition, a stronger stimulation is given. Larger, more tightly rolled cones are selected, and a greater number are used, one after another. On occasion, the moxa may even be lightly fanned to accelerate the burning.

As with acupuncture treatments, there is a number of tsubo, conditions and body parts forbidden to moxibustion, although in a non-technical book like this, these need not be detailed. Anyone wishing to learn self-application is advised to get professional advice.

The procedure for applying moxibustion is as follows:

- The area to be treated is disinfected.
- The exact location of the point is noted.
- The practitioner rolls a cone of moxa of appropriate size and density, and places it on the skin.
- The moxa is ignited with an incense stick, not a match, and allowed to burn down. The patient indicates when the heat becomes intense, and the practitioner immediately removes the moxa.
- These last two steps may be repeated several or more times, depending on the practitioner's judgment.
- The treatment ends with the area being disinfected a second time.

Side Effects

During a moxibustion application, the skin reddens in response to the heat, and often, a small blister forms. The strength of such reactions, and the length of time they persist, varies according to the patient's condition. As mentioned earlier, many people have a thin layer of fat under the skin, produced by the regular consumption of simple sugars, and fatty, greasy foods, including animal food. During treatment, the heat (yang) draws this fat and liquid (yin) to the surface, creating a blister. This is a natural reaction and occurs to some degree to everyone.

However, if the individual's condition is extreme, the skin may rupture and a larger blister and later a scab may form. Under such circumstances, the healing process may take several weeks or more, and the abrasion may leave a scar. If the internal condition and the skin are more tight, dry and clean, the size and intensity of a blister and scab will be milder, and healing may be accomplished in as little as a few days to a week.

To avoid such disagreeable complications, practitioners have the option of using stick moxa, which is passed back and forth over the tsubo rather than coming in direct contact with the skin. Or, the moxa may be placed on top of another substance for an indirect application, as explained above. Of course, the length and intensity of an application can also be varied in consideration for individual condition.

Acupuncture and moxibustion are, respectively, the yin and yang tools that a physician uses to manipulate Ki. There are, however, numerous methods to vary and adjust the effects of these opposite applications. In acupuncture (essentially a yin function), the needle serves either as an antenna to attract energy from the environment, or as a safety valve for the release of excess energy. The charge of Ki produced by the burning moxa (a more yang function) can be adjusted to either tonify or sedate, depending on the need and the degree of stimulation.

Once again, the fundamental value of the concept of complementary opposites becomes apparent. In traditional and Oriental medicine, the dynamics of yin and yang are utilized in a flexible way to suit not only the individual but the environmental factors within which he lives.

In Part 3, we will follow this concept further, as we focus on the specifics of first personal and then family health. The last chapter addresses the broader issue of social well-being.

Part Three: Macrobiotic Healing: The Medicine-to-Be

INTRODUCTION TO PART 3

In the first chapter of this book we examined three categories of medical practice: (1) modern, Western medicine, (2) Chinese medicine as it is currently practiced, and (3) traditional and Oriental medicine, which we also characterized as the medicine-to-be. In subsequent chapters we explored in detail the theory and practice of the latter two, and made comparisons with the first. Now it is time for a comprehensive examination of the medicine-to-be.

One need not be a social scientist to realize that modern civilization is being swept by revolutionary changes. This grassroots reformation is reflected in movements for issues as diverse as: political and economic independence; nuclear disarmament; human rights; a safe environment; natural foods and organic agriculture; Far-Eastern meditation, medicine and exercise regimens; and even a budding resurgence in organized religion. Despite the apparent disparity of these concerns, an understandable pattern can be perceived. Collectively, we are beginning to sense—in different ways according to personal vantage point—the price we are paying for our one-sided approach to life. We are learning that short-term benefits, based on narrow considerations, are inefficient, unnatural, and ultimately ruinous.

Macrobiotics—a synonym for the medicine-to-be—has been a leader in this social reorientation. Reasoning from the total spectrum of human considerations—physical and mental health, family and social well-being, economics, ecology, technology, and so on—macrobiotic education has brought home the true impact of our lifestyle choices and governmental policies.

The macrobiotic approach to healing, or the medicine-to-be, is holistic in the truest sense of the word. Starting by establishing personal well-being, it moves on to the wider concerns of civilization. Following this progression, chapter 1 addresses the dynamics of individual development. Family health is the next subject to be considered. In the final chapter, we examine the broader applications of macrobiotic healing: an approach that is already beginning to influence society at large, and that will ultimately reach every member of the global family of humanity.

1. Personal Well-being

An ironic yet accurate bit of folk wisdom states that the more often and widely a particular value or virtue is publicly discussed, the more likely that specific quality is to be in short supply. In recent times, there has been an explosion of discussion on health-related topics. As a society, we seem to be obsessed with issues of health, or more precisely, the lack of it. The air waves are jammed with radio and television specials devoted to the subject, book-store shelves bulge with many hundreds of health-related titles, the vitamin and food-supplement industry is booming, and the weight-loss business has mushroomed into a multi-billion dollar industry.

Obviously, there is nothing wrong with such concerns. Yet, the very fact that we worry so much about the qualities of health and sickness, and talk so much about them, indicates our inability to realize physical and mental well-being. And, as the status of our individual and collective health continues to decline—as reflected by the flood of studies from both public and private sources—increasing amounts of time and money are being spent examining the reasons why. But what exactly does the concept of health entail.

According to *Webster's Ninth New Collegiate Dictionary*, *health* is defined as: "the condition of being sound in body, mind, or soul." The implication is that our physical body—blood, cells, organs, glands, nerves, and systems—is functioning properly, that is, without the need for artificial or extraordinary support (examples of which include synthetic hormones, artificial joints and heart pacemakers). In addition, our emotions are appropriately expressed, and our mentality is clear and stable. Interestingly, included in this description of health is the idea of the soul, which can be described as the comprehensive state of awareness produced by the interaction of physical and mental functions. Consciousness, or soul, is a product of these two processes, and the scope of one's consciousness depends directly on the quality of body and mind.

This is a surprisingly broad definition, one each of us would do well to consider. It implies that health is a dynamic interaction of all aspects of the Self—physical, emotional, mental, and spiritual. By extension, it supports what common sense already tells us: if there is a problem in one area, the individual as a whole will be affected. This relationship has been discussed in detail in earlier chapters, and researchers are beginning to confirm it.

The macrobiotic principles that whatever has a front has a back, and the bigger the front the bigger the back, are clearly echoed in the case of the AIDS disease. The threat of weakened immune ability is gradually bringing us to the recognition of the wider implications of health. Over the past several years vast amounts of resources have been devoted to the investigation of the human immune system. Scientists are now reporting that the mind plays an important role in our state of health, and conversely, our physical condition affects our attitudes and views. This concept is now moving from the research labs and medical journals to the mass media.

The cover story of the November 7, 1988 issue of *Newsweek* magazine was titled, "Body & Soul: Scientists Discover the Links between the Brain and Your Health." The article is a report on "new discoveries linking the brain to the immune system," and it suggests that "state of mind can affect us right down to our cells." Two major points in the article support our discussion of traditional and Oriental medicine:

1. *The Intimate Connection between Mind and Body.* Higher rates of illness were reported among individuals who have recently lost a spouse. "For all age and sex groups, mortality was three times higher among those with the fewest close relationships. Similar correlations turn up among nursing-home patients who sense no 'control' over their daily lives, breast-cancer patients who are pessimistic about recovering, and partners locked in strife-torn marriages."
2. *The Dualism That Characterizes Modern Society in General and Our Approach to Medicine in Particular.* "An abiding mystery of the mind-body connection is that it should seem mysterious at all—an indication, perhaps, of how deeply conditioned we have been by 'dualism,' that doctrine, laid down more than three centuries ago by French philosopher Rene Descartes, sees mind and body as distinct entities, to be treated separately. It become the paradigm for modern medicine, and still dominates medical thinking."

Several decades ago, macrobiotic teacher George Ohsawa listed a series of seven requirements for health. In retrospect, these conditions clearly anticipated the holistic approach to well-being that is emerging today. In particular, they depict the two-way relation between physical and mental health. The starting points for qualifications one to three are physiological (although they have psychological corollaries as well), and those for numbers four through six are psychological in nature. The last, which Ohsawa considered most important, is related to one's view of life and can be considered the base of all the others. These conditions were intended to be used for self-evaluation. As you read them, assess your own state of health.

1. *No Fatigue.* Our ability to take up any task or face any challenge with physical vitality and mental alertness is a sign of health. Responses such as "It is too difficult," or "I can't do it," reflect a weariness of both spirit and body. This does not mean that we are not tired after a full day's work, but rather that a night's rest is sufficient to replenish our strength and renew our outlook.
2. *Good Appetite.* If one is satisfied with simple, wholesome food, and eats with hunger and gratitude, one is generally in good health. Appetite, of course, includes the desire for knowledge, experience, activity, sex, and in general, a hunger for life. Curiosity and a sense of adventure reflect a sound appetite for this more refined type of food.
3. *Deep Sleep.* A healthy person can fall asleep quickly—within two or

three minutes of lying down. He sleeps peacefully, is not bothered by nightmares or chaotic dreams, and wakes refreshed and ready for a new day. People generally sleep too long; an individual in good health should find six hours sufficient.

4. *Good Memory.* Memory is the foundation of our personality, and the source of our powers of judgment. This concept not only includes the recall of names, facts, and dates, but also the more basic memory of our origin and purpose in life.
5. *Good Humor.* A healthy individual is free from fear, and remains cheerful under all circumstances. One barometer of this precept is how often we get angry. Ohsawa stated that a truly healthy person never gets angry due to his wide perspective on life. The number of close friends one has is another measure of our humor. A large number and variety of friends indicates a deep understanding of the working of life and the consequent appreciation of all people.
6. *Clarity in Thought and Action.* Healthy individuals are able to think, judge, and act with promptness and clarity. Promptness, says Ohsawa, is the expression of freedom. Such people distinguish themselves by their ability to establish order everywhere. Beauty of action or form is a reflection of one's comprehension of the infinite universe.
7. *A Sense of Justice.* Our inclination to live in accord with the principles of life is an indication of our health on this level. It is revealed in our ability to recognize front and back, or the dynamics of yin and yang in every phenomenon, be it physical, mental, or spiritual. Existing hand-in-hand with a sense of justice is the feeling of gratitude for all the events and experiences in our lives. With understanding, even hardships and difficulties become our benefactors.

A Holistic Look at Illness

With this broad, clear definition of health, it will be easier to understand the purpose, value, and mechanism of illness. "Wait just a minute," you may be saying, "What could possibly be the purpose of sickness, other than to cause pain and suffering?" The answer frames the outline to the macrobiotic approach to healing.

We start by realizing that sickness is not an adversary or malevolent force trying to harm or even destroy us. Nor is it a punishment for improper behavior. Whatever form it takes, and whatever the symptoms, sickness is the means by which the totally of an individual—body and mind—adapts to the biological extremes that an imbalanced way of life has produced. In this sense, sickness is a process of harmony, whereby the various aspects of the Self respond and compensate for the disorder we have created for ourselves.

What we call illness is actually a self-preservation process, in which adjustments, sometimes desperate ones, are made to safeguard the overall biological and psychological integrity of the concerned individual. In doing so, the Self maintains the balance necessary to sustain life to the limits of biological and psychological compensation. The scientific term for this process is *homeostasis.* It is defined as "the maintenance of equilibrium, or constant conditions, in a biological system by means of automatic mechanisms that counteract influences toward disequilibrium." Homeostatic mechanisms occur on all levels of organization in living systems, including the molecular, cellular, and organismic levels. In the broadest sense, the entire Self is a homeostatic system that serves to maintain individual harmony. What we call sickness of body or mind is simply one—and certainly not the preferred—self-regulating mechanism used.

Difficulties Benefit Us

Individuals new to the orientation offered by macrobiotics are often surprised by accounts of men and women who have reversed a serious problem through the macrobiotic way of life. The point that seems to startle is not the fact that the individual was able to recover from a severe, sometimes life-threatening illness—although in many instances, the return to health is truly dramatic. More often, it is the gratitude expressed for the health crisis that comes as a shock to the uninitiated.

The explanation is that the suffering and threat posed by a serious sickness was the motivator that prompted that particular individual to examine his or her way of life, and perhaps, for the first time, see how dissatisfying, empty, and self-destructive it was. This realization, we often hear, changed the person's entire life. From this point, goals shifted, lifestyles were rearranged, and values were fundamentally altered.

For many, the idea that we should be grateful for difficulties, and that hardships foster personal development, is a novel one. And yet, too often, the only time people make the effort to see how their behavior and attitudes are responsible for the circumstances of their life is during a period of crisis. Difficulties benefit us by sharpening our judgment, focusing our attention, stanching our resolve, shaking off our lethargy, and spurning us on to efforts we would think impossible under normal circumstances. In short, they put us in touch with reality.

Sickness is indeed our benefactor, performing two extremely important functions:

1. It serves as information, warning us that in some way our lives are out of harmony with the forces of nature. If we did not receive this feedback, we could continue our inappropriate behavior until our condition became dangerously imbalanced, and we would suddenly and without warning fall seriously ill and perhaps die. Long before this happens, however, we are alerted by physical and psychological alarms, or symptoms. If we heed these early-warning signs, minor complaints can be eliminated before they develop into major problems.
2. By either discharging or localizing excessive and/or toxic substances, the body preserves the overall integrity of the organs, systems, and so on. This is vital because despite the body's best efforts, many people have quite a lot of internal excess caused by the habitual consumption of extreme foods. If allowed to freely circulate, the cells, blood, and other body

fluids would soon become septic, resulting in a condition of toxemia. Through the above mechanisms, homeostasis is maintained, providing us with ample opportunity to recognize and correct the condition.

Unfortunately, these positive functions too often go unrecognized, and are instead labeled as sickness. What is worse, we make ever effort to interfere with the body's self-adjusting processes, thereby thwarting its natural immune responses, and creating the conditions for much more serious problems. Fever, for example, is a means used by the body to cleanse itself of excessive yin or yang factors. Doctors understand that a temporary, low-grade fever, benefits the individual. The slightly elevated temperature activates certain antibodies, kills many micro-organisms outright, and enhances the elimination of excess.

Skin disease is another internal house-cleaning process. It is the body's attempt to discharge excess via the skin pores, thus ensuring that the internal condition remains relatively clean. With medications we may succeed in slowing or even stopping what is perhaps an uncomfortable and/or unsightly skin breakout. But think of the consequences. Instead of humbly accepting the body's natural response to our unnatural lifestyle, we: (1) interfere with the body's self-regulating response, and (2) force excessive or toxic substances inside, greatly increasing the likelihood of a more severe form of adjustment later on. Because of its essential role in the maintenance of health, more will be said about the mechanism of discharge in just a moment.

Our current attitude toward, and treatment of, illness fails to recognize these beneficial and educational factors, putting each of us at risk. Geared toward isolation and analysis, the modern approach to healing is predicated on the crippling emotion of fear. Affected individuals are perceived as helpless victims of the disease process. Symptoms and their assumed causes—bacteria and viruses—are viewed as enemies that must be destroyed, quickly and ruthlessly. We thus have "the war on cancer," "the war on AIDS," and even the "war on the common cold." In each of these struggles, the fighting takes place within our own body, and the adversary is actually ourself!

Mechanism of Illness

We have already seen that illness is the result of a disruption in the body's energy system, and can be identified as being either Kyo, or deficient energy, or Jitsu, or excessive energy. The physical process of sickness can likewise be classified into two general categories according to their mechanism and function:

1. *Sickness of Adjustment.* A healthy body responds to an imbalanced condition by discharging toxins either externally or internally. This often happens in the spring and fall as we expell the excess taken in during the previous season. Such elimination can manifest as the common cold, flu, or tonsillitis. Hay fever and certain types of allergies are additional examples. This "housecleaning" is of course a beneficial process, and should not be seen as a sickness at all. That is, unless it happens on a frequent basis. If so, the

indication is that deeper problems are developing in response to the individual's way of life.

2. *Degenerative Sickness.* In cases of degenerative disease, the body's self-regulating mechanisms are either overwhelmed or seriously depleted, and the structure and functions of the body begin to break down. Although it represents a life-threatening condition, degenerative disease is the final means the body has to adapt to extreme and long-term abuse. Excess may be localized in the form of a tumor, for instance, to prevent its circulation throughout the body. Or, it may be stored within and around an organ, whose functions and structure then begin to give out.

In the chapter "Food as Medicine" we say that human life is an ongoing process of interaction between the individual and the forces of nature, far and near. That is to say, we continually take in and give out energy in various forms. In the developed nations the first half of this cycle, the taking in, is secured. In fact, we consume too much of everything—we glut ourselves with food, natural resources, information, entertainment, and all the other products of modern civilization. Our parents, grandparents, and earlier generations succeeded too well in their efforts to secure for us the physical aspects of life. Our challenge is twofold and is concerned with the opposite process of balancing our material wealth with spiritual values. We must: (1) use our judgment to set healthful limits to our consumption patterns, and (2) devise the means to share our bounty with the rest of the world.

In health, the second phase of this exchange—the giving back—occurs through the specific processes of bowel movement, urination, the exhalation phase of the cycle of respiration, and perspiration. Women have the additional processes of menstruation, childbirth and lactation as ways to maintain equilibrium. Physical activity, emotions, and thoughts are caloric and energetic forms of discharge.

If we take in more than these routine processes can return to the environment, the body adjusts by periodically increasing the pace of exchange through such mechanisms as the common cold and the flu. The symptoms of these so-called illnesses are all those of elimination: low-grade fever, runny nose, watery eyes, swollen glands, sore throat, achy joints, a cough, sneezing, diarrhea, and similar processes help keep the internal environment clean.

If our way of life, and in particular our daily diet, is chronically imbalanced, the body is forced to initiate a constant process of elimination. This can include regular headaches, or pain and swelling in some other area, persistently blocked nasal passages and/or runny nose, excessive perspiration, body odor, recurrent infections, constipation or diarrhea, skin disease, and chronic low-grade fevers. In woman this may mean routine menstrual problems.

Over time and with continual abuse, these self-adjustment responses of elimination begin to break down. Homeostasis must still be maintained, however, and so the body begins an alternative method of harmony. Lacking an efficient means of elimination, excess is isolated and stored internally to prevent it from affecting the entire body. This process is called *accumulation*.

Initially, accumulation begins in the peripheral areas, as the body attempts to localize, neutralize, and discharge excess. The sites are those that have access to the outside, such as the inner ear, the nasal sinuses, the bronchi and lungs, the intestines, kidneys and bladder. In men the prostate gland is another area of storage. In women the breasts, uterus and vagina serve this purpose.

The problem is that although these sites are capable of holding and then discharging toxic and excessive substances, they lack the active and specific self-cleaning processes that the conventional organs of discharge possess. This is the reason why these areas are frequent sites of infection, and are where polyps, stones, cysts, and tumors are likely to develop.

With continual abuse, the self-regulating mechanism of localization is either overwhelmed or depleted, and excess begins to gather deeper within the body. This marks the beginning of tissue build-up, chemical and hormonal changes, and ultimately organ degeneration. In this process, the body's last available response is to initiate structural changes that mark the beginning of degenerative disease.

The same process of homeostatic response occurs on the mental level as well. Psychologically, periodic elimination may be achieved through such exaggerated behavioral traits as a fit of anger, a bout of depression, or even uncontrollable laughter. The chronic process of discharge can take the form of gradual changes in personality and behavior along lines similar to the periodic symptoms of bodily elimination. The psychological corollary to physical accumulation is the suppression of thoughts and feelings and the beginnings of distorted attitudes and emotional responses. In the degenerative process, character traits begin to break down and consciousness grows increasingly deluded. The individual loses touch with the reality of life, creating instead bizarre visions that reflect his own imbalanced condition.

Impaired Discharge Ability

If the process of exchange between the individual and the environment is orderly and efficient, serious sickness will not arise. That is to say, if we maintain proper consumption patterns, and either use or give back what we take in, our condition will remain clean and harmonious, resulting in a state of health. It is only when we take in more than we give out that problems begin. There are three major reasons why this exchange does not go smoothly.

1. *Discharge Ability Overwhelmed.* This occurs when we habitually take in more than we can naturally and efficiently put to use. In addition, it happens when we consume extreme items that the body cannot properly metabolize.

   There are two points to address in this case: (1) Slow the rate of consumption to levels appropriate to one's condition and lifestyle, while eliminating any dietary extremes. (2) Accelerate the elimination of already existing excess via physical and mental activity, and with other practices that will be mentioned shortly.

2. *Discharge Ability Blocked.* The implication of blocked discharge ability is that the organs and systems are in some way impaired, and can no

longer perform their functions effectively. Examples include intestinal problems leading to poor digestion and assimilation, and to constipation or diarrhea. As another example, there may be fat accumulations in the kidneys, disrupting their function of filtering wastes from the blood.

A major factor in diminished discharge ability is the progressive blockage of the skin pores. The body's largest organ is the skin, and its functions include the discharge of excess via perspiration, and the regulation of body temperature by contracting the pores, thus holding onto heat, or by expanding them, thus releasing energy. The discharge and absorption of Ki is another function that takes place, via the *tsubo*, on the skin's surface. The skin also breathes, and this respiratory function will be diminished if the skin pores are clogged. Many people have accumulations of fat under the skin, preventing or disrupting these essential activities. This is a serious problem in itself, and it can produce further complications.

The factors leading to skin blockage include the long-time consumption of dairy products and other fatty, greasy foods. Overeating and a sedentary lifestyle are contributing factors. Even after one or two years of balanced dietary practice, some people do not lose weight, and their condition may be slow to improve. The cause is the diminished efficiency of the internal organs, and the fatty accumulations that prevent discharge through the skin.

To help open skin pores, a daily body scrub, done with a hot or cold cotton towel, is recommended after a bath or shower. Briskly rubbing the skin until it begins to turn red increases the circulation of blood, lymph fluid, and Ki energy, and helps break down fatty deposits under the skin. Exercise is an additional aid, as it promotes perspiration and circulation, and strengthens the overall metabolism.

A sudden shock or extreme tension can cause the same effect. In such cases, the external stress or pressure contracts the internal organs and tissues, and this response is balanced by a simultaneous expansion on the surface, or the skin.

3. *Discharge Inhibited by the Mind.* Elimination can also be blocked by the mind. In this case, individuals are mentally controlling their thoughts, emotions, and behavior. Although psychological in nature, the basis for this blockage is the individual's physical condition.

For instance, if there is a hardening of the pancreas, the hormones that regulate blood-sugar levels, insulin and anti-insulin, are either secreted in insufficient amounts, in improper proportions, or their quality is weakened to the point where they are unable to work effectively. The emotions of the affected individual swing widely in response to the consequent irregular blood-sugar levels. This often produces a sense of anxiety and depression. Lacking a stabilized, peaceful feeling, the individual begins to lose faith in himself and may compensate by rigidly controlling his feelings and thoughts.

If the function of the kidneys is disturbed, from fat accumulations or stones, for instance, or perhaps from being overworked by excess or extreme liquid intake, the individual may begin to grow fearful. His confidence and self-esteem may diminish, and, as a result, the individual may adopt self-defensive traits as a way to compensate.

These examples present a challenge. To change our physical condition, we must first discharge any excessive or toxic substances, but in these situations, exaggerated psychological mechanisms resist such release. While this mental state exists, the condition may be slow to change, or may even worsen. Once blockage is opened, discharge proceeds smoothly through the processes mentioned above, and rapid personal change takes place.

Ways to Accelerate Discharge

Supporting or reestablishing the body's discharge functions are crucial factors in the macrobiotic approach to healing. There are numerous ways to do this, and in fact, every aspect of daily life should perform this function. Specific recommendations include:

1. Daily body scrub to open the tsubo and skin pores.
2. Singing, chanting, or praying out loud daily. We have already seen the importance that sound has on lives. Vocalizing is a form of release in itself, and it activates the metabolism as well.
3. Keep active, physically and mentally.
4. Eat to only about 80 percent of capacity. It takes a few moments for the stomach's message that it is full to reach the brain. Eating slowly helps insure that we are aware when we reach this point. Many people habitually overeat, and this causes various forms of stagnation in the body. As an additional measure to prevent stagnation, if at all possible, avoid going to bed for about three hours after a meal.
5. Chew your food very well. The process of digestion begins in the mouth with the mechanical breakdown of food, and the chemical breakdown of carbohydrates by the enzymes in saliva.
6. Wear natural fiber clothing. Items that directly touch the skin should be made of cotton or other natural fiber. This enhances the numerous functions of the skin.
7. Maintain a well-ventilated home and work space, and go outdoors in the fresh air and sunlight daily.
8. In certain cases, home-care preparations may be necessary, on a short-term basis, to foster the functions of the organs, systems, and discharge functions.
9. Shiatsu, acupuncture, herbal remedies, or other more natural therapies may be useful on a temporary basis. Their purpose is the same as that for number eight above.
10. When necessary to save or protect the individual's life, there are situations when modern medicine offers the only practical alternative.

Macrobiotic Healing

The techniques, purpose and philosophy of macrobiotic healing contrast sharply with those embraced by our current medical strategies. Based on the principles of life itself, the macrobiotic approach to personal well-being is oriented around the concept of harmony. Establishing balance within and between the myriad aspects of the Self, and between the Self and the environment, is the goal.

Rather than being limited to the narrow realm of recovery, macrobiotic healing develops the whole person—body, mind, and spirit. This unique orientation fosters the development of free individuals, capable not only of solving their own problems, but of understanding the mechanism and purpose of life. This is medical practice in the largest sense of the word. Fostering the realization of one's full potential as a human being is the ultimate intention. As we achieve this maturity, we assume the responsibilities of adulthood, including the desire to extend help to our juniors and seniors, and to care for and protect the environment and our fellow inhabitants of this planet.

We are accustomed to thinking that the process of physical maturation is automatic, and to a certain extent this is true. By a certain age, generally at the time the wisdom teeth emerge, we all reach physical adulthood. And yet, the quality of our biological constitution varies greatly according to the strength of our parent's reproductive cells, and to the nature of our own upbringing. The fact is, many of us fail to reach our full potential for health and vitality.

Mental and spiritual development parallel this process. Although each of us has the capacity for unlimited growth toward self-realization, few individuals achieve this state. Many of us fail to grow at all on these levels, and, sadly, some of us actually begin to regress.

As we grow older, the accumulation of learning and experience naturally increases the scope of our lives. We gain more friends, more interests and options, and greater flexibility in the way we approach life. For many people today, the opposite is true. As they age, their capacity for life diminishes, leading to less interests, ambition, and participation, and to a deepening rigidity of body, mind and spirit.

The major causes of death in the industrialized countries are the degenerative diseases. The body grows progressively stiff and painful, or swollen and weak as these conditions slowly unfold. Emotions, thoughts and spiritual consciousness, as we have seen, are not exempt from this process. To prevent or reverse this situation, to reclaim our heritage as human beings, a return to the basic aspects of daily life is required.

Keys to Healing

The keys to macrobiotic healing and personal development include:

1. *Daily Diet.* By basing our diet on high-quality food, chosen and prepared in a manner appropriate to our personal condition, we secure both our present condition and our orientation for the future.
2. *Enhancing Our Discharge Ability.* By strengthening the discharge func-

tions, we facilitate the elimination of excess, and in this way we reconstruct our past.
3. *Various Lifestyle Adjustments.* The above two factors are reinforced by our simple, day-to-day activities.
4. *Self-reflection.* Using the experiences in our lives as learning opportunities, we begin to perceive the order of life, and the principles upon which existence is based. If we have a problem, we come to realize how and why we created it, or, in other words, we embrace the concept of personal responsibility. In this way, we take a positive and active role in creating our future.

The dictionary offers an assortment of definitions for the verb *to heal.* These explanations fall into two interesting and revealing categories. To "make sound or whole" and "to restore to original purity or integrity" suggest a renewal and a moving forward. "To patch up" and "to cause an undesirable condition to be overcome" imply a willingness or necessity to make due, to accept less that might be possible. If we are willing to settle for the second set of implications, we need not take responsibility for our condition, nor need we examine and change the way we live. If, however, our desire is for complete and lasting healing, and for personal growth, we must start at the beginning.

Everyone must eat, and we have already seen the primary influence that daily diet has on all aspects of the Self. Whatever type of difficulties we may be experiencing, our principal means of eliminating them is by day-to-day diet. If we are capable of flexibly adjusting diet to the ever-changing circumstances in our lives, we will achieve freedom. From the base of dietary adjustment, we can begin to take positive steps to influence the other aspects of our Self in a practical way.

Because of the sophistication of science, technology, and medicine, it is understandably difficult for many of us to appreciate the importance of the simple aspects of daily life in the role of prevention and relief of illness. However, if we approach the subject with an open and inquiring mind we will realize that an individual life, or microcosm, is an encounter with the universe, or the macrocosm. We have already examined the ways we interact with the multiple dimensions of existence. They include:

1. The mineral, vegetable and water environment, by "eating" in the common understanding of the word
2. The atmospheric environment, through the process of respiration
3. The world of energy, or long-wave vibrations, via activity, which stimulates the meridians and tsubo
4. The realm of short-waves, through thinking or consciousness
5. The world of universal consciousness, in the form of the very short-waves originating beyond our galaxy

We have total control over the first category, and progressively less direct influence over each of the subsequent levels. And yet, by regulating daily diet, we determine the quality and quantity of all the other levels of life we receive.

Numerous approaches to well-being are being put forth today. And each may be beneficial to particular individuals, and in specific circumstances. Clearly, they are addressing some strongly felt needs, or they would not be in such demand. Almost without exception, however, they emphasize one or another of the higher levels of interaction, for instance, stressing the importance of exercise, breathing practices, positive thinking or stress reduction, and various types of meditation. Failing to address the primary influence on our lives, and the most effective means for self-development, these strategies in effect try to make change by working from the outside in. This involves varying degrees of strain and force. They can effect temporary results, but unless and until the primary influence of dietary practice is recognized and addressed, such efforts will be short-term. Intellectually, we are all aware of the necessity for "learning to walk before trying to run." An yet far too many of us insist on doing just the opposite in our pursuit of physical health and emotional, mental and spiritual well-being.

Food plus alpha, beta, and omega, is the macrobiotic orientation. In other words, starting with dietary change, any other practice can be used. These additional factors vary according to individual need, and within the individual, often change during the healing process. Physical exercise may be required in some cases, while attention to spiritual, intellectual, or emotional concerns may be needed in others.

The tools we use to secure well-being and to foster personal growth are the principles of yin and yang. Without the dynamic application that this understanding allows, our efforts can never be fully effective. Although we may be able to create temporary balance, as circumstances change, we will be powerless to appreciate and harmonize with them.

The simple example of knee pain offers a clear illustration of how practical this orientation is. In general, the complementary types of knee pain are: (1) Pain that occurs during movement—walking, running, and so on, and (2) pain that arises when sitting, lying down, or perhaps during simple bending and stretching movements. In the first case, the cause is excess yang, produced, for example, by meat and eggs. The area is tight and hard, and movement is difficult. Chemically, there is an excess of uric acid. In the second case, the cause is excess yin, from sugar, alcohol and tropical fruits, for instance. During periods of inactivity, the area becomes swollen as excess accumulates, making bending difficult.

The treatments for these apparently similar yet actually distinct problems will consequently be opposite. A hot external application will have an expansive, dispersing effect, and is appropriate for the yang-caused condition. A cold application will produce a contracting influence, and is called for in the yin-caused problem. By using the principles of yin and yang, we can respond appropriately to any situation.

Compare this simple approach to the complexity of our current strategies. We can see how unnecessary and in some cases dangerous they can be. With state-of-the-art technology, highly paid technicians and specialists, and thousands of medications, we squander our resources and time in a futile effort to eliminate symptoms. Yes, the effects of an illness can be temporarily relieved, but a permanent recovery can never be achieved.

Cancer, for instance, is treated by surgical removal, burning with radiation, or poisoning with chemotherapy. The trouble is that a cancerous growth is merely the flower, or final product of the disease process. The stem lies in the individual's blood quality, the root in his way of life, and the soil that produces the malignancy is his view of life. What modern medical treatments accomplish is to cut away the most obvious aspect of the disease. Failing to address the source, it is no surprise that in many, many cases, the illness returns.

The same is true of other diseases: the symptoms of asthma are treated with medications to dilate the bronchial tubes; diabetes with synthetic insulin, mental illness with behavior-altering drugs, and in severe cases institutionalization; the solution to crime is punishment in the form of fines or incarceration. Each of these approaches is a passive, defeatists, and ultimately futile exercise, and each repudiates its reason for existence: therapy geared toward eliminating the cause of the problem and returning the individual to a productive way of life.

Macrobiotics of course, does not rule out the use of modern therapies. After all, we have seen how anything can be used as medicine, and that in life-threatening situations, Western medicine does save lives. As long as the distinction is made between symptomatic relief and permanent recovery based on cause elimination, we need not fear or exclude any practices. Several key factors determine to what extent an individual will need to depend on the more complex and professionally oriented therapies.

1. The strength of one's basic constitution.
2. The individual's present condition, including the effectiveness of the discharge functions.
3. The individual's will to live. An optimistic outlook and the desire to get well play a key role in recovery.
4. Proper practice. In order to recover, the individual needs to correctly apply the Unifying Principles of yin and yang to dietary and lifestyle changes. This includes not only eating the proper foods, but of cooking them correctly. As one's condition begins to change, additional adjustments are usually necessary. To support this, reading, attending classes, and meeting with a qualified macrobiotic teacher are recommended. All this can be done while consulting with the appropriate health-care professional.
5. Self-reflection. By examining our habits of body and mind we come to understand our own responsibility in creating the problem. We develop a sense of gratitude for the illness, and for all those individuals and influences that are supporting our return to health.

The context in which many people are introduced to macrobiotics is through the relief of sickness. This is unfortunate, although, as already mentioned, illness may be the only impetus sufficiently strong to prompt major lifestyle changes. Many people begin out of fear, but with self-reflection and improving health, this emotion is soon replaced by a sense of faith. This faith is firmly rooted in an understanding of the orderliness and oneness of life, however, and is not the blind faith based on wishful thinking. As Jesus said: "If you had faith as a grain of mustard seed, you might say unto this sycamine tree, 'Be thou plucked by the root, and be thou planted in the sea,' and it should obey you." The faith of the mustard seed is the faith in the natural order of life.

The fear that so many people live with is an illusion created by a severely imbalanced physical and mental condition. Paradoxically, it is both a symptom of illness and a cause of it. There is no enemy in life, no suffering or punishment, and no alienation. There is only harmony, self-adaptation, and opportunity for growth. Each of these more negative perceptions and others like them, are the products or reflections of our own condition. In the Shinto shrines of Japan sits a mirror. Its significance is twofold: to see God one must merely behold oneself. And, to know the source of our happiness and the cause of our problems, one must likewise look inward. Whatever qualities we see in the world around us are a reflection of what we are.

Curing an Illness

Just as there are narrow and wide definitions for the concepts health and sickness, so too are there distinctions in the perception of what constitutes a cure. Medically speaking, if the symptoms of an illness are removed, or repressed, and do not reappear within a certain period of time, a cure or permanent remission is assumed. This is the source of the well-known "five-year recovery rate" that is used to determine successful treatments for such diseases as cancer. The scientific yardstick for a cure is clearly symptom elimination.

Fig. 64 Changing One's Direction toward Health

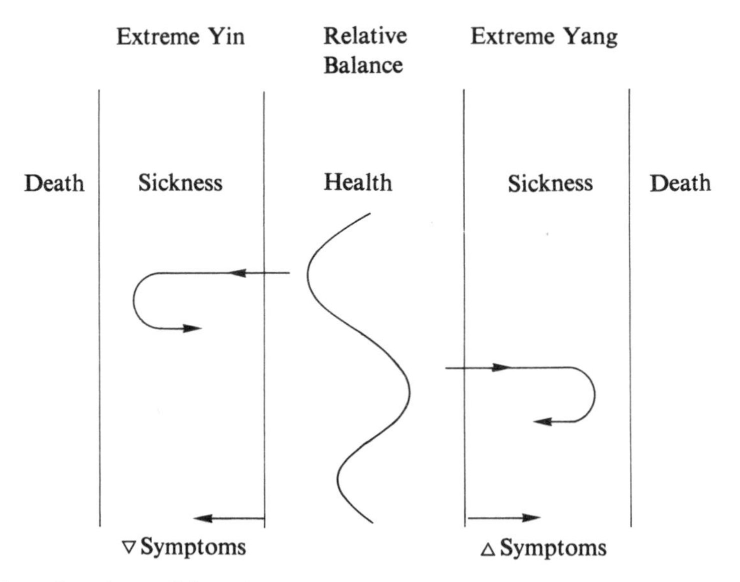

As the direction of one's condition changes toward balance and health, the symptoms that reflect the previous, extreme state begin to disappear.

The macrobiotic meaning of cure is far broader. George Ohsawa, recognizing that all disorders are the result of an energetic imbalance—either too yin, too yang, or a combination of both extremes—declared that a cure came about when an individual accomplished a change of direction, moving his condition from one of excess toward one of balance. In this basic way, Ohsawa stated, practically any problem could be relieved in ten days, which was the time it took to begin this reorientation. By using macrobiotic principles, an individual could effect a change in direction within this relatively short time span. Accordingly, Ohsawa defined cure as "a change of direction" in one's condition, lifestyle, and outlook. Once this process was underway, symptoms would gradually begin to fade.

From the scientific point of view, the idea that a serious illness can be reversed in ten days is absurd. After all, the symptoms are probably still manifesting, especially in cases of degenerative disease like heart disease, arthritis, or diabetes. Lacking the concept of yin and yang, modern medicine cannot appreciate the value and implications of changing the direction of one's condition. However, once this process is underway, the individual is on the road to recovery.

Over the years, experience has helped us expand on Ohsawa's definition. Direction change is the necessary first step toward recovery. And, achieving a balanced condition will certainly relieve the symptoms of an illness, although it may take several months to several years. But even at this point, we cannot say that a cure has been achieved. As discussed earlier in this book, we must move from the symptoms of sickness to the underlying cause and on to the source of the problem before a final and total cure can be assumed.

In this broad sense, a cure is achieved when an individual becomes free from physical and psychological delusion. That is to say, when he or she gains an understanding of the principles of life, and thus self-mastery. At this point, a person no longer needs to depend on another to solve his troubles. If a difficulty arises, the individual self-reflects to discover how he created it, and how to relieve it. He understands the results of his actions, and knows how to offset them to regain balance. This is what is meant as a free human being, the development of which is the goal of macrobiotic healing.

Reaching this point can take a long time, perhaps ten or twenty years. It involves study, experience, and reflection. On the other hand, it can happen instantaneously as the result of some sudden shock or insight. Once again, the crucial point is that we realize that we, ourselves, are the source of our difficulties, and that we have the ability to turn them into opportunities for personal growth.

One final aspect of human development requires explanation if we are to properly appreciate the role of macrobiotics in the realm of personal healing.

Spiritual Development

The complementary aspects of individual existence are physical growth and spiritual development. Physical existence is the result of the contracting spiral of creation. The reverse process, in which we develop our spiritual consciousness, unfolds in the opposite, or expanding spiral. This evolution should unfold smoothly, moving from natural conception and birth, to a natural way of life, and finally to a natural death. Each stage along the way is a preparation for the next.

Human life begins in the dark, warm, watery environment of the womb. Fetal growth is directed toward developing our protoplasmic body for life in the atmosphere. At birth, as we move into the world of air and alternating patterns of light and dark, the placenta and umbilical cord are no longer needed. During life the physical body takes over the role of the placenta—it nourishes the growth and development of the spiritual body for the next stage of life.

What we call death is actually birth into the more refined world of vibrations. If during our life as human beings, we developed a mature consciousness, or spiritual body, this birth will be smooth and peaceful, and our new life in the vibrational world will proceed naturally. On the other hand, if we fail to reach spiritual maturity during this life, we will experience various self-imposed difficulties, much as a poorly developed newborn has difficulty adjusting to life outside of the womb.

On earth, ideas and concepts take time to materialize and require concentrated attention to achieve. In the spiritual world, thoughts manifest immediately. If we are filled with delusional thoughts—such as fear, greed, or hate—when we die, we will create these same states for ourselves in our new life. This is the basis for the concepts of purgatory and hell found throughout the world.

The quality of consciousness we develop on earth determines the type of experiences we will have in the next stage of life. Seeking as it does the development of humanity, macrobiotics is actually the most practical of spiritual movements. It is a continuation of the work of the philosophers, saints and sages who have striven to teach humanity the purpose of life.

2. Family Health

If you glanced through the table of contents before starting to read this book, you may have wondered what a chapter on the family is doing in a work on traditional and Oriental medicine. Having come this far, the answer should now be evident. Family concerns are tied to the wider implications of health—extending beyond, but intimately connected to, issues of individual welfare—and to the full range of "medicine" in the largest interpretation of the word.

Health, as we have seen, is a dynamic state, maintained by the interaction between the individual and the environment. Healing, in turn, is a holistic process, in which individual well-being is established on a biological, psychological, and spiritual level. Personal development—the natural outcome of a life lived consciously—is an evolutionary course, which gradually extends beyond individual concerns to include one's family, community, and ultimately, to society as a whole.

In this chapter, we discuss the subject of family health. Issues on a social scale are addressed in chapter 3. Although appearing unrelated, the family and society are simply extensions of the individual, and their degree of soundness is an echo of individual vitality. Anyone involved in the health-care profession, for instance, is well aware of the link between individual and family well-being. People with strong family ties get sick less often, and when they do, a supportive family often is the decisive factor in whether an individual recovers from a severe illness. Friends and the community constitute an extended family, and play an essential role in personal health.

The Basis of Society

In the life sciences, the *cell* is commonly defined as the fundamental, irreducible unit of life. By definition, all living organisms are composed of cells. There are trillions in an individual human body, and their quality determines the state of one's physical and mental health.

Just as the cell is the elementary building block of biological life, the family is the basic unit of society. Of all our social institutions, the family is perhaps the oldest and most enduring. Long before mankind's most ancient civilizations flourished, the family provided the thread from which human culture was woven. It has survived repeated natural and social disasters, and the rise and fall of countless civilizations. As the *Academic American Encyclopedia* states: "In traditional societies and, to a lesser but still important extent in modern nations, the ties of kinship form the basic pattern of social interaction and organization."

Healthy families, united by strong ties, are the cornerstone of an orderly and prosperous society. When the family is sound, so too are the social institutions that make up a culture or a nation. If the family structure weakens, society as a whole begins to degenerate. The numerous social problems that we face today—including crime, drug and alcohol abuse, mental illness, degenerative and infectious disease, declining educational standards and work efficiency—can be traced, in one way or another, back to the disintegration of the modern family.

By any criteria, the viability of families in the world's developed nations is in doubt. Divorce and abandonment are rampant, spouse and child abuse are frightening and growing problems, and declining reproductive ability poses the ultimate threat to family unity. A few statistics will help clarify the current situation. The following figures pertain to the United States, but similar tendencies can be seen in modern societies in general. (They are taken from the book, *Macrobiotic Diet*, by Michio and Aveline Kushi, Japan Publications, Inc., 1985.)

- *Divorce:* The divorce rate in the mid-1980s was one divorce for every two marriages. This contrasts with 1 in 3 in 1970; 1 in 6 in 1940; and 1 in 12 in 1900.
- *Family Violence:* Nearly half a million cases of family violence are reported to authorities each year. It is thought that numerous other instances go unreported. About half of the reported cases involve spouses or ex-spouses. The rest involve parents, children, siblings, or other relatives.
- *Birth Defects:* In the last 25 years the number of children born with physical abnormalities, mental retardation, or learning disabilities has doubled. In the late 1950s the total was 70,000, in 1983 it stood at 140,000. This figure represents a jump from 2 percent to 4 percent in the number of infants born with birth defects each year.
- *Sexually Transmitted Disease:* An estimated 30 million Americans have herpes or other "new" STD. Syphilis, gonorrhea, and other, older types of venereal disease affect slightly more than 1 million people.
- *Reproductive Disorders:* One out of every four or five American couples is infertile. More than 20 percent of sexually active males are estimated to be sterile. Sperm counts have dropped 30 to 35 percent since 1920. There are about 4.2 million operations on the female genital tract every year, including about 700,000 hysterectomies. About 1 in 5 babies is delivered by Caesarean section.
- *Sterilization:* Eighteen percent of couples of childbearing age have been voluntarily sterilized to avoid pregnancy. Between 1965 and 1982 female sterilization rose from 7 to 26 percent, and male sterilization rose from 5 to 15 percent.
- *Abortion:* Currently, there is 1 abortion for every three live births in the United States. The yearly total is about 1.5 million abortions.
- *School Violence:* In a typical month, 282,000 secondary students are physically attacked, 112,000 robbed, and 2.4 million report thefts at school.
- *Alcohol Abuse:* An estimated 14 million Americans are alcoholics, about 1 in 10 adults. Alcohol abuse is involved in a large percentage of spouse and child abuse, and divorce or separation.

Each of these statistics carries a double-edged threat: (1) It represents an assault on the family structure, and by extension, on the general welfare of society, and (2) it reflects the declining health of the individuals that make up the family unit.

Beyond Personal Health

After establishing personal well-being, the natural progression for a mature, fully functioning adult is to begin to extend this order to one's family. If an individual is in good health, this process proceeds naturally, that is, without any special efforts or prompting. In harmony with the principles of life, this course automatically returns benefits to the individual involved: to receive, we must give.

A microcosmic and macrocosmic relation exists between the individual and the family. The condition of the one is reflected in the condition of the other. There is a two-way pattern of influence at work in this relationship: The health of its individual members affects the collective soundness of family life, and the quality of family relationships has a direct impact on individual well-being.

The family is thus the pivot upon which civilization turns. It is the point of transmission where individual energy is transformed into social prosperity. Recognizing this vital role, our attention necessarily turns to the question of how to establish and maintain the integrity of the family. This concern is not the providence of any particular group. Government, religion, education, industry, law enforcement, all have a direct and vested interest in ensuring family unity.

Any attempt to secure the family as a viable social institution must begin with a practical concept of what the family is: a working definition is required of its purpose and function, and the dynamics that create and nurture family ties need to be clarified. Interpretations of family life vary according to the particular time, location, and group involved. *Webster's Ninth New Collegiate Dictionary* offers a variety of broad definitions:

1. A group of individuals living under one roof
2. A group of persons of common ancestry
3. A group of people united by certain convictions or a common affiliation

There are, of course, additional explanations, but these are the most common. A family, then, is a group of individuals living together, sharing a common ancestry, and united by common convictions. *Sharing* is a key word in this description, and a concept basic to family life. A family shares a variety of important factors:

1. *Genes and Blood Quality.* From ancient times relatives were described as "blood kin," or "blood relatives," and even today we use the term "in-law" to distinguish relatives by marriage from blood relations.

   It is through the genetic material that inherited characteristics are passed from one generation to the next. A common blood quality is both our link with the past and our bequest to the future.
2. *Food and Drink.* Food has a direct and profound influence on blood quality and thus on our emotions and thoughts, as well as the quality of physical health. By following specific patterns of consumption, families engender distinctive physical and psychological characteristics in their members.
3. *Time and Experiences:* Sharing the pleasures and difficulties of life,

families forge a strong communal bond. As members proceed through the stages of life—birth, childhood, adolescence, marriage, old age and death—the group gains important insights into the meaning of life. Until very recent times, the kitchen and mealtimes were the primary stage for family interaction. The decline in this practice is an overlooked but fundamental reason for the growing sense of alienation and fragmentation between family members.

4. *Values and Goals.* Children start to fashion their orientation to life at a very early age, and in fact, this education begins in the womb and is influenced by a mother's thoughts and emotions. In the Orient, a sophisticated concept of "embryonic education" has been practiced for thousands of years.
5. *The Family Spirit.* Family members share influences passed on from their ancestors that go beyond the hereditary factors carried by the genes. A certain vision, dream, and orientation to life is transmitted from one generation to the next, and can have a strong influence on one's life.

In direct contrast to this ethic of sharing and unity, the hallmark of modern society is of individual gratification and separation. When individuals pursue personal happiness with little or no regard for the welfare of other family members, how can we expect to create a compassionate and caring society. Millions of people today are plagued by deep feelings of isolation. They are emotionally and spiritually disconnected from parents, spouse, children, brothers and sisters. This is the natural and perhaps final outcome of civilization's attempts to separate the spiritual from the physical, the body from the mind.

Love and Marriage

To properly assess the importance and purpose of family life, a comprehensive or "macro" starting point is essential. Behavior based on this broad understanding differs greatly from that produced by more limited visions of reality. In setting goals, solving problems, and making the choices and decisions that are an inevitable part of daily life, we are often faced with what seem to be conflicting demands. If we are to successfully address the complimentary considerations of short-term and long-term need, of personal pleasure and growth, and of individual, family, and social benefit, our values must indeed be broad-based. From this starting point, we fashion the answers to such germane questions as: What is the basis of sexual attraction? What is love? What is a family? What is the purpose of children?

The significance of marriage clearly starts with the man and woman involved. Initially attracted by the polarities of yin and yang, a couple enters into a relationship to establish harmony and balance in their daily life. In traditional cultures, the relationship was not limited to the husband and wife, however. Marriage was seen as a tying together of two families. This is the reason for the so-called arranged marriages still practiced in traditional and Oriental countries.

Recognizing that a young couple often based their choices solely on the basis of sexual attraction or emotional appeal, the opinion of family members with wider experience in life was solicited. Not so long ago, the concept of marriage as a lifelong commitment was taken seriously, and many factors of character and background were used to determine the suitability of a partner. Of course, when abused, this system can degenerate from one of advice and mutual consent to one of unwilling partners being pushed into unwanted relationships.

After living together for a period of months or years, a certain balance is struck between the partners as the various polar tendencies of the couple balance each other. As this stage is reached, the strong attraction between the male and female may diminish, and the relationship could be threatened if an outside influence, such as another person or even an engrossing activity attracts one or both the partners' time and energy. In the natural course of events, this eventuality does not occur.

Children are a key to a couple's living together. The implications of marriage begin to take on wider meanings with the coming of the first child. A new set of energetic dynamics begins—between father and baby, mother and baby, husband and wife, and parents and child. Each member affects and is influenced by the other family members.

A child widens the parent's vision of life. The emphasis shifts from personal concerns to factors beyond the individual. A couple's awareness broadens in both the dimensions of space—concerns for the home, the neighborhood, the school—and time. The future now has a compelling significance. The parent's orientation expands from the limited concerns of personal satisfaction to the wider demands of raising healthy offspring.

Sexual attraction is the magnetism created by the male's yang energetic nature and the female's yin energetic orientation. During sexual intercourse, these energies are temporarily neutralized, and children are the result of this consequent harmony. In health, attraction between the sexes automatically arises, and children are conceived and born. The focus of marriage, from the large perspective, does not change with the birth of a child, it widens to include the preservation and improvement of the human species.

In contrast to this function, the values of modern relationships are often superficial and temporary. Far too frequently, the expectations of marriage are limited to sensory satisfaction, or to issues of emotional or financial security. Building a relationship on such transient goals is one of the main reasons why marriages fall apart when difficulties arise. If the expectations of one partner are not satisfied, or if a better opportunity presents itself, the lifetime commitment made during the wedding ceremony may readily be abandoned. There are, of course, justifiable reasons for divorce, but they do not include the failure to satisfy the transient desires of a consumer-driven view of life.

In the value systems of certain cultures and in the particular time frame of the late twentieth century, such considerations may be important. In the eyes of nature they are meaningless, beyond whatever value they have in helping the individual recognize the scope and purpose of life. Wealth, fame, an active social life, academic degrees, material goods, power or influence, are not related to quality of life, enduring happiness, spiritual growth, and the type of death we eventually experience. Far more significant are the issues of establishing our health, maintaining personal development, and then producing and developing offspring. For this reason attraction between man and woman occurs, love develops, and a couple establish a home.

It is natural for parents to love their children, to try to protect them, and to want the best for them. But many couples do not know how to realize these goals. The central issue for parents is the criteria they use to decide what it is that will best serve their children. Many families are building their future on illusion. Acting from a limited perspective, and pursuing narrow goals, a marriage may easily end in divorce. Or, parents may fail in their efforts to teach their children how to find lasting happiness.

Before moving on, one final point regarding marriage needs to be addressed. A couple that remains childless—either by choice or because the partners are unable to reproduce—faces the question of how to compensate for the sense of sharing and the impetus for growth that children provide. Their challenge is to articulate a goal toward which both partners can dedicate their lives. This "dream" must be large enough to accommodate the multidimensions of the Self. It must be comprehensive enough to fully engage the couple's energies and to foster the development of their consciousness. Lacking such a compelling orientation, the possibility that the partners will drift apart is great.

The Changing Family

The family has undergone profound changes since the Industrial Revolution. It has evolved from the *extended family*—composed of three or more generations living in the same household—to the *nuclear family*, made up of parents and children. In recent years the phenomenon of the *single-parent family* has emerged. Because of divorce, separation, or death of a spouse, one parent—most often the mother—faces the twin tasks of raising the children and earning a living.

Very recently, a totally new family orientation has emerged. The *artificial family*—in which children are produced through such high-tech procedures as in vitro fertilization and artificial insemination—is a troublesome warning not only of declining reproductive abilities but of a society-wide weakening of overall health. Many couples are unable to produce children naturally. In their despair and desperation, they search for help in the laboratories of science and the inventions of technology. (For a discussion of the macrobiotic approach to infertility, readers are referred to *Macrobiotic Health Education Series: Infertility and Reproductive Disorders*, Michio Kushi, Japan Publications, Inc., 1988.)

The news media regularly carry stories of the latest "miracle" in artificial birth techniques. A recent UPI article was reported in the *Japan Times* newspaper under the headline, "Wonder of Science." It was the story of a woman whose ovaries were removed because of an unspecified infection, making her incapable of conception. However, following the surgery, a number of her eggs were removed from the ovaries and fertilized with her husband's sperm in vitro, that is, in a laboratory dish. The fertilized eggs were then frozen and some months later were thawed and inserted into the woman's uterus, where implantation took place.

From the narrow view of contemporary society, this birth is undeniably a miracle. A woman without ovaries who nonetheless gives birth is a fantastic story. From a larger view, the episode could be seen as a tragedy. Failing to prevent the illness that affected her reproductive organs, and unable to treat it, the medical concept of a cure was to remove the ovaries. Then, sterility, one side effect of the treatment, was overcome by artificial fertilization and insemination.

And what is the cost of this miracle? In economic terms, it certainly involved many thousands of dollars. The woman will be unable to have more children unless additional eggs were removed from her ovaries and are now frozen. She will take artificial hormones to replace those naturally produced by the ovaries, and face the consequent risks to health. The implications to the child are unknown, and perhaps no one is even asking. Most bothersome is the fact that the primary role of medicine, to prevent illness or, failing that, to restore health, was not achieved.

The human race faces a crisis: we are losing our ability to produce healthy children, and to raise them to be responsible, independent members of society. Under these circumstances, if the declines in physical and mental health—as reflected in the statistics given earlier—continue, image what the situation will be like in just twenty-five years.

Family unity is a far more important issue to a nation than its Gross National Product or trade balance. Its implications are much more serious and immediate than even environmental deterioration or the threat of nuclear war. In fact, in a very real sense, these problems are merely reflections of family decline. Decreasing worker productivity, wasteful patterns of consumption, and international tensions, are the result of individual choices. Choices, we might add, that are profoundly influenced by the orientation received from one's family. The issue of family health is directly related to whether we, as a species, will be able to reverse these trends, and whether we, as a civilization, will survive beyond a few more generations.

Rebuilding Family Health

The principles for establishing family health are the very same guidelines used for creating individual well-being. The progressive steps for producing family unity include:

1. Recovering or improving our reproductive abilities.
2. Ensuring the optimum biological strength of our children. We start with the quality of our own reproductive cells, and then focus on the quality of the child's life in the womb.
3. After an infant is born, parents can see to it that the influences that shape the child's formative years continue to be those that produce health and vitality.
4. Raising our children with the understanding of the order of life, and the Unifying Principles of yin and yang.

Three primary factors must be considered in respect to the above guidelines.

Dietary Practice: The number one issue for family well-being is balanced dietary practice. Meals should be centered around such traditional and natural foods as whole grains, fresh vegetables, beans and other complex-carbohydrate items found in the macrobiotic way of eating. Daily diet is directly responsible for an individual's physical and psychological health, as discussed in Part 2. Comprised of a group of individuals, a family's physical, mental, and spiritual orientation are equally dependent on day-to-day diet.

If a family is eating poorly, its members will be susceptible to a variety of self-inflicted problems. Family unity may be lost due to the lack of appreciation, concern, and communication between members as individual biological and psychological vitality diminishes. Serious illness and even death may result. Such strains can severely affect the family. If it is already troubled, the family could collapse. At the same time, reproductive ability will decline, reducing the chances of offspring in the present and next generation. As values shift to reflect the weakening biological quality, many adults will choose not to have children. The next several decades will see the end of many families, and with them, the spirit and heritage of countless generations will disappear.

Sharing Meals: Included in proper dietary practice is the sharing in the preparation and consumption of meals. If this is not possible every evening, families should eat together as often as possible. In this way family members share their experiences of the day, receive encouragement and advice, and gain the sense of belonging that is so important to all human beings.

Care for Family Members: An additional point is that family members should care for each other. This may seem obvious, and should be a natural response, but unfortunately, many families resemble a group of strangers sharing the same living space for economic and other considerations of convenience. The idea of care includes a genuine concern for the welfare of family members, and the willingness to share in problems and concerns. It implies the readiness for personal sacrifice, if necessary, to help others.

Spiritual Healing

As human beings, we have both a physical and spiritual existence. Our influence can and should stretch in both domains. This means that we extend our feelings of gratitude and love not only to living family members, but also to those who have passed on. We have already seen that life on earth is preparation for existence in wider dimensions of reality. Individuals who die before their consciousness is fully developed often experience a kind of purgatory in which they exist in the vibrational realm and yet are strongly attached to the material world.

To help these individuals adjust to the reality of their new life, several simple practices are recommended. First, if at all possible, we should be with our relatives at the time of their death. We make them comfortable, thank them for sharing their life with us, pray for them, and in general are there to comfort and care for them at the time of their transition.

For the first seven days after a relative's death, we eat simply, avoiding animal food completely, to make our own condition as clean and peaceful as possible. During this period, we spend thirty to sixty minutes in a daily session of prayer and remembrance, extending our love to the deceased individual. Following this initial seven days, we continue offering daily prayers for a total of forty-nine days, extending our wishes for peace and happiness in their new life. After this period, we can devote a special time for prayer each week or month, and on the anniversary on the individual's passing into the spiritual world.

Fig. 65 Family Memorial

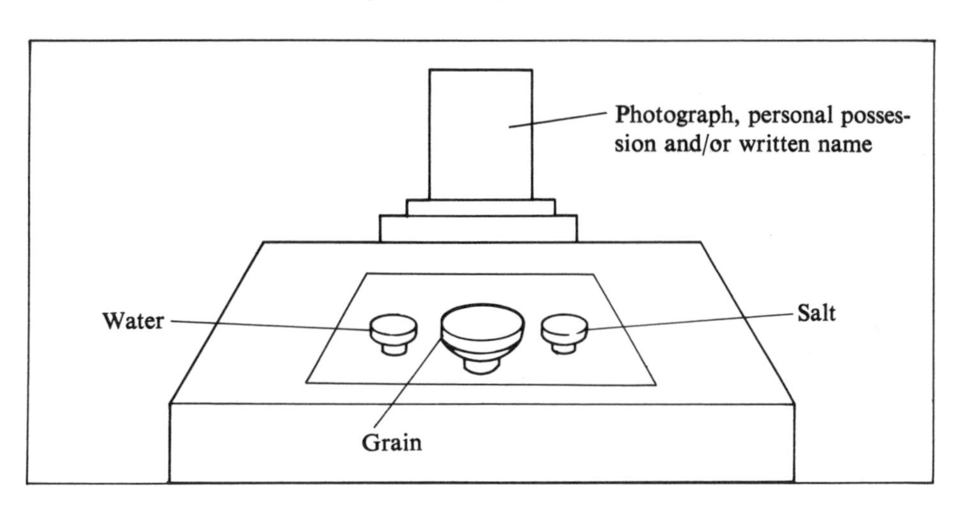

The family memorial is placed in a quiet place in the home. White candles, incense and flowers can be used in addition to the items listed above. Religious objects related to one's faith may also be included.

As a supplement to these practices, a simple memorial can be created in a quiet place in the home. This can be used both for recently deceased relatives, and for family members from earlier generations. In a quiet room in the home, put up a small shelf or wooden table. Then, because of the profound influence that dietary practice has on consciousness, we can aid the spirits of the departed by sending them the energy of high-quality food.

The minimum requirements are a small portion of uncooked grain, sea salt and fresh water. According to the principles of yin and yang, the grain, being most balanced, is placed in the center. The most yang item, the salt, is situated on the left side of the shelf (your right as you face it), and the most yin, the water, is on your left. These items are not symbolic. We are offering the Ki of each substance for the spiritual nourishment of the deceased.

A photograph, personal belonging, or simply the name of the deceased written on a piece of paper may also be placed on the memorial. Such articles help establish our energetic connection with the individual, and serve to focus our image as we pray. In cases of a recent death, spend the recommended time in front of this memorial, praying for the peace and happiness of the relative. For individuals who have passed away further back in time, we can occasionally pray for them, perhaps once a week, or monthly.

One additional practice can be very useful both for consoling the spirit of a departed relative and for engendering a feeling of family unity. The entire family can gather annually for a family memorial on the anniversary of a parent's or other family member's death. On this day, family members can once again eat together, talk about the departed relative and their shared experiences, and keep the others up to date on their personal lives. The gathering should begin with a common prayer for particular relatives and for all family members who are now deceased. It can also include any other type of commemorative activity deemed appropriate.

If we have this kind of gratitude and appreciation for our parents, close family members, and other relatives, our family experience will be a rewarding one. If we lack this sense of appreciation and desire to help and share, we are no longer biologically and spiritually strong. Our personal health is probably declining, and our family is already in jeopardy.

The Time for Commitment

Because of the increasing assaults on our biological and psychological well-being, we no longer have the luxury of being complacent. The situation in the areas of health, environment, social and international affairs, is grave. If we kiss someone we may get herpes. If we make love, we may be exposing ourselves to the AIDS virus. Our air and water are being poisoned, our emotions and intellect are being abused, and our spirit is ignored, all in the name of convenience and a misplaced confidence in modern values.

We must ask ourselves what constitutes personal and family happiness. Is it simply doing whatever we want, satisfying the desires of the moment and either ignoring the consequences or choosing to pay for them at a later date? Or does the concept of happiness embrace the more profound vision of living in harmony with the forces of life, even at the expense of short-term pleasures, so that continual development on a personal, family, and planetary scale are assured.

The family is the source of nourishment and renewal for our offspring and for mankind in general. It is precious. Parents are encouraged to devote their efforts toward making their children physically and spiritually healthy. Women, please remember that you are the center of the home, and by extension, of society itself. By the power of your vision and dream, and with the tools of your physical and spiritual nourishment, you create and guide the next generation. Men must regain their biological strength. If a man's sperm is weak or if he cannot create a child, he is losing his masculine quality. If his thinking is unclear, his emotions unstable, or he has no direction in life, he is biologically weak. Biological strength is synonymous with spiritual strength.

Parents need a dream, a purpose for which they devote their life. This vision must embrace one's spouse and children or we are dualistic. Pursuing personal goals while ignoring one's family is a type of schizophrenia. As we address the daily concerns of raising a family, our judgment matures. We begin to see what is really important, and the quality of our life increases accordingly. Gradually our concept of family expands to include all children, and all elderly people become our parents. We automatically extend our respect, love and care to them. In this way we come to realize that our family ties extend to humanity in general: we are members of the human family. We know this not in an intellectual way, but truly and instinctively experience it.

Before we begin to actively participate in these wider dimensions of life, however, we must first establish the welfare of our immediate family. If we cannot make ourselves and our own family healthy, happy and peaceful, we will be unable to do so in society. There are many people in the world who would be leaders and teachers. One measure of their abilities is their families. While such individuals speak of peace and love, their own families may be suffering. If so, they are talking but not living peace. They cannot be your guide.

Macrobiotics is clearly far more than a means of recovering individual health, or even of fostering personal development. After these qualities are secured, we go on to establish them in our own families. From the experience and insights gained in the process, we are ready for the final application of macrobiotic healing: society and the world.

3. Society and the World

In just a few short years humanity will usher in the twenty-first century. It will be a time of worldwide celebration and hopeful expectation. Perhaps because it marks the start of a new millennium, the year 2001 has a powerful hold on the imagination. It carries images of the ultra-modern, of almost inconceivable scientific advances used for the benefit of humanity. How is it then, that in the last years of the twentieth century, despite our undeniable technological prowess, degenerative disease poses the biggest threat to individual, family, and social well-being? And why is it that the spector of environmental deterioration, war, and the ultimate threat of nuclear annihilation grows with each passing year?

It was over thirty years ago that the age of space exploration began. Twenty years ago, the first human walked on the moon. The Voyager 2 spacecraft is even now traveling to the outer limits of this solar system. The computer micro-chip—capable of storing reams of information on tiny wafers of silicone—is changing every aspect of life, including the way we work, study, and relax. Advances in science and medicine are so rapid and so profound, that the genre of science fiction is a threatened art. The irony is that the more sophisticated our technology grows, the more susceptible we seem to become to physical and mental disorders, and that the farther our power extends over nature, the more our judgment and common sense appear to diminish.

In this final chapter, we address these concerns. For answers, we look to the order of life, the Unifying Principles of yin and yang. Let us hope that the creativity, vitality, and optimism that characterizes the human spirit will soon find expression in a comprehensive vision of life.

An Epic End

We are quickly approaching the conclusion of the recent epic in human history. For thousands of years humanity has pursued the course that can broadly be described as *materialism. The New American Desk Encyclopedia* explains materialism this way:

> Any view asserting the primacy of matter; in psychology, any theory denying the existence of mind, seeing mental phenomena as the mere outworking of purely physio-mechanical processes of the brain; in the philosophy of religion, any synthesis denying the existence of an immortal soul in man. The growth of modern science brought a revival of materialism, which many have argued is a prerequisite for scientific thought, particularly in the field of psychology.

Proponents of materialism based their orientation on two basic assumptions: (1) They hoped that by understanding and harnessing the forces of nature, the human condition could be dramatically improved. (2) They reasoned that only phenomenon that could be measured in a repeatable and consistent manner had any practical value in this pursuit. There have been dissenters to this line of thought in every age. But they have not been taken seriously by the social institutions who insisted on the completeness of the scientific orientation. The teachings of such individuals have been dismissed, ignored, or relegated to the supposedly impractical areas of philosophy and religion. It seems that only in times of desperation have individuals and groups turned to such guidance for solace and inspiration.

For the past 6,000 years or longer, civilization has been developing along the pattern that naturally emerges from the materialistic view of existence. This orientation is now reaching its logical conclusion. We have taken the materialistic world view just about as far as we can without inflicting grievous harm to ourselves and our planet.

Modern civilization is wonderful. Its fruits of prosperity, comfort and material wealth are perhaps unheard of in human history. The average citizen in industrial nations is surrounded by more luxury than kings and queens of old. Yet we are reminded of the principles of nature that whatever has a front has a back, and that the bigger the front, the bigger the back.

In the midst of this great material wealth, the spiritual values of humanity are disappearing. Our development has been one-sided, and, like a child allowed to eat as many sweets as he likes, we have gorged ourselves on the products of our consumer-driven economy, with no consideration for the consequences. As we have already seen, this short-sighted lifestyle is affecting both the individual and the family. It is echoed on the individual level in the degeneration on the body, mind, and spirit. Practically everyone in the United States faces the threat of ill health. Indeed, this is the biggest problem in the modern world. The concept of family, as it has existed since the beginnings of human history, faces a similar fate.

To cope with the inevitable side effects that our modern value system has generated, we have introduced the forces of science, technology and medicine into every area of our lives. The scope of this intervention is astounding. From artificial fertilization techniques to industrially made body parts, from the cloning and re-engineering of biological life to the chemical manipulation of human emotions and behavioral patterns, humanity is abdicating its biological integrity, its cultural heritage and its spiritual origins.

It is no secret that new medical therapies and technological advances repeatedly cause problems more serious than they were intended to cure. In such cases, who takes responsiblity? Recent examples include the routine removal of the tonsils, which researchers are now reporting to be a vital part of the immune system; the introduction of the contraceptive pill, and later the intrauterine device, or IUD, both of which have subsequently been proven to have severe and unanticipated side effects; practices related to pregnancy and childbirth like Caesarean section and *ultrasound scans*, in which high-frequency sound waves (two-thousand cycles per second) are bounced off the fetus, even at the earliest stages of fetal development.

As far back as the 1950s, nuclear power was touted as a clean, inexpensive source of energy. The recent disclosure that for the past thirty years, a nuclear-weapons plant in Ohio has been releasing tons of radioactive material into the atmosphere every year has stunned and angered people throughout the United States. Microwave ovens are now almost as common as refrigerators in the modern kitchen. They are used in schools, hospitals, restaurants, airlines, and, in fact, anywhere food is prepared. This trend continues despite well-documented research indicating that foods cooked with microwaves may produce tumors and accelerate the growth of already existing tumors. As many social commentators have noted, the public has become the unwitting guinea pigs of science and technology.

Crisis and Opportunity

Among the definitions listed for the word *crisis* are:

- A turning point for better or worse in an acute disease or fever
- An emotionally significant event or radical change of status in a person's life
- An unstable or crucial time or state of affairs in which a decisive change is impending
- A situation that has reached a critical phase

Civilization faces a crisis, a time of decision and unlooked for opportunity. From our front-and-back perspective, we see that the threats facing modern civilization can be turned into benefits. And, because of the extent of the problems, the promise is great. The difficulties we face are of our own making. They result from our orientation to life, which has generated the personal and social conditions that are causing our problems.

The challenges confronting modern civilization, and indeed the world, can be summed up as:

1. *The Threat of Nuclear War.* Although relations between the Soviet Union and the United States are improving, the proliferation of nuclear weapons continues, putting the world at risk. Nuclear war, even a limited one, would cause unimagined suffering for humanity. It could very well mean the end of civilization, of countries as national entities, and of the family unit. Social patterns might continue in isolated areas, but for most of mankind, there would be nowhere to take shelter, and no one to turn to for help.
2. *The Deteriorating Environment.* Our lives are directly dependent on the natural world, as reflected in such commonly used phrases as "mother nature" and "mother earth." As the quality of our air, water, and soil continues to decline, the incidence of environmentally related sickness—both physical and mental—can be expected to rise. It is estimated, for instance, that for every 1 percent drop in the earth's protective ozone layer, levels of skin cancer can rise by as much as 2 percent. Desertification and changing weather patterns are additional environmental changes produced, in great part, by modern civilization.
3. *The Destruction of Civilization by Disease of the Body and Mind.* In this scenario, as the rate of physical and psychological illness continues to

increase, nations, deprived of the productivity of their citizens, and plagued by widespread social disorder, would collapse from within.

At one time, there was the possibility that the threat of cancer would be sufficient to awaken society to its destructive habits. Not so long ago cancer was a feared and much-dreaded disease. Unfortunately, we have grown accustomed to the idea of cancer and no longer feel the horror that the disease once elicited. Many of us now suppose that cancer is under control, that it can be cured, and that it is not such a widespread problem. Comparatively speaking, this may be true. We now have AIDS to worry about, and heart and circulatory disease is still the leading cause of death in the United States and many industrialized countries.

However, if readers are inclined to discount the menace of cancer, please consider the personal, family, and social implications of the following information. In 1985, it was estimated that one out of every three children born that year would suffer from cancer at some point in their life. This contrasts to one in eight in 1950, and one in fifteen at the turn of the century. Is it possible that we have become numb because of the pervasiveness of the disease?

Acquired Immune Deficiency, or AIDS, is the disease that now grabs the headlines, and poses the greatest potential for social chaos. But people do not die from AIDS. Because of weakened immune ability, infected individuals are instead susceptible to a host of common illness that would not necessarily be fatal to a healthy individual. As our collective immune ability drops below a certain level, and increasing numbers of individuals succumb to routine infections, perhaps we will waken to our mistakes. If so, the AIDS disease will indeed turn into our benefactor, for it will have alerted us to our self-destructive lifestyles.

Macrobiotics has already been noted for its ability to slow or arrest the development of AIDS. It is just a matter of time until research confirms that proper diet and lifestyle can prevent or relieve the disease. When this happens, we can expect a total reevaluation of goals and policies to implement them, by government, science, medicine, education and other social institutions.

If this does not happen, it may be that an even more dreadful illness will arise to give notice that we are violating the principles of life. As we saw in the chapter on individual health, sickness, in whatever form it takes, is a warning that individually and collectively, we are creating extreme conditions in our lives. By heeding the message, finding and changing the cause, we erase the problem. Ignoring the warning is a reckless, dangerous course.

Good Intentions Are Not Enough

Many groups and organizations are working hard to improve the condition of mankind. Their starting points differ—some focusing on the plight of the poor, others on helping underdeveloped nations, saving endangered animal species, protecting the environment, and there are many groups devoted to world peace. These organizations exert a necessary and beneficial influence, and their work helps to highlight problem areas. We all owe a debt of gratitude to those who devote their lives to the betterment of humanity.

The focus tends to be on the symptoms of a particular problem or range of problems, however, and despite their good intentions, such groups cannot achieve the lasting resolution of the conditions they are addressing. No one seems to be directly approaching the biological and psychological root of society's and civilization's dilemma. No matter how complicated the problem—poverty, crime, famine, war, environmental decline—it can be traced back to a common root, the deteriorating quality of human judgment and physiology.

Macrobiotics has been a pioneer in the field of prevention and relief of illness through dietary practice. Yet, although the natural-food movement has spread practically worldwide, and numerous governmental and scientific organizations have issued dietary guidelines for disease prevention, these steps are not enough. Do not make the mistake of thinking that macrobiotics is a diet, or that diet alone can solve our problems. Macrobiotic dietary recommendations are one application of the Unifying Principles. The ease with which they can be implemented, the economic savings they produce, the environmentally sound farming practices they entail, and their undeniable rejuvenating abilities, are reflections that these guidelines are based on the order of life. Such broad-based benefits should be enough to prompt the immediate application of these same principles to other areas of human activity, perhaps starting with a national policy on agriculture and then education and developing a nonpolluting source of energy.

As they now exist, our social institutions cannot protect us from the decline of modern civilization. Educational systems are failing us, our children, and our future. Instead of teaching the order and purpose of life, and then using this foundation to fashion a practical and comprehensive education, students learn from their earliest years the values of consumption and competition. Government fails to look out for the welfare of its citizens, religion has lost its relevance to day-to-day life, medicine is preoccupied with symptomatic relief, science with ever-smaller areas of life, and technology has forgotten its purpose of improving the lot of humanity.

Solutions

How have we reached such desperate straits? What is the cause of our problems and suffering? Simply stated, it is our forgetfulness. We have forgotten who we are, where we come from, and why we have come to this life on the planet earth. In Part 1, the process by which we materialized as human beings was discussed. Infinite oneness, or the large I, physicalized into individual consciousness, or the small I, by means of a seven-orbited spiral. Each of us has come from infinity, descending through each level of life, finally emerging as human beings.

This journey has taken billions of years, and every human being has passed through it. The memory of this heritage resides in each of us. Deep inside, we all know that we are brothers and sisters. Because we share this common origin, the principles that govern life are the same for all of humanity. Always and everywhere in the realm of relative existence, creation is guided by the dynamics of yin and yang, of attraction and repulsion, for the purpose of establishing and maintaining harmony and peace.

Dualism—the concept of struggle and reward, of good and bad, right and wrong, enemy and friend—is the foundation of modern civilization. It is reflected in our personal and collective approach to life. And, it is an illusion, a self-imposed distortion of reality. Our concepts of suffering, punishment, struggle, and hell are products of dualism.

There is no enemy in this life, and there could never be. If, however, the small I thinks "I am right," then someone else must obviously be wrong. If we insist that we are blameless when misfortune or sickness strikes, then indeed, we simultaneously fabricate an enemy to shoulder the blame. It could be a virus or bacteria, an industry for producing cancer-causing chemicals, defective hereditary factors that predisposed us to certain illnesses or destructive behavior, a cruel fate that dealt us difficult circumstances, or we may even start to question the existence of God, or blame Him for our troubles.

This makes no sense. Paradise is here and its time is now. We fail to recognize and experience this reality because of our insistence that we already know what is right. For many thousands of years, civilization has been blinded by the delusion of dualism. Only recently have we begun to recognized the seriousness of our error.

Throughout history there have been philosophers, teachers and religious leaders who have tried to warn us of our mistake. As just a single example, in *The Gospel According to Thomas*, Christ said:

> If those who lead you say to you, "See, the Kingdom is in the sky," then the birds of the sky will precede you. If they say to you, "It is in the sea," then the fish will precede you. Rather, the Kingdom is inside of you, and it is outside of you. When you come to know yourselves, then you will become known, and you will realize that it is you who are the sons of the living Father. But if you will not know yourselves, you swell in poverty and it is you who are that poverty.

Did we come from infinity to struggle and suffer, to live in fear of threats, internal and external? Is not something dreadfully wrong? If our approach to life is correct, then why do we and our children suffer from degenerative disease, why must we bar our doors even during the day for fear of intruders, and why do we face extinction by nuclear war or environmental disaster?

If we suffer, it is our own fault. Our problems are self-made; the product of our own misperception. The solution to such difficulties lies within ourselves. We need not depend on any external force or influence for relief. Indeed, to the extent that we do so, we will fail to realize our happiness and freedom. As a society, suffering has a similar origin. Social problems are, after all, people problems. As such, the solution centers around basic questions pertaining to individual and family well-being.

A New Human Species

The first step toward realizing social harmony and global cooperation is to establish the biological and psychological health of humanity. In one sense, this work can be described as creating a new human species; one which lives in cooperation with the forces of nature. Actually, this new species is a very old variety: it represents the return to the original quality of human beings. The key to humanity's future lies in its past. This is the basis for the assertion that traditional medicine, or macrobiotics, is the medicine-to-be.

To establish this change in humanity, we cannot use violence, and our outlook cannot be based on fear. Violence always turns against itself, and fear is based on ignorance. To accomplish our essential task of regeneration, our judgment must be clear, and predicated on the understanding of the Unifying Principles of life.

What is needed is a revolution in ideology and philosophy; a reformation of civilization. Because in many ways the world is a global community, a renaissance on a global scale is needed. Yet how can such a revival be accomplished? Imagine that the leaders of the social institutions of the nations of the world gathered to determine a common definition of peace, prosperity, God, and similar broad concepts. There would be endless discussion, and no agreement. The basic problem would not be cultural or national distinctions, but basic biological differences between participants.

Even though we share a common origin, and we are all human beings, sensations, emotions, thinking, perception, and understanding, differ dramatically according to the quality of our blood, our brain cells and nervous system, and the breadth of our consciousness. These factors, in turn, are produced by distinctive qualities of food and drink. It would only be a slight exaggeration to say that the participants would constitute different biological and psychological orientations.

Different areas of the brain are activated or suppressed according to specific dietary habits. Emotions and perceptions are affected in the same manner. Because of these variations, individuals and groups have different opinions and desires, and perceive different degrees of reality. To some extent this is natural. The dictates of geography, climate, and cultural traditions produce unique cuisines and lifestyle patterns that in turn generate singular physical, psychological, and spiritual orientations.

Within this natural pattern of diversity, however, there are common human perceptions generated by human-quality food—grains, beans, vegetables, and so on. When we consume extreme foods—foods for which the human body cannot efficiently metabolize—our thinking, emotions, perceptions and behavior become unbalanced. Examples of such foods include simple sugars, meat and dairy products, refined, chemicalized, and highly processed foods, and products from climatic regions that differ from that in which we live—eating, for instance, tropical foods in a temperate climate, or beef, poultry and eggs in tropical regions. As these dietary extremes are now quite common, it is no surprise that the world is full of violence, strife, and personal tragedy.

Conflicting Opinions

Civilization lacks a consensus about its most basic terminology. Numerous concepts carry such emotional weight that they repeatedly spark heated and conflicting reactions. The notion of God is an example. Christians, Jews, Muslims, Hindus, Buddhists, and followers of Shintoism all use the word, but the underlining meaning differs greatly. Wars have been fought, individuals persecuted and even put to death over the meaning of God. Is it possible to unite these contending opinions and beliefs?

Truth is another difficult idea to define. The meaning differs according to the particular perspective employed. Varieties of truth include the scientific, religious, philosophical, national, and personal. The concepts of good and bad, and right and wrong, are undependable. To kill another human being is generally considered wrong. Yet in times of war, killing makes one a hero. And of course there are many types of murder. With education we can dispatch a child's curiosity, and parents and teachers can kill a child's sense of worth. Through economic manipulation, a culture can be destroyed. The earth itself can be mortally wounded through misguided agricultural and industrial practices, and modern social values.

Love is a prime example of the relativity of concepts. There is sexual love, emotional love, parental love, the love of ideas, of country, and of God. In our age, the concept of peace has particular importance. Many consider peace to be achieved when there are no wars going on. But what about the struggle between the rich and poor, the law abider and the criminal, economic and environmental violence, the misuse of animals in scientific and medical experiments, and we have already mentioned the medical wars waged against cancer and the common cold. As long as the underlying fighting mentality exists, war will be found in every realm of life.

Those who aspire to the role of peacemaker must find a way to reconcile these and similarly broad-based concepts. Doing so requires transcending relative values, conditioned on particular times and cultural orientations. We must see what is love, truth, peace, and God, from the perspective of the universe. Otherwise our solutions will be temporary, and in all likelihood, will produce results opposite to those intended.

The Macrobiotic Solution

The goal of macrobiotics extends far beyond the establishment of individual health. The objective is twofold:

1. To reverse the self-destructive trend in the modern world in order to secure the future of human society. Obviously, it is easy to criticize and to make predictions of gloom and disaster, but the facts of our decline are well-documented, and originate from many sources. Unless mankind alters its orientation, civilization could come to an end within fifty years. The threats issue from every area of human endeavor, and are in fact, part of the fabric of our view of life.
2. Securing the future, macrobiotics seeks to insure the full development of the human species. This process was discussed in chapter 1 of this part.

The methods employed in the revolutionary work of reorienting the direction of modern society are the very same ones used in establishing personal and family well-being. The Unifying Principles apply to all areas of human endeavor.

Change Moves from the Bottom up

There is a complementary relationship between individuals and social institutions. Recognizing the futility of our one-sided view of life, and the practicality of a more holistic outlook, individuals and families enjoy the freedom and flexibility to alter their lifestyle. Social institutions, being more insulated from economic, health, and ecological realities, and possessing less adaptability, require more time to change their policies. Even in the face of overwhelming evidence, other considerations may hold sway. Factors such as the influence of special-interest groups, a lack of understanding of how to implement new policy, or a reluctance to upset the status quo, often are the determining factors.

Ironically, social change in the modern world often happens from the bottom up. Personal habits change, move up through the social and economic ladder, and when they have become an established, though as yet unsanctioned way of life, they begin to attract recognition by the governing boards of various institutions and agencies. As they do so, the larger concerns of community and society begin to reflect this shift in values.

There is a revolution taking place in modern society. For the most part ignored by the mass media, and scorned by policy makers, this reformation is none-the-less well under way. The message is clear: individuals and families can make a difference. As they take responsibility for their own well-being, the larger concerns of community and society begin to respond.

The Crossroad

Humanity stands at a crossroad. The choices before us are clear. One road continues in the direction that has brought humanity to this point in history. It is a continuation of the symptomatic, fragmented approach to life, and offers only measures to cover up our problems. The other path presents a new, and yet familiar direction. It is not a renunciation of the first, but rather a synthesis. Once again the mind will be connected to the body, spiritual concerns will take their place along side the material, and our options will not be limited to either fighting or perishing.

The physical structure of a planetary commonwealth is established. Inexpensive and comfortable travel, instantaneous communication, and the rapid flow of information, puts us in touch with all corners of the planet. Whether we go beyond this reality of a technologically united civilization to create a brotherhood and sisterhood of humanity is the decision we now must make. Macrobiotics, the medicine used many thousands of years ago, and the medicine-to-be, is the course toward biological and spiritual evolution. Let us walk together down this road.

Bibliography

Aihara, Herman. *Basic Macrobiotics*. Tokyo and New York: Japan Publications, Inc., 1985.

Anatomical Atlas of Chinese Acupuncture Points. Jinan, China: Shandong Science and Technology Press, 1982.

Asano, Hachiro. *Hands: The Complete Book of Palmistry*. Tokyo and New York: Japan Publications, Inc., 1985.

Ballentine, Rudolph, M.D. *Diet and Nutrition: A Holistic Approach*. Honesdale, Pa.: The Himalayan International Institute, 1982.

Becker, Robert O., and Gary Selden. *The Body Electric: Electromagnetism and the Foundation of Life*. New York: William Marrow and Company, Inc., 1985.

Berry, Wendell. *The Unsettling of America: Culture and Agriculture*. New York: Avon Books, 1977.

The Bhagavad Gita. Translated by Juan Mascaro. Middlesex, England: Penguin Books Ltd., 1962.

Briscoe, David, and Charlotte Mahoney Briscoe. *A Personal Peace: Macrobiotic Reflections on Mental and Emotional Recovery*. Tokyo and New York: Japan Publications, Inc., 1989.

Duckheim, Karlfried. *Hara: The Vital Center of Man*. London: George Allen and Unwin Ltd., 1962.

Esko, Edward and Wendy. *Macrobiotic Cooking for Everyone*. Tokyo and New York: Japan Publications, Inc., 1980.

Essentials of Chinese Acupuncture. Beijing: Foreign Language Press, 1980.

The Four Books: The Great Learning, The Doctrine of the Mean, Confucian Analects, and the Works of Mencius. Translated by James Legge. Colo.: Oriental Bk Store, 1983.

The Gospel According to Thomas. Translated by Pico Iyer. London and Santa Barbara, New York: Concord Grove Press, 1983.

Hashimoto, Keizo, M.D., with Yoshiaki Kawakami. *Sôtai: Balance and Health through Natural Movement*. Tokyo and New York: Japan Publications, Inc., 1983.

Hippocratic Writings. Edited by G.E.R. Lloyd. Middlesex, England: Penguin Books Ltd., 1978.

How to Know God: The Yoga Aphorisms of Patanjali. Translated by Swami Prabhavananda and Christopher Isherwood. New York and Toronto: Mentor, 1953.

Hunter, Beatrice Trum. *Consumer Beware: Your Food and What's Been Done to It*. New York: Simon and Schuster, Inc., 1971.

I Ching or *Book of Changes*. Translated by Richard Wilhelm and Cary F. Baynes. Princeton: Bollingen Foundation, 1950.

Illich, Ivan. *Limits to Medicine: Medical Nemesis, The Exploration of Health*. Middlesex, England: Penguin Books, Ltd., 1977.

Ineson, John. *The Way of Life: Macrobiotics and the Spirit of Christianity*. Tokyo and New York: Japan Publications, Inc., 1986.

The Journey to the West. Translated by Anthony C. Yu. Chicago and London: The University of Chicago Press, 1977.

Kapit, Wynn and Lawrence M. Elson. *The Anatomy Coloring Book*. New York: Harper and Row, 1977.

The Koran. Translated by N.J. Dawood. Middlesex, England: Penguin Books Ltd., 1956.

Kushi, Aveline, with Alex Jack. *Aveline Kushi's Complete Guide to Macrobiotic Cooking*. New York: Warner Books, 1985.

Kushi, Michio. *The Book of Dō-In: Exercise for Physical and Spiritual Development*. Tokyo and New York: Japan Publications, Inc., 1979.

———. *The Book of Macrobiotics: The Universal Way of Health, Happiness and Peace*. Tokyo and New York: Japan Publications, Inc., 1986 (Rev. ed.).

———. *Crime and Diet: The Macrobiotic Approach*. Tokyo and New York: Japan Publications, Inc., 1987.

———. *How to See Your Health: The Book of Oriental Diagnosis*. Tokyo and New York: Japan Publications, Inc., 1980.

———. *Natural Healing through Macrobiotics*. Tokyo and New York: Japan Publications, Inc., 1978.

———. *Your Face Never Lies*. Wayne, N.J.: Avery Publishing Group, 1983.

Kushi, Michio and Aveline, with Alex Jack. *Food Governs Your Destiny: The Teachings of Namboku Mizuno*. Tokyo and New York: Japan Publications, Inc., 1991.

———. *Macrobiotic Diet*. Tokyo and New York: Japan Publications, Inc., 1985.

Kushi, Michio, with Marc Van Cauwenberghe, M.D. *Macrobiotic Home Remedies*. Tokyo and New York: Japan Publications, Inc., 1985.

Kushi, Michio, and Martha C. Cottrel with Mark N. Mead. *AIDS, Macrobiotics, and Natural Immunity*. Tokyo and New York: Japan Publications, Inc., 1990.

Kushi, Michio, with Olivia Oredson. *Macrobiotic Palm Healing: Energy at Your Finger-Tips*. Tokyo and New York: Japan Publications, Inc., 1988.

Lao Tzu. *Tao Te Ching*. Translated by D.C. Lau. Middlesex, England: Penguin Books, Ltd., 1963.

Levin, Cecil Tovah. *Cooking for Regeneration: Macrobiotic Relief from Cancer, AIDS, and Degenerative Disease*. Tokyo and New York: Japan Publications, Inc., 1988.

Masunaga, Shizuto. *Zen Imagery Exercises: Meridian Exercises for Wholesome Living*. Tokyo and New York: Japan Publications, Inc., 1987.

Masunaga, Shizuto, with Wataru Ohashi and the Shiatsu Education Center of America. *Zen Shiatsu: How to Harmonize Yin and Yang for Better Health*. Tokyo and New York: Japan Publications, Inc., 1977.

McNaught, Ann B., and Robin Callander. *Illustrated Physiology*. Edinburgh, London and New York: Churchill Livingstone, 1975.

Muramoto, Naboru. *Healing Ourselves*. Edited by Michel Abesera. New York: Avon Books, 1973.

The Nag Hammadi Library. James M. Robinson, general editor. San Francisco: Harper and Row, 1978.

Needham, Joseph. *Science and Civilization in China* (multi-volume series). London: Cambridge University Press.

Ohsawa, George. *Acupuncture and the Philosophy of the Far East*. Boston: Tao Books, 1973.

Omura, Yoshiaki. *Acupuncture Medicine: Its Historical and Clinical Background*. Tokyo and New York: Japan Publications, Inc., 1982.

Ornstein, Robert and Paul Ehrlich. *New World New Mind: Moving Toward Conscious Evolution*. New York: Simon and Schuster Inc., 1989.

Porkert, Manfred. *The Theoretical Foundations of Chinese Medicine.* Cambridge, Ma. and London: The MIT Press, 1974.

Reed, William. *Ki: A Practical Guide for Westerners.* Tokyo and New York: Japan Publications, Inc., 1986.

Sergel, David. *The Macrobiotic Way of Zen Shiatsu.* Tokyo and New York: Japan Publications, Inc., 1989.

Serizawa, Katsusuke, M.D. *Effective Tsubo Therapy: Simple and Natural Relief without Drugs.* Tokyo and New York: Japan Publications, Inc., 1984.

———. *Tsubo: Vital Points for Oriental Therapy.* Tokyo and New York: Japan Publications, Inc., 1976.

Serizawa, Katsusuke, M.D., with Mari Kusumi. *Clinical Acupuncture: A Practical Japanese Approach.* Tokyo and New York: Japan Publications, Inc., 1988.

Sheldrake, Rupert. *The Presence of the Past: Morphic Resonance and the Habits of Nature.* New York: Vintage Books, 1988.

Swami Vishnu-devananda. *The Complete Illustrated Book of Yoga.* New York: Harmony Books, 1960.

Takahashi, Masaru, and Stephen Brown. *Qigong for Health: Chinese Traditional Exercise for Cure and Prevention.* Tokyo and New York: Japan Publications, Inc., 1986.

Tara, William. *Macrobiotics and Human Behavior.* Tokyo and New York: Japan Publications, Inc., 1985.

Taylor, Louise, and Betty Bryant. *Ki: Energy for Everybody.* Tokyo and New York: Japan Publications, Inc., 1990.

Tohei, Koichi. *Book of Ki: Co-ordinating Mind and Body in Daily Life.* Tokyo and New York: Japan Publications, Inc., 1979.

———. *Ki in Daily Life.* Tokyo: Ki no Kenkyukai, 1978.

The Upanishads: Breath of the Eternal. Translated by Swami Prabhavananda and Fredick Manchester. Hollywood, Calif.: Vedanta Press, 1947.

Vermes, G. *The Dead Sea Scrolls in English.* Middlesex, England: Penguin Books Ltd., 1962.

Whitehead, Alfred North. *Science and the Modern World.* New York and Toronto: Mentor, 1925.

Wu Ch'eng-en. *Monkey: Folk Tale of China.* Translated by Arthur Waley. New York: Grove Press Inc., 1943.

Yamamoto, Shizuko. *Barefoot Shiatsu.* Tokyo and New York: Japan Publications, Inc., 1979.

The Yellow Emperor's Classic of Internal Medicine. Translated by Ilza Veith. Berkeley: University of California Press, 1949.

The Yellow Emperor's Classic of Internal Medicine and the Difficult Classic. Translated by Henry C. Lu. Vancouver: Academy of Oriental Heritage, 1985.

Index

abandonment, 244
abdominal center, 53
abdominal chakra, 54, 163, 168, 169, 175
abdominal cramps, 113
abdominal diagnosis, 126, 210, 213
abdominal energy center, 163
abdominal pain, 113
abdominal palpation, 125
abdominal spasms, 113
abortion, 244
abscesses, 22
absolute consciousness, 42
Academic American Encyclopedia, 243
accumulation, 232
achy joints, 232
acupressure, 210
acupuncture, 22–24, 31, 45, 156, 164, 177, 210, 216–21, 224, 235
Acupuncture and the Philosophy of the Far East, 28, 86
Acupuncture Medicine, 112
age of space exploration, 254
aggressive behavior, 143
AIDS, 19, 220, 227, 231, 257
AIDS virus, 19, 252
Aikido, 197
air, 140
alcohol abuse, 148, 243, 244
allergies, 231
American football, 196
amma, 208–10, 213
anemia, 131
angina pectoris, 143
antibiotics, 18
antithesis, 64
arrhythmia, 113
arthritis, 45, 205, 241
artificial family, 284
artificial fertilization, 249, 255
artificial insemination, 248, 249
aspirin, 151, 154
asthma, 143, 239
asthma attacks, 205
athletics, 196
atmospheric energy, 148
Aurelius, Marcus, 126
aurora australis, 51
aurora borealis, 51
autoclave, 221
awareness, 41
Ayurvedic medicine, 22, 207

backaches, 45
back-and-forth pulse, 128
balanced breathing, 183
baldness, 59
baseball, 196
basic sounds, 165
Bible, 34, 40, 67, 164, 165, 177
bio-force, 43
birth defects, 244
Bladder Meridian, **96**
    diagnostic points of, 123
blunt-point type needles, 218
Bodily Organs and the Five Transformations, **72**
body scrub, 234
Body's Major Energy Centers, **52**
bodywork, 204, 208
boils, 22
Book of Changes, 66, 67
Book of Dō-In, The, 171, 197, 213, 214
Bo points, 105
Bo Shin, 119, 118
Brahman, 67, 142
breast cancer, 228
breathing practice, 22, 23, 177, 238
breathing techniques, 182, 213
bronchitis, 113
Buddha, 24
Buddhism, 67, 261
Bun Shin, 117

Caesarean section, 244 255
cancer, 45, 59, 129, 151, 231, 238, 240, 257, 259, 261
carbohydrates, 140, 141
Celestial Origin of the Meridians, **103**
cell, 243
cell division, 83
center of gravity, 83
centrifugal force, 48
centripetal force, 48
ceremony, 247
chakras, 52, 170, 175, 178, 183
    activating, 169
    treating, 185
Changing One's Direction toward Health, **240**
chanting, 23, 162, 177, 213, 214
Characteristics of Yin and Yang, **61**
chemical analysis, 118
chemotherapy, 239
Ch'i, 43
Chieh Chen, 117
child abuse, 244
children, 247
China, 21, 24, 207–9, 213, 222
Chinese medicine, 24
Chinese needles, 218
Christ, 34, 67, 259
Christians, 261
Chu Yaku, 155
circulatory disease, 257
cirrhosis, 148
colic, 113
colon cancer, 59
coma, 113
Combination of Yin and Yang in Herbal Preparations, **161**
common cold, 113, 231, 232, 261
Complementary Orientation of Modern and Traditional Societies, **20**
Complementary Relation of the Digestive and Nervous Systems, **139**
Complementary Spirals of Life, **40**
Complementary Writing Styles: East and West, **29**
Conception and Governing Vessels, **88**
Confucianism, 67
Confucius, 67
constipation, 109, 115, 201, 205, 232, 234
contagious disease, 220
contraceptive pill, 255
Correlation between Abdominal Areas and Specific Organs, **125**
Correlation between Areas of the Tongue and

Digestive System, **131**
Correlation between Arm and Oragan Spirals, **106**
Correlation between the Face and Body Organs, **119**
Correlation between the Face and Organ Systems, **120**
Correlation between the Meridians and Constellations, **102**
cosmic rays, 48
coughing, 112, 160, 185, 232
cramps, 205
crime, 19, 239, 243
crisis, definition of, 256
crown chakra, 54, 163
cure
    definition of, 241
    meaning of, 241
cysts, 22, 128, 160, 175

dead pulse, 129
deafness, 113
deep pulse, 127–29
degenerative diseases, 232, 233, 236, 241, 243, 254, 259
depression, 201
Descartes, Rene, 47, 228
desertification, 256
destitute, 19
destructive agricultural practices, 20
diabetes, 45, 143, 239, 241
diabetes millitus, 147, 205
diagnosis, 114–34
    by listening, 121
    methods of, 116
    principles of, 114
    purpose of, 116
    by seeing, 118
    by touching, 123
    using tongue, 129
Diagnostic Points on Each Meridian, **123, 124**
diarrhea, 205, 232, 234
diet, macrobiotic approach to, 142
dietary practice, 250
digestive difficulties, 146
digestive system, 139, 184
discharge, recommendations for accelerating, 235
divorce, 244, 247, 248
dizzinees, 220
Dō-In, 197, 213
dragon lines, 82
drug abuse, 19, 29, 243
dualism, 258
duodenal ulcers, 143

earaches, 146, 205
Earth's Electromagnetic Field, **50**
Earth's force, 50
Eastern exercise, 197
Eastern massage, 208
eating, concept of, 137
ecliptic, 103
Egypt, 207
eight extra meridians, 88
Einstein, 36, 37
Einstein's theory, 37
Ei points, 107
electromagnetism, 43
electronic microscope, 118
embryonic education, 246
emotional ailments, 189
Emotional Characteristics and the Five Transformations, **76**
emotional consciousness, 42
emotional disorders, 75
emotions, 75, 187
Emphasis in Yin and Yang Breathing Techniques, **182**
empty-mind exercise, 174
empty-mind meditation, 172, 173, 214
Energetic Forces in the Solar System, **48**
Energetic Nature of Fruit, **51**
Energetics in the Plant Kingdom, **68**
Energetics of Cell Division, **83**
energy, points of, 104
energy circuit, 178
Energy Cycle along the Meridians, **89**
energy cycles, 58–80
energy diagnosis, 183
energy flow, course of, 89
Energy Spirals on the Palm and Fingers, **179**
energy treatment, 183
enlightenment, 197
environment, deterioration of, 256
environmental disaster, 259
environmental pollution, 20
enzymes, 141
escape velocity, 50
Esoteric Buddhism, 174
evolution of judgment, 41
Examples of Diagnostic Points on Each Meridian, **123, 124**
Examples of the Yin and Yang Cycle, **62**
excess fear, 143
excess perspiration, 232

exercise, 22, 45, 189–201, 205, 208, 213, 215, 234, 238
    Eastern approach to, 195
    five guidelines for, 192, 193
    traditional approach to, 195
    two poles of, 194
    Western approach to, 195
Exercise for the Heart and Small Intestine Meridians, **199**
Exercise for the Heart Governor and Triple Heater Meridians, **200**
Exercise for the Kidney and Bladder Meridians, **199**
Exercise for the Liver and Gallbladder Meridians, **200**
Exercise for the Lung and Large Intestine Meridians, **198**
Exercise for the Spleen-Pancreas and Stomach Meridians, **199**
extended family, 248
extremely fine short-wave vibrations, 140

face
    correspondences with organ systems, 119
    correspondences with trunk, 118
facial diagnosis, 118
fainting, 113
family
    definition of, 245
    loss of, 19
    sharing factors of, 245
    steps for producing, 249
family members, care for, 250
Family Memorial, **251**, 252
family violence, 244
Far-Eastern massage, 207
fatigue, 146, 228
fats, 141
female, 54
female pulses, 127
Feng-shui, 82
fever, 146, 160, 208, 231, 232
Fifty Basic Sounds, **166**
figurine, 24
Five Element Theory, 70
Five Stages of Energy Transformations, **70**
Five Transformation Points, 109, **110, 111**
five transformations, 69

of energy, 149, 159
flat-headed needles, 218
flu, 231, 232
folk remedies, 154
food
energetics of, 147
infinite range of, 137
for medicinal applications, 142
relationship of to body, 150
seven stages of, 139
treating symptoms with, 151
use in healing, 151
Foods Categorized by Yin and Yang, **144–46**
foot reflexology, 109, 117
Formation of the Meridians and Organ and Limb Spirals, **84**
Fu, 85
Fu-Hi, 64–66
Fu-Hi's Eight Trigrams, **65**

Galen, 126
gallbladder disorders, 131
Gallbladder Meridian, **100**
diagnostic points of, 124
gallstones, 205
genital region chakra, 53, 54, 163
Gen points, 106–8, 133
Geographic Regions of Oriental Medicine Practice, **21**
Ge Yaku, 155
Ghee, 43
God, 260
Go Kou, 117
gonorrhea, 244
Go points, 106–8
Gospel According to John, The, 164
Gospel According to Thomas, The, 46, 60, 67, 187, 259
governing vessel, 88
graying hair, 143
Greeks, 202, 207
guide tube, 220

hair loss, 59
hand, three general areas of, 179
hand reflexology, 117
Hara, 53, 184
focusing on, 175
Hara chakra, 182, 183
hatha yoga, 195
hay fever, 231
headaches, 45, 146, 151, 177, 205, 210, 212, 232
healing
definition of, 237
keys to, 236
modern approach to, 231
healing abilities
generating, 180
source of, 179
health
definition of, 227
seven requirements for, 228
heart chakra, 53, 54, 163, 183, 187
heart disease, 241, 257
Heart Governor Meridian, **98**
diagnostic points of, 124
Heart Meridian, **94**
diagnostic points of, 123
heart/small intestine
correspondences with the nonphysical qualities of the self, 77
listening diagnosis of, 121
Heaven's force, 50
Hegel, George Wilhelm Friedrich, 64
hemorrhoids, 205
herbal medicine, 22, 23, 31, 45, 153–61, 164, 177, 235
preparations of, 150
standard application of, 155
value of, 154
herbs, modern and traditional uses of, 153
hernia, 143
herniated spinal discs, 205
herpes, 244, 252
hexagrams, 66
high blood sugar, 147
high fever, 151, 185
Hindu, 142, 260
Hinduism, 67
holistic medicine, 33, 203, 206
homeless, 19
homeostasis, 229, 231–33
How to See Your Health, 117
Huang Ti Nei Ching, 22, 66
Husband-and-Wife Cycle, **78**
husband-wife relationship, 77
hypoglycemia, 148
hysterectomies, 244

I Ching, 66
ideological consciousness, 42
illiteracy, 19
illness
curing, 240
holistic look at, 229
mechanism of, 231
immune ability, 35, 46, 132, 227, 257
immune function, 193
immune responses, 231
immune system, 34, 175, 227, 228, 255
impaired discharge ability, 233
India, 21, 22, 24, 207, 209, 213
Industrial Revolution, 196
infectious disease, 221, 243
infectious hepatitis, 220
infertility, 244, 248
Infertility and Reproductive Disorders, 248
injury, 205
insufficient lactation, 113
intellectual consciousness, 42
intestinal problems, 234
intrauterine device (IUD), 255
in vitro fertilization, 248
irregular pulse, 128

Japan, 21
Japanese needles, 218
Japan Times, 249
Jaundice, 148
Jesus, 34, 46, 60, 67, 177, 187, 240
Jews, 260
Jitsu, 125, 132, 149, 150, 160, 170, 178, 185, 211, 217, 223, 231
Jitsu-Sho, 56
joints, manipulation of, 211
Jo Yaku, 155
jumpy pulse, 128

Kami-Musubi, 67
Keats, 63
Kei points, 107
Ki, 43
arrival of, 220
in the body, 47
definition of, 37
detecting, 183
to generate, 180
in healing, 45
problems with, 56
in traditional societies, 43
two types of, 51
kidney/bladder

correspondences with the nonphysical qualities of the self, 77
listening diagnosis of, 121
Kidney Meridian, **97**
diagnostic points of, 123
kidney problems, 113, 151
Ki energy, 25, 36
Ki exercises, 197, 212
Ki Kai, 53, 82
knee pain, 238
Kojiki, 67
Korea, 21, 24
Ko-Tei, 66
Koto Dama, 165
Krishna, 67
Kun-Shin-Sa-Shi, 160
Kyo, 125, 132, 150, 160, 170, 178, 185, 211, 217, 223, 231
Kyo-Sho, 56

Lao-Tzu, 67
Large Intestine Meridian, **91**
diagnostic points of, 123
Laws of Change, 66
learning desabilities, 244
leukemia, 59, 143
ley lines, 82
life-force, 43
listening diagnosis, 121
List of Correspondences within the Five Transformations, **73**
liver disorders, 131
liver/gallbladder
correspondences with the nonphysical qualities of the self, 77
listening diagnosis of, 122
Liver Meridian, **101**
diagnostic points of, 124
liver troubles, 75
Location of the Wrist Pulses, **126**
logarithmic spiral, 40
love, 246, 261
low blood pressure, 56
low blood sugar, 148, 155
lung/large intestine
correspondences with the nonphysical qualities of the self, 77
listening diagnosis of, 121
Lung Meridian, **90**
diagnostic points of, 123
lung problem, 151

Macrobiotic Diet, 244
macrobiotic healing, key to, 236
Macrobiotic Home Remedies, 146
male, 54
male impotency, 205
male pulses, 127
malignancies, 221
malnutrition, 129
marriage, 246
martial arts, 194
massage, 22, 23, 31, 45, 104, 156, 164, 177, 189, 202–10 213
benefits of, 205
decline of, 204
origin of, 203
origin of the word, 202
Masunaga, Shizuto, 212
materialism, 254
Matsuo Basho, 222
mechanical consciousness, 41
medical practice, three levels of, 30
medications, traditional and modern approaches compared, 156
meditation, 23, 31, 46, 162, 171–77, 213, 214, 222
for healing, 175
memorial, 251
menstrual irregularities, 146
menstrual problems, 232
mental ailments, 189
Mental and Spiritual Qualities and the Five Transformations, **76**
mental characteristics, 75
mental disorders, 75
mental illness, 45, 239, 243
mental retardation, 244
meridian diagnosis, 132, 210
meridian exercises, 197–201
meridian pairs, 86
meridians, 81–103
celestial origin of, 103
in the embryo, 82
origin of, 102
relationship of to constellations, 102
metaphysics, 18, 19
methodology, 47
micronutrients, 141
microwave oven, 256
midbrain, 184
focusing on, 175
midbrain chakra, 53, 54, 168, 175, 176, 182
middle pulse, 128, 129
mind, 75
minerals, 140, 141
Modern and Traditional Approaches to Medicine, **32**
modern exercise, 194
modern worldview, 19
mother-child relationship, 78
moxa, 221
production of, 222
use of, 222
moxibustion, 22, 23, 104, 175, 221–24
origin of, 221
mucus deposits, 56
mudras, 178
muscle cramps, 209
Muslims, 260

narrow pulse, 128
nasal sinusitis, 112
Natural Cycles and the Five Transformations, **71**
needles, 24, 217–19
insertion methods of, 220
material of, 217
shape of, 218
thickness and length of, 218
needle sterilization, 221
needling techniques, 218
Nei Ching, 23, 24
nervous system, 139, 184
neuralgia, 209
New American Desk Encyclopedia, The, 254
Newsweek, 228
niacin, 59
night sweats, 113
Nihon Shoki, 67
nonphysical food, 139
nosebleed, 205
nuclear annihilation, 254
nuclear family, 248
nuclear power, 255
nuclear war, 256, 259
nuclear-weapons plant, 255

odors
relationship of to five transformations, 122
relationship of to organ pair, 122
Odors and the Five Transformations, **122**
Ohsawa, George, 28, 62, 86, 228, 229, 241
Omura Yoshiaki, 112
optical microscopes, 118

Order of the Pulses in Males and Females, **127**
Order of the Universe, 62
organs, treating, 186
Organs Classified by Structure and Function, **86**
organ spiral, 106
organ systems, activating, 169
Oriental medicine, 21
five principles of, 24
foundation of, 20
ovarian cancer, 146
over-the-counter medications, 157

palm healing, 22, 23, 31, 177–88, 208
palm reading, 117
paralysis, 208
parent-child relationship, 78
parents, 247
Parvati, 67
peace, 261
philosophical consciousness, 42
physical abnormalities, 244
physical activity, 190–93, 201
advantages of, 190
physical exercise, modern approach to, 196
physical food, 39
physical health, 190, 193, 197
physicalization, 40
physicalization progress, seven stages of, 41
physics, 18, 19
planetary body, 48
Planetary Energy Body, **49**
plant kingdom, energies in, 68
pneumonia, 113
polarity, 58
Polo, Marco, 207
polyps, 233
poor digestion, 193
Prana, 43
prayer, 22, 23, 31, 46, 156, 162–78, 251, 252
prescription medications, 157
pressure, application of, 211
primary channel, 52, 137
toning of, 167
primary consciousness, 41
principal fire, 77
Principles of the Universe, 66
Progressive Categories of Food Intake, **140**
prostate cancer, 143
prostate problems, 205
protein, 140, 141
psychosis, 143
pulses, 126

Qigong, 197

Radha, 67
radiation, 238
rapid pulse, 128
razor-edge style needles, 218
regulating cycle, 78, 79
Rei-Su, 66
rejuvenation, 151
relative's death, 251
reproductive disorders, 244
rhinitis, 112
rice vinegar, 75
rigid pulse, 128
ringing in the ears, 113
runny nose, 74, 232
Rutherford, Ernest, 36, 164

sauerkraut, 75
schizophrenia, 143, 252
school dropouts, 19
school violence, 244
Scientific Revolution, 204, 207
scurvy, 143
secondary fire, 77
sedation, 206, 207, 217, 219, 223
Sei, Gen and Go Points, **108**
Sei points, 106–8
Self, 46
self-image, 189
self-massage, 197, 203, 206, 208
self-realization, 41, 197
self-shiatsu, 213–15
self-treatment, 187
sensory consciousness, 42
separation, 248
Setsu Shin, 117
seven-orbited spiral, 107, 137, 165, 258
Seven Universal Principles, 62
sexually transmitted disease (STD), 244
sexual revolution, 204
sharing, 245, 248
sharing meals, 250
sharp-pointed type needles, 218
She Chen, 117
shiatsu, 203, 208–15, 235
shiatsu treatment, 212
Shin-No, 66
Shintoism, 240, 261
Shiva, 67
Shoku Shin, 125
shortness of breath, 112
short temper, 143
sickness
of adjustment, 231
classification of, 231
function of, 230
silent prayer, 162
Silk Road, 207
single-parent family, 19, 248
skin cancer, 256
skin discharges, 146
skin diseases, 231, 232
slow pulse, 128
Small Intestine Meridian, **95**
diagnostic points of, 123
sneezing, 232
social consciousness, 42
society, basis of, 243
solar plexus, 53
solar plexus chakra, 54, 163
solar system, energetic forces in, 48
solar wind, 48, 49
So-Mon, 66
song, 162
sore throat, 232
Sound Energies and Their Related Organs, **170**
sounds, 162–71
combinations of, 170
as energy, 163
healing with, 167
how we use, 162
spinal correction, 211
spirit, 75
spiritual channel, 52
spiritual characteristics, 75
spiritual development, 241
spiritual healing, 250
spiritualization, 40
seven stages of, 41
Spleen Meridian, **93**
diagnostic points of, 124
spleen-pancreas/stomach
correspondences with the nonphysical qualities of the self, 77
listening diagnosis of, 122
spouse abuse, 244
stagnated pulse, 129
standard macrobiotic diet, 143
standard macrobiotic way of eating, 142
sterility, 249
sterilization, 244
stiffness, 201, 208
stimulation, 206, 207
stomachaches, 146, 177

stomach chakra, 53
Stomach Meridian, **92**
diagnostic points of, 124
stones, 56, 128, 129, 160, 233, 235
stress, 189, 195, 201
stress reduction, 195, 205
strong pulse, 128
Structural Features of the Tongue, **130**
Study of History, A, 60
stuffy nose, 112
Sumerian civilization, 24
"super" bacteria, 18
superficial pulse, 127–29
Support and Regulating Cycles, **78**
surgery, 31
Swedish massage, 208
swelling, 146
swollen glands, 232
symptomatic medicine, 33
symptoms, attitude toward, 34
synthesis, 64
syphilis, 244
systematic exercise, 190

Tai-chi, 194, 197
Takami-Musubi, 67
Tanasue-no-Michi, 177
Tan Den, 53
Taoism, 67, 209, 213
Te Ate, 22, 177
teenage pregnancies, 19
Ten-Mei, 67
thesis, 64
thoughts, 162
throat chakra, 53, 54, 165
thumbtack-tape needles, 218
Tibet, 21
Time, 34
tongue, relationship of to digestive systems, 130
tongue diagnosis, 129
tonification, 207, 217, 219
tonsillitis, 231
tonsils, removal of, 255
toothaches, 45, 205
tooth decay, 143
touching diagnosis, 123
Tower of Babel, 165
toxemia, 231
Toynbee, Arnold, 60
traditional diagnosis, value of, 133
traditional worldview, 19
Treating the Large Intestine's Gen Point, **109**
treatment, 36, 184
classes of, 31
trigrams, 65
Triple Heater, **87**
Triple Heater Meridian, **99**
diagnostic points of, 124
true sound, 164
truth, 261
tsubo, 104, 216, 234
tuberculosis, 121
tumors, 22, 59, 129, 175, 232, 233, 256
Twelve Laws of Change, 62
Two-Way Influence on the Self, **45**

ultrasound scans, 255
umeboshi vinegar, 75
Unifying Principles, 62, 67
universal consciousness, 42
unwed mothers, 19
Upanishads, 142

Van Allen belts, 49
Various States of Water, **38**
Vedanta, 67
venereal disease, 244
vibrations, 140
visual diagnosis, 118
visualization, 162, 171, 173, 176, 181, 213
vitamin A, 59
vitamin B_2, 59
vitamin B_6, 59
vitamin C, 59
vitamin D, 59
vitamin E, 59
vitamin K, 59
vitamins, 141
voices
relationship of to five transformations, 122
relationship of to organ pair, 122
"Voices" and the Five Transformations, **122**
vowels, 165, 166
Vowels and Their Meaning, **165**

Wang Chen, 117
war, 261
water, 140
watery eyes, 232
Ways to Adjust Yin and Yang Qualities, **159**
weak pulse, 129
Webster's Ninth New Collegiate Dictionary, 202, 227, 245
weight loss, 192, 195
well-being, macrobiotic approach to, 197
Wen Chen, 117
Western diet, 196
Western massage, 206–9, 213
wide pulse, 128
withdrawal, 143
Wu Hsiang, 117

X-rays, 118

yang breathing, 182
yang diet, 195
yang exercise, 194
yang foods, 196
yang meridians, 84
Yellow Emperor, 23, 24
Yellow Emperor's Classic of Internal Medicine, The, 22, 66, 126, 208, 221
yin and yang, 58, 194, 196, 197, 201, 207, 217, 219, 224
characteristics of, 61
cycle of, 62
yin and yang functions, balancing, 168
Yin and Yang in the Plant Kingdom, **158**
yin and yang meditation practices, 171
yin breathing, 182
yin diet, 195
yin exercise, 194
yin meridians, 84
Yin Yang Go Gyo, 70
yoga, 172, 197, 209, 215
Yu and Bo Points, **105**
Yu points, 96, 104, 105, 107, 181, 211

Zang, 85
Zang and Fu Organs, **85**
Zen Imagery Exercises, 212
Zetsu Shin, 117, 129